Research and survey in nature conservation

No. 39

A review of the scarce and
threatened flies of Great Britain
(Part 1)

Steven Falk

Further copies can be obtained from
Publicity Services Branch
Nature conservancy Council, Northminster House
Peterborough, PE1 1UA

PREFACE

The Diptera or true flies, are often perceived as undesirable because some species spread disease or are agricltural pests. In fact the great majority of flies in Britain and elsewhere, are either harmless or are beneficial to man. Flies are of considerable ecological significance in breaking down and re-cycling of organic material, as pollinators of flowers and as enemies of insect pests such as aphids.

Furthermore, many flies are of actual or potential conservation significance. There are many specialised species, often associated with ancient habitats, which are sensitive indicators of environmental conditions. For example, there are species associated with our most ancient woodlands whose larvae develop in dead wood, and which have been unable to colonise newer woodlands. Other species develop in the stems and roots of plants which are in turn restricted to unimproved semi-natural habitats.

The fly fauna of Great Britain comprises over 6,000 species which exploit niches in probably all terrestrial and fresh water habitats; a few species have even colonised the inter-tidal zone of the marine environment. Thus flies have the potential to be used in site assesment and monitoring very widely. They have the added advantage that traditional sampling techniques (such as sweeping) and more systematic surveys using trapping methods, both yield a good variety of species in many ecological situations. It is hoped that the publication of this Review will enable the lists of flies obtained by these means to be more readily interpreted in the future.

This Review will be published in two parts. Volume one provides accounts for the better known families and those for which records are most likely to be forwarded to the conservation manager. All species of fly currently assigned to Red Data Book and Notable categories are also listed. Volume two will include species accounts for a selection of the species not included in volume one.

CONTENTS

INTRODUCTION

The National Review of Diptera has been produced to highlight the large number of scarce or threatened species within the order and to assist in safeguarding their presence at known sites. There are over 1500 Red Data Book and Notable species, (those estimated to occur in 100 or less post 1960 10 km squares) included in this publication, making it one of the most extensive works on British Diptera. The review provides a natural succession from two previous works, The IUCN Invertebrate Red Data Book (Wells, Pyle & Collins, 1983) and British Red Data Books: 2. Insects (Shirt, 1987). The latter included a small representative selection of RDB1 and RDB2 Diptera species amongst its species accounts and provided lists of all RDB and Appendix species. This review is one of a series of similar reviews covering most invertebrate groups in Britain.

In the past, invertebrate conservation has been largely confined to the more attractive and easily identified groups with comparatively few species such as butterflies and dragonflies, even though many species in other groups were known to be in need of protection. Groups such as butterflies and dragonflies are not necessarily representative of the invertebrate fauna as a whole and conservation management for these groups alone will not necessarily benefit all other groups of invertebrates. It is becoming increasingly apparent that the use of a wider range of invertebrates will provide a more balanced approach to conservation management as it will require the consideration of a far wider range of ecological situations. The Diptera, with some 6000 known British species (over one quarter of the British insect fauna), exploit an enormous variety of ecological niches and are particularly important in this respect.

Much of the past neglect of groups such as the Diptera in conservation has resulted from the sheer size of the group and the difficulty of identification. There are three other contributory factors.

1. Many entomologists are amateur collectors who have had little if any active involvement in conservation and comparatively few professional entomologists exist within the conservation movement.

2. Much relevant information has not been published, even when it is well known to specialists. Even when published information is available, it may be scattered widely in British and European literature so that collation is a lengthy task.

3. Often, where species are comparatively well known, the information is often not available for use in management, especially where the management body is lacking in entomological expertise. Such management bodies may have long lists of the invertebrates on their sites, with no means of interpreting them.

The production of data sheets on the scarce and threatened species (Red Data Book and Notable species) will hopefully resolve many of these problems. Information from a wide range of published and unpublished sources, including the leading specialists, has been compiled and presented in a form that can be incorporated more easily into a management plan.

The amount of information available for a species can vary greatly. Rarity is a factor which can either impede our understanding of a species through an inability to find and study it, or it may actually define a species' requirements by demonstrating a direct association with a habitat or host that is itself rare or restricted. Even a rare species can be abundant under suitable conditions. The data sheets vary in detail according to the amount of information available. Those of the less well known species are often generalised, especially in their threat and management sections and may list operations that are likely to be detrimental to that species given the available information. Data sheets of the better known species can assert more positively the "do's and don'ts", and provide justifications for these recommendations in the sections on habitat and ecology.

The Review is thus aimed at a double audience:

1.   **Conservationists** involved in site management (e.g. Wardens and Assistant Regional Officers of the NCC, County Trusts and other wildlife groups) where there may be a desire to incorporate the needs of invertebrates, especially threatened species, into the management of their sites, but a lack of entomological expertise.

2.   **Entomologists** who encounter a vast number of species on their travels, but do not fully appreciate the significance of their finds, or know how to place them into a conservation or ecological context. Much of the literature on Diptera lacks ecological statements and distributional information is often incomplete or misleading. The data sheets should provide the most accurate and up to date accounts available. It is hoped that as a consequence of this Review, entomologists will be encouraged to actively pursue gaps in our knowledge concerning our rarer Diptera and also to keep detailed and accurate information concerning their captures, especially ecological notes.

There is a need to discover the larval development sites and other conditions required by scarce and threatened species. The development of more precise recording of situations exploited by the immature stages and adult flies is essential if we are to conserve these insects in future.

RARITY CATEGORY DEFINITIONS AND CRITERIA

Grading of the species in the manner used in the Red Data Books allows a rapid assessment of the conservation status of a species based on degree of threat. Rarity alone does not necessarily reflect the degree of threat as it does not account for differential rates of loss in different habitats or other factors responsible for the different rates of species declines. Seven categories are used in this review. The definitions and criteria of RDB 1, 2, 3 and Appendix closely follow Shirt (1987) with some slight modifications. **However, this is not a Red Data Book and the threat categories designated here should be considered provisional until they are published in a Red Data Book.** RDBK is used in a similar context to that used in The IUCN Invertebrate Red Data Book (Wells, Pyle & Collins 1983), though the definitions and criteria have been redefined to suit the needs of this review.

2

RDB1 - ENDANGERED

Definition. Taxa in danger of extinction and whose survival is unlikely if the causal factors continue operating.

Included are taxa whose numbers have been reduced to a critical level or whose habitats have been so dramatically reduced that they are deemed to be in immediate danger of extinction. Also included are taxa that are believed to be extinct but with records for this century.

Criteria
- Species which are known, or believed to occur as only a single population within one modern 10 km square of the National Grid.

- Species which only occur in habitats known to be especially vulnerable.

- Species which have shown a rapid and continuous decline over the last twenty years and are now estimated to exist in five or fewer modern 10 km squares.

- Species which are believed extinct but which if rediscovered would need protection.

RDB2 - VULNERABLE

Definition. Taxa believed likely to move into the Endangered category in the near future if the causal factors continue operating.

Included are taxa of which most or all of the populations are decreasing because of over-exploitation, extensive destruction of habitat or other environmental disturbance; taxa with populations that have been seriously depleted and whose ultimate security is not yet assured; and taxa with populations that are still abundant but are under threat from serious adverse factors throughout their range.

Criteria
- Species declining throughout their range.

- Species in vulnerable habitats.

- Species whose populations are low.

RDB3 - RARE

Definition. Taxa with small populations that are not at present Endangered or Vulnerable, but are at risk.

These taxa are usually localised within restricted geographical areas or habitats, or are thinly scattered over a more extensive range.

Criteria
- Species which are estimated to exist in only fifteen or fewer modern 10 km squares.

RDBK - INSUFFICIENTLY KNOWN

Definition. Taxa suspected to fall within the RDB categories but with too little information to allow confident assignment to any of the previous categories.

Criteria   - Species recently discovered or recognised in Britain which may prove to be more widespread in the future (though some recent discoveries may be placed in previous categories if felt not be substantially under recorded).

- Species with very few or perhaps only a single known locality belonging to poorly recorded or taxonomically unstable groups such as the Phoridae, Anthomyiidae etc.

- Species with very few or perhaps only a single known locality, inhabiting inaccessible habitats such as caves or montane situations. This leads to difficulty in assessing the distribution and frequency of the species within the available habitat (this does not apply to all montane species).

- Species with very few or perhaps only a single known locality and of questionable native status, but not clearly falling into the category of recent colonist, vagrant or introduction, e.g. <u>Laphria</u> <u>gilva</u> (Asilidae), <u>Rhamphomyia</u> <u>marginata</u> (Empididae).

APPENDIX

Taxa which were formerly native to Britain but have not been recorded since 1900.

N - NOTABLE

Species which are estimated to occur within the range of sixteen to one hundred modern 10 km squares. The subdividing of this category into Na and Nb has not been attempted in this review.

INTRODUCED

In a small number of cases, RDB species originally regarded as native are now believed to be introductions, e.g. <u>Cephenemyia</u> <u>trompe</u> (Oestridae), which was probably introduced with reindeer into Scotland. These species are not regarded as having conservation value, though data sheets have been provided to clarify their new status. Introduced species which were never regarded as RDB species despite rarity have been ignored. This has also been the policy with recent colonists (e.g. a number of rare syrphids associated with spruce or commercial conifer plantations) and vagrants (e.g. the calliphorid <u>Stomorhina</u> <u>lunata</u> which is associated with locust swarms, and migratory syrphids such as <u>Scaeva</u> <u>albomaculata</u> and <u>Metasyrphus</u> <u>lundbecki</u>).

Changes in status from the Insect Red Data Book (Shirt 1987)

Given the extra information obtained for most of the scarce and threatened species during the course of this review, it has been felt necessary to revise the status of many species. An accompanying statement is provided in the data sheets under the section on status, giving the original grade. Changes in status are inevitable, though hopefully as our knowledge improves, the status of most species will become more stable, or at least reflect genuine declines or increases rather than recording level or taxonomic stability.

Further notes on the assessment of status

For a small number of Diptera species we can feel reasonably confident that our idea of the modern distribution and precise localities involved is a fairly accurate one. Such species are usually associated with very restricted habitats, hosts etc. which are themselves well mapped. For the vast majority of species however, we have to make subjective estimates of status based on many factors, including the distribution of apparently suitable habitat, the apparent frequency or distribution of the species within this habitat, and the rate of either habitat loss or species decline. Other factors which may also entail adjustment of the grades are discussed below.

1. **Taxonomic difficulties.** This may affect individual species, genera or whole families and may result in comparatively little collected material of the species being confidently determined, and also lead to much inaccurate data. The author has attempted to eliminate obvious misidentifications, either at source (collections, old literature etc.) or through reassessment of records following aberrant habitat, date or distributional information. Leading specialists have also been consulted.

2. **Popularity of the group.** Some families such as the Syrphidae, which are relatively attractive, easily recorded and identifiable, receive considerably more attention by recorders than most fly groups. A species from one of the less well known families with a similar frequency and distribution to a syrphid, will have only a fraction of the number of records by comparison and thus a degree of adjustment to its grade will be required to compensate for the different levels of recording. Obviously such adjustment is subjective, though without it the grades of many species would be meaningless.

    A number of families (e.g. Psychodidae, Chironomidae, Simuliidae, Sciaridae, Scatopsidae, Cecidomyiidae and Sphaeroceridae) are not dealt with in this review due to a combination of taxonomic difficulties and low levels of recording, though it is likely that they contain species of RDB status and probably some useful indicator species habitat quality. Other families such as the Phoridae, Anthomyiidae and Agromyzidae have received only sparse coverage in the review. These families may receive more detailed coverage in the future. In families such as the Helcomyzidae, Dryomyzidae and Coelopidae, the lack of apparent coverage is simply through none of the species being rare enough to warrant inclusion in the review.

    Where families are poorly recorded but appear to include reasonably good RDB candidates, the category RDBK is frequently used, as it is inappropriate to place such species alongside RDB1 species that are genuinely in need of protection. This policy has been adopted for certain species within the families Culicidae, Phoridae, Anthomyiidae, Fanniidae and difficult genera within other families.

3.   **Geographical, habitat or temporal factors.** Inaccessible locations such as cliffs, mountain tops and certain offshore islands may be under recorded or even completely unworked for invertebrates so that species associated wich such situations will tend to be poorly recorded.   In the case of montane habitats the problem is exaggerated by a compressed recording season combined with unpredictable weather patterns.   Again, RDBK has been used for some species.

An autumnal or early spring flight period can also lead to under recording, even in the case of relatively popular groups such as syrphids, hence Melangyna species tend to be under recorded in the spring whilst Xanthandrus comtus and the conopid Leopoldius signatus are possibly overlooked in the autumn.

INFORMATION ON THE DATA SHEETS

The data sheets are designed to provide a fast and efficient system for obtaining information on the Red Data Book and Notable species.   The format consists of sections on distribution, habitat, ecology, status, threat and management.   These are explained more fully below.

1.   **Distribution**

This is based on Watsonian vice counties (Dandy J.E 1969 Watsonian vice-counties of Great Britain. The Ray Society, London), though for the sake of time and convenience certain vice counties have been amalgamated.   The relevant vice counties have been tabulated as follows:

Amalgamated Vice Counties used in this review	Actual Vice Counties
Cornwall	W Cornwall, E Cornwall
Devon	S Devon, N Devon
Somerset	S Somerset, N Somerset
Wiltshire	N Wiltshire, S Wiltshire
Hampshire	S Hampshire, N Hampshire
Sussex	W Sussex, E Sussex
Kent	E Kent, W Kent
Essex	S Essex, N Essex
Suffolk	E Suffolk, W Suffolk
Norfolk	E Norfolk, W Norfolk
Gloucestershire	E Gloucestershire, W Gloucestershire
Lincolnshire	S Lincolnshire, N Lincolnshire
Lancashire	S Lancashire, W Lancashire
Yorkshire	SE Yorkshire, NE Yorkshire, SW Yorkshire, MW Yorkshire, NW Yorkshire
Perthshire	W Perthshire, M Perthshire, E Perthshire
Aberdeenshire	S Aberdeenshire, N Aberdeenshire
Sutherland	E Sutherland, W Sutherland

Where a species is particularly widespread, with a distribution involving perhaps a dozen or more vice counties, a more generalised statement is used. When a distribution has a southern or northern bias, the vice counties delimiting its range are usually given. Outlying records are also given, either as a vice county, or if particularly significant, as an exact locality. Apart from the rarest species with few records (where full, dated localities are given) the distributional information is intended to give a general impression of distribution based on all known records and makes no attempt to highlight any change in status or to differentiate between pre and post 1960 information. This is dealt with more fully under status.

2.   **Habitat**

A brief description of habitat requirements is given. Where a range of habitats is used, any preferences are identified and if a more specific situation occurring in a range of habitats is exploited, this is also stated. Special requirements such as standing water, dead wood and old or diseased trees are also stated to emphasise the importance of these components within the habitat.

The terminology used in the habitat descriptions is subjective as it was found that the rigid use of categories such as defined in the NCC/RSNC habitat classification were for many species oversimplifications and occasionally misleading. The use of phytosociological associations could eventually provide a more accurate and informative means of expressing the habitat requirements of certain species, though for others it is clear that the physical structure of the habitat, irrespective of the plant communities, is the most important factor.

For many species of Diptera, the available habitat information is too sketchy to allow anything more than a vague idea of the requirements and where the habitat requirements are unknown, this is stated as such. However if the species is known to belong to a group of predominantly woodland or shade preferring species or wetland species, and the known localities contain such habitat, this is stated as a possible habitat requirement without attempting to lead the reader into a false understanding of the species.

3.   **Ecology**

This provides information on the larval biology and developmental site where known and again may state a possible larval developmental site where this is unknown. Adult flight periods are also given, plus any further information on adult behaviour such as flower-visiting, predatory behaviour and activities such as basking on foliage (the latter might suggest open ride and clearing management for a woodland species). The habitat requirements of the larvae and adults may differ quite considerably in some species, especially flower-visiting, predatory or blood-sucking species, and a loss or degradation of the adult habitat could prove as deleterious to the species as the loss of the larval developmental site. This is why structural diversity of habitat and habitat mosaics are often so important in invertebrate conservation.

7

4.   **Status**

This deals with a number of different aspects.

a.   Any apparent declines or increases in status are noted where
      the data appears to be sufficiently reliable. For some
      species in poorly recorded groups, the age class and
      geographical spread of the records will closely follow
      recording effort, which is usually of an uneven temporal and
      geographic nature and hence the discussion of changing
      status in such species becomes rather speculative. For some
      groups however such as syrphids, Larger Brachycera and
      species associated with diminished habitats such as
      heathland, downland, coastal grazing marsh, ancient woodland
      and Caledonian pine forest, an obvious decline may be
      apparent, often involving both a contraction in range or
      loss of sites, and often decreased population levels at
      modern sites. The latter is usually through habitat
      degradation (especially departures from traditional
      management policies which may now be uneconomic), habitat
      fragmentation etc. For a smaller number of species there
      has been an obvious increase in status, especially species
      utilising conifers. These species may have originally been
      confined to Caledonian pine forest but are now able to use
      commercial plantations or pines on heathland and other
      habitats more widely in Britain, e.g. <u>Didea</u> <u>intermedia</u>,
      <u>Xylota</u> <u>coeruleiventris</u> (both Syrphidae) and <u>Chyliza</u>
      <u>fuscipennis</u> (Psilidae). These species often still fall
      within the Red Data Book and Notable categories, though
      obviously their conservation value becomes more limited once
      they exploit these new situations. Some species have
      exhibited changes in status that are clearly not linked
      directly to habitat loss or gain, or to changes in recording
      level, eg. the dramatic increase of the large and attractive
      <u>Stratiomys</u> <u>potamida</u> (Stratiomyidae). The factors behind
      such phenomena can only be speculated upon at present but
      may include climatic factors or parasite/predator cycles.

b.   The number of post 1960 localities known are cited, and for
      the rarer species (where not already included in the
      distribution section), the full dated post 1960 information
      is given here to assist in locating the species for further
      studies. Post 1960 information gives some indication of
      modern status and the number of localities is unquestionably
      more useful in assessing rarity and vulnerability than
      simply using the number of vice counties, especially where a
      clumped distribution is involved, and additionally sites
      provide the most meaningful units of distribution. An
      attempt has been made to take account of all known records
      up to and including the 1989 field season.

c.   Any taxonomic or nomenclatural confusion surrounding the
      species, or recent name changes that may mislead users of
      the review, are briefly discussed. A number of species
      included in the review are recent discoveries in Britain and
      not included in standard checklists or identification
      guides. A small number of species have not yet been

formally published as British and have been included by kind permission of the discoverers. Some species, whilst long recognised as British, have undergone recent name changes, either of the specific name, generic name and occasionally both. This is usually the result of recent European revisions and brings the British nomenclature into line with that abroad. Whilst this may confuse some users, these revisions are usually the result of accurate and detailed taxonomic studies that are intended to introduce stability in the future.

d. Where the group to which the species belongs has received relatively low levels of recording, irrespective of taxonomic or nomenclatural stability, this is stated.

e. For particularly rare species an attempt has been made to provide information on the known sites ie. whether NNRs, SSSIs or reserves of any sort, whether the owners are sympathetic to nature conservation and whether the sites are threatened, degraded or destroyed. This is because as a species becomes progressively rarer, its conservation status becomes increasingly a function of the individual sites rather than that of the overall habitat requirement. Consequently two rare species occurring at the same number of localities could have quite different conservation status, depending on the threats faced by the individual sites and the differential rates of their loss.

f. The European or world distribution is given where felt to be reasonably accurate and up to date, though this has only been possible for a few groups that have undergone a relatively recent revision. Whilst some species regarded as rarities in Great Britain are widespread and even common abroad, others show a decline throughout much of Europe, such as those species associated with ancient broadleaved woodland.

g. Where the status of the species has been provisionally modified from that in the Insect Red Data Book (Shirt 1987), a qualifying statement is given at the end of the status section ie. "Status revised from ......".

5. **Threat**

This outlines the operations which will render a site unsuitable for the species concerned. It is usually a generalised list of operations that form the prevalent threats to the habitat, breeding location or adult requirements. Specific threats affecting individual sites are only discussed for the rarest species. It should be noted that irrespective of the listed threats, habitat fragmentation and reduction of habitat area at a site can lead to extinction; indeed this is possibly the most under-estimated danger. Even where habitat continuity has occurred at a site, species have frequently become extinct, presumably in many cases because their populations have been forced to such low levels that they succumb to bad weather, parasite/predator cycles, the effects of inbreeding etc.

6.   **Management**

This outlines any positive active management, precautionary management or passive measures required to maintain the required habitat of a species in a suitable state for the species concerned, in the long term. Some species do not require much active management, simply a lack of disturbance and the maintenance of breeding locations, while others need continuation of practices such as coppicing or traditional patterns of grazing. As in the threat section, management for specific sites is only discussed for the rarest species, and for poorly known species the statement may be generalised and precautionary, such as advocating the use of habitat mosaics to maintain diversity at a site, or the continuation of traditional management policies.

Coverage

This is confined to Great Britain but not the Isle of Man, Republic of Ireland, Northern Ireland or the Channel Islands, which are outside the executive powers of the NCC.

Species lists & nomenclature

These are based upon the 1985 checklist of the Passmore Edwards Museum which is an updated version of A Checklist of British Insects, Part 5: Diptera & Siphonaptera, 2nd Edition (Kloet & Hincks 1976). Some further modifications have been necessary during the course of this review, either through the addition of species, the synonymising of others or due to name changes.

Abbreviations

NHML - The Natural History Museum of London [formerly the British Museum (Natural History)]
BRC   - Biological Records Centre (Institute of Terrestrial Ecology, Monks Wood)
CAB   - Commonwealth Agricultural Bureaux
FBA   - Freshwater Biological Association
ISR   - Invertebrate Site Register (NCC)
ITE   - Institute of Terrestrial Ecology (a component of NERC)
IUCN - International Union for Conservation of Nature and Natural Resources
LNR   - Local Nature Reserve
N   - Notable
NCC   - Nature Conservancy Council
NNR   - National Nature Reserve
NT   - National Trust
RDB   - Red Data Book (grading)
RSPB - Royal Society for the Protection of Birds
SSSI - Site of Special Scientific Interest

SOURCES OF INFORMATION

During the preparation of this work it was felt necessary to obtain as much distributional and ecological information for the Red Data Book and Notable species as was possible (within the constraints of a two year contract), rather than relying solely upon the leading specialists and key literature sources (the latter are frequently now outdated). It was not possible to survey comprehensively all literature, examine all collections or contact every recorder, though approximately 120 recorders eventually contributed to this review to varying extents (see Acknowledgements). Other sources of information are given more fully below.

Literature

Post 1960 runs of the following major British entomological journals were examined for all records of Red Data Book and Notable species:-

> Entomologist's Monthly Magazine
> Entomologist's Record & Journal of Variation
> Proceedings and Transactions of the British Entomological and Natural History Society (latterly the British Journal of Entomology and Natural History)
> Entomologist's Gazette
> Irish Naturalists' Journal
> The Entomologist

In addition, a good number of the more important papers in pre 1960 runs of these journals and (of any year) other journals such as County Naturalist Reports, county or regional journals, entomological newsletters and foreign literature, have been examined. Where foreign information has been incorporated into data sheets, this is stated, because the ecology and habitat requirements of certain species in Britain varies from that abroad. Unfortunately time has not permitted the citing of references used in, or relevant to, the data sheets, though details of information sources are obtainable from the author.

Museums

The Diptera collections of the following museums were examined by the author:-

- The Natural History Museum of London, including the A. Low collection which was temporarily housed here during the period of the visit.

- Department of Zoology Museum, University of Cambridge.

- Doncaster Museum and Art Gallery, including the card index of the Yorkshire Naturalist Union.

- Hope Department of Entomology, Oxford University Museum.

- Castle Museum, Norwich.

- Royal Scottish Museum, Edinburgh.

Further museum collections have been examined by other members of the ISR team for county reports and some of this information will have been included. A number of the recorders contacted individually are based at local museums or have access to the collections of such museums and have kindly passed on information, whether this be for all groups or selected families. This situation is referable to local museums at Coventry, Southend, Dorchester, Furzebrook, Reading, Glasgow and the Passmore Edwards Museum of London. Some published county lists also include a large proportion of records available in institute and museum collections e.g. papers by Kidd and Brindle on the Diptera of Lancashire and Cheshire cover much of the material in the Manchester Museum.

Recording Schemes

Records were obtained from the following national recording schemes:-

-      Tipuloidea and Ptychopteroidea (for selected genera and species)

-      Dixidae

-      Culicidae

-      Mycetophilidae

-      Lonchopteridae

-      Conopidae (limited species)

-      Opomyzidae

-      Sepsidae

-      Sciomyzidae

The vast amount of information accumulated by the Larger Brachycera and Syrphidae recording schemes, means that the information was not in a form that could be examined readily or rapidly and has therefore not been extracted for the review. Much of the relevant information has probably been intercepted through contact with the major recorders, especially for the rarest species, though there will undoubtedly be some important records that have been missed.

ACKNOWLEDGEMENTS

The author is greatly indebted to the large number of individuals (and certain organisations) who responded to requests for information, whether it be for records of Diptera, information on sites and habitats, or for allowing access to private collections. Whilst these efforts may not have accounted for all records of SSSI criteria species, the information gathered has been invaluable in confirming the modern status of many species throughout the country and in some cases quite radically altering our views on species. Without such a full response this would probably not have been achievable. A full list of contributors and advisors is given below.

D M Ackland, Dr K N A Alexander (NT), A A Allen, Sir C H Andrews, D Appleton, Dr S G Ball (NCC), D G Bartram, T J Bennett (Warden, Wicken Fen), C Bentley, Dr N L Birkett, Dr K P Bland, M G Bloxham, A Brackenbury, J H Bratton (NCC), M C Brian, Dr N R H Burgess, Dr N E Buxton (NCC), J Breed (Warden, Braunton Burrows), E J F Cameron (Warden, Glen Tanar), H Carter, P J Chandler, D Clements (NT), L Clemons, B Cogan, S J Coker, J H Cole, G A Collins, Dr J C Coulson, R Crossley, S B Cull, I P Davies (Warden, Thursley Common), Prof L Davies, W F Dean, J Deeming, Dr R H L Disney, J Dobson, Dr C M Drake (NCC), C E Dyte, M Edwards, G R Else, W A Ely, P F Entwistle, B C Eversham (ITE), L Farrell (NCC), E A Fonseca, G Forrester, A P Foster (NCC), A P Fowles (NCC), M Furse (FBA), S E Garnet (NCC), D Gibbs, Dr F Gilbert, G Glombeck, Dr H C J Godfray, A R Godfrey, A J Halstead, K H Halstead, E G Hancock, M W Hanson, P T Harding (ITE), R Harold (Warden, Woodwalton Fen), F Hatcher, D J de C Henshaw, P J Hodge, P Holmes (NCC), D Horsfield (NCC), I R Hudson, A M Hutson, Dr P Hyman, D Iliff, Dr A G Irwin, Dr J W Ismay, A W Jones, N P Jones, R A Jones, Dr R S

Key (NCC), Dr P Kirby (NCC), Dr J Lane, R Leeke, D A Levy, E T Levy, D Lott, I MacGowan (NCC), G McGavin, Dr I F G McLean (NCC), H Mendel, K Merrifield, S R Miles, D Moore, I K Morgan (NCC), M J Morgan, R K A Morris, J Mousley, J M Nelson, M Oates, Prof J Owen, C J Palmer, J Parkin (Warden, Dinnet), M Parsons (NCC), Passmore Edwards Museum, R M Payne, R G Payne, I Perry, E Philp, C W Plant, A C Pont (NHML), Dr K Porter (NCC), M N Pugh, S Randolph, M Rawes, A T Rees, D M Robertson, Dr G E Rotheray, Dr T A Rowell (NCC), Dr D A Sheppard (NCC), P Skidmore, D A Smith, K G V Smith (NHML), Dr K Snow, Dr M C D Speight, D Stephens, A E Stubbs (NCC), E Thorpe, Dr R Titchener, D M Unwin, R I Vane-Wright BM(NH)), K R Watt, P Waring (NCC), T J Wells (Warden, Moor House), Dr R P H Welsh (NCC), Dr I M White (CAB), D Whiteley, P Withers, Dr A Wright, M Wright (Warden, Chippenham Fen), N Wyatt (NHML), I R Wynne, Yorkshire Naturalist Union, Dr M Young.

Further mention must also be made of a number of entomologists who provided specialist advice on certain families and assisted the author in the production of data sheets and/or proof reading.

D M Ackland	-	Anthomyiidae.
P J Chandler	-	Mycetophilidae, Platypezidae, Otitidae, Pallopteridae, Odiniidae, Carnidae, Periscelididae, Aulacigastridae, Anthomyzidae, Asteiidae, Diastatidae, Drosophilidae, Scathophagidae and for volunteering useful information on numerous other areas of this review.
J Cole	-	Empididae, Dolichopodidae.
R Crossley	-	Empididae.
Prof L Davies	-	Calliphoridae.
Dr R H L Disney	-	Dixidae, Phoridae.
Dr C M Drake	-	Lonchopteridae, Opomyzidae, certain Larger Brachycera.
Dr A G Irwin	-	Ephydridae.
Dr J W Ismay	-	Chloropidae.
Dr I F G McLean	-	All data sheets with specialist advice particularly for the Chamaemyiidae and Sciomyzidae.
J M Nelson	-	Scathophagidae.
A E Stubbs	-	Trichoceridae, Tipulidae, Ptychopteridae, Thaumaleidae, Anisopodidae, Stratiomyidae, Xylomyidae, Xylophagidae, Rhagionidae, Tabanidae, Asilidae, Therevidae, Scenopinidae, Acroceridae, Bombyliidae, Pipunculidae, Syrphidae, Conopidae, Clusiidae.
Dr I M White	-	Tephritidae.
P Withers	-	Heleomyzidae, Clusiidae.

Acknowledgement is also due to BRC for allowing the use of their data for certain families (these are listed under Sources of Information) and to the Museums listed under Sources of Information for allowing me access to their collections and for making my presence so welcome.

Finally I would like to thank all my colleagues at the NCC for their advice and encouragement and especially the Word Processing Section at NCC Peterborough for their endless patience during the past few years.

This review is the result of a two year period appointment initiated in May 1985 and funded by the NCC.

CORRESPONDENCE

The ISR is maintaining data files on all British Red Data Book and Notable species of Diptera and would be pleased to receive modern records and biological information on any of the species included in the review, as well as views on the inclusion, exclusion or grading of any species. The biology and habitat requirements of many species are insufficiently known. This information is essential if the correct management is to be assessed and where possible implemented for the conservation of these species. Please address all correspondence to: The Nature Conservancy Council, Northminster House, Peterborough PE1 1UA.

RECORDING SCHEMES, STUDY GROUPS AND NEWSLETTERS

Many of the families included in this review are covered by national recording schemes, either formally in conjunction with BRC, or on an informal basis (eg. Lonchopteridae and Opomyzidae). Regular newsletters are available for some of the schemes. These schemes and their organisers are listed below:-

- Cranefly (Tipuloidea & Ptychopteroidea) recording scheme; organiser:-A E Stubbs, NCC, Northminster House, Peterborough, PE1 1UA.

- Dixidae recording scheme; organiser:- Dr E K Goldie-Smith, 44-46 Military Road, Rye, E Sussex, TN31 7NY.

- Mosquito recording scheme; organiser:- Dr N R H Burgess, Royal Army Medical College, Millbank, London, SW1P 4RJ.

- Mycetophilidae (Fungus Gnat) recording scheme; organiser:- P J Chandler, Weston Research Laboratories, Vanwall Road, Maidenhead, Berks, SL6 4UF.

- Larger Brachycera recording scheme; organiser:- Dr C M Drake, Nature Conservancy Council, Northminster House, Peterborough, PE1 1UA. This scheme has a regular newsletter.

- Dolichopodidae and Empididae Study Group; not a recording scheme but with a regular newsletter; organisers:- Dr A Bainbridge, 166 Farnborough Road, Farnborough, Hants, GU14 7IJ and R Crossley, 46 St Davids Road, Otley, West Yorkshire, LS21 2AW.

- Hoverfly (Syrphidae) recording scheme; organisers:- Dr S G Ball & R K Morris, The Nature Conservancy Council, Northminster House, Peterborough, PE1 1UA. Various regional organisers. This scheme has a regular newsletter edited by Dr G E Rotheray, Dept of Natural History, Royal Scottish Museum, Chambers Street, Edinburgh, EH1 1JF.

- Conopidae recording scheme; organiser:- D Clements, 9 Cecily Hill, Cirencester, Glos, GL7 2EF.

- Tephritidae newsletter; editor:- Mr L Clemons, 70 Tonge Road, Sittingbourne, Kent, ME10 3SR.

- Sciomyzidae recording scheme; organisers:- Dr S G Ball and Dr I F G McLean, NCC, Northminster House, Peterborough, PE1 1UA.

- Lonchopteridae and Opomyzidae recording schemes; unofficial schemes for 2 poorly recorded families; organised by Dr C M Drake, NCC, Northminster House, Peterborough, PE1 1UA.

- Diptera Recording Schemes Bulletin - a regular newsletter providing a general overview of the study of Diptera in Britain, providing information on field and indoor meetings, recording schemes and study groups, new literature and other events. Information can be obtained from the co-ordinator A E Stubbs, NCC, Northminster House, Peterborough, PE1 1UA.

- Dipterists' Digest - a new British based journal for Diptera which commenced with Issue No 1 in November 1988. For details contact the editor:-Derek Whiteley, 730 Ecclesall Road, Sheffield, S11 8TB.

BIBLIOGRAPHY

The following is a list of the more important literature relevant to species covered in this review. It is neither a comprehensive bibliography of the British Diptera fauna, or a complete list of references used in the compilation of this review, the latter amounting to over one thousand articles. The bibliography attempts to enable accurate identification of the majority of SSSI criteria species and concentrates on the most recent key works on families or genera, also including any further papers that clarify, modify or provide additional information to such key works. The arrangement is in taxonomic order, like the data sheets.

General

Colyer, C.N. & Hammond, C.O. 1968. Flies of the British Isles, 2nd ed. London, Warne.

Falk, S.J. 1985. A Provisional Review of the Status of British Diptera. NCC (unpublished) (ISR report no. 62, CSD report no. 529).

Kloet, G.S. & Hincks, W.D. 1975. A check list of British insects, part 5: Diptera and Siphonaptera, 2nd ed. (revised K.G.V. Smith et al). Handbooks for the Identification of British Insects, 11(5).

Shirt, D.B. (ed) 1987. British Red Data Books: 2. Insects. Peterborough, Nature Conservancy Council.

Sims, R.W., Freeman, P. & Hawksworth, D.L. 1988. Key works to the fauna and flora of the British Isles and north-western Europe. Oxford, The Systematics Association, Special Volume No 33.

Stubbs, A.E. & Chandler, P.J. 1978. A dipterists handbook. Hanworth, Middlesex; Amateur Entomologists' Society.

Wells, S.M., Pyle, R.M. & Collins, N.M. 1983. The IUCN Invertebrate Red Data Book. Gland, Switzerland: IUCN.

Trichoceridae

Brindle, A. 1962. Taxonomic Notes on the Larvae of British Diptera. 11. Trichoceridae and Anisopodidae. The Entomologist, 95: 284-288.

Coe, R.L., Freeman, P. & Mattingley, P.F. 1950. Diptera. 2. Nematocera: families Tipulidae to Chironomidae. Handbooks for the Identification of British Insects, 9(2).

Laurence, B.R. 1957. The British species of Trichocera (Diptera: Trichoceridae). Proceeding of the Royal Entomological Society of London (A), 32: 132-138.

Tipulidae

Brindle, A. 1958. Notes on the Identification of Limnophila larvae (Diptera -Tipulidae). Transactions of the Society for British Entomology, 13: 57-68.

Brindle, A. 1960. The Larvae and Pupae of the British Tipulidae (Diptera - Tipulidae). Transactions of the Society for British Entomology, 14: 63-114.

Brindle, A. 1967. The Larvae and Pupae of the British Cylindrotominae and Limoniinae (Diptera, Tipulidae). Transactions of the Society for British Entomology, 17: 151-216.

Brindle, A. & Bryce, D. 1960. The Larvae of the British Hexatomini (Dipt., Tipulidae). Entomologist's Gazette, 11: 207-224.

Chandler, P.J. & Stubbs, A.E. 1977. Tipula (Lunatipula) dilatata Schummel 1833 (Diptera: Tipulidae) new to Britain. Proceedings and Transactions of the British Entomological and Natural History Society, 10: 85-87.

Coe, R.L., Freeman, P. & Mattingley, P.F. 1950. Diptera. 2. Nematocera: families Tipulidae to Chironomidae. Handbooks for the Identification of British Insects, 9(2).

Edwards, F.W. 1938. British Short-palped Craneflies. Taxonomy of Adults. Transactions of the Society for British Entomologists, 5: 1-168.

Edwards, F.W. 1939. Additions to the list of British Craneflies. Entomologist's Monthly Magazine, 75: 241-249.

Hutson, A.M. & Stubbs, A.E. 1974. Limonia (Dicranomyia) omissinervis De Meijere (Diptera: Tipulidae) new to Britain, and the identity of L. (D.) patens in Britain. Entomologist's Gazette, 25: 297-301.

Hutson, A.M. & Vane-Wright, R.I. 1969. Corrections and additions to the list of British Nematocera (Diptera) since Kloet and Hincks' 'A Check List of British Insects' (1945), Part 1 - Introduction and families Tipulidae, Trichoceridae and Anisopodidae (Tipuloidea). Entomologist's Gazette, 20: 231-256.

Stubbs, A.E. 1977. Gonomyia (Protogonomyia) limbata (Ros.) and Molophilus variispinus Stary (Dipt: Tipulidae) new to Britain from Wales. Proceedings and Transactions of the British Entomological and Natural History Society, 10: 100-103.

Stubbs, A.E. & Chandler, P.J. 1973. Molophilus lackschewitzianus Alexander 1952 (Diptera: Tipulidae) new to the British Isles. Proceedings and Transactions of the British Entomological and Natural History Society, 6: 18-19.

Stubbs, A.E. & Little, C.J. 1974. Dicranoptycha Osten-sacken (Diptera, Tipulidae), a cranefly genus new to Britain. Proceedings and Transactions of the British Entomological and Natural History Society, 7: 44-46.

Ptychopteridae

Brindle, A. 1962. Taxonomic notes on the larvae of British Diptera. 9. The family Ptychopteridae. The Entomologist, 95: 212-6.

Edwards, F.W. 1941. Notes on British Fungus-Gnats (Dipt, Mycetophilidae). Entomologist's Monthly Magazine, 77: 21-32, 67-82.

Hutson, A.M. 1979. Notes on Sciophilinae (Dipt., Mycetophilidae) with a revision of Palaearctic Syntemna Winnertz. Entomologist's Monthly Magazine, 114: 131-145.

Hutson, A.M., Ackland, D.M. & Kidd, L.N. 1980. Mycetophilidae (Bolitophilinae, Ditomyiinae, Diadocidiinae, Keroplatinae, Sciophilinae and Manotinae). Handbooks for the Identification of British Insects, 9(e).

Larger Brachycera

(General publications covering the Stratiomyidae, Xylomyidae, Xylophagidae, Rhagionidae, Tabanidae, Asilidae, Therevidae, Scenopinidae, Acroceridae, Bombyliidae. Those dealing with families individually are given separately).

Oldroyd, H. 1969. Diptera Brachycera. Handbooks for the Identification of British Insects, 9(4).

Verrall, G.H. 1909 British Flies, 5: Stratiomyidae to Cyrtidae. London, Gurney and Jackson.

Stratiomyidae

Brindle, A. 1962. Taxonomic notes on the larvae of British Diptera. 7. The genus Pachygaster Meigen (Stratiomyidae). The Entomologist, 95: 77-82.

Brindle, A. 1964. Taxonomic notes on the larvae of British Diptera. 16. The Stratiomyinae (Stratiomyidae). The Entomologist, 97: 91-96.

Brindle, A. 1964. Taxonomic notes on the larvae of British Diptera. 16. The Clitellarinae (Stratiomyidae). The Entomologist, 97: 134-139.

Rozkosny, R. 1973. The Stratiomyidae (Diptera) of Fennoscandia and Denmark. Fauna Entomologica Scandinavica, 1.

Rozkosny, R. 1982-83. A Biosystematic study of the European Stratiomyidae (Diptera) in 2 vols. Series Entomologica, 25.

Speight, M.C.D. 1981. Chorisops nagatomii, an insect new to Ireland and its segregation from C. tibialis (Diptera: Stratiomyidae). Irish Naturalists' Journal, 20(8): 327-329.

Xylophagidae

Brindle, A. 1961. Taxonomic notes on the larvae of British Diptera. 2. The genus Xylophagus Meigen (Rhagionidae). The Entomologist, 94: 144-8.

Stubbs, A.E. 1972. A Review of Information on the Distribution of the British species of Ptychoptera (Dipt: Ptychopteridae). The Entomologist, 105: 23-38; Part II: 308-312.

Dixidae

Disney, R.H.L. 1975. A key to British Dixidae. Freshwater Biological Association Scientific Publication, 31.

Culicidae

Cranston, P.S., Ramsdale, C.D., Snow, K.R. & White, G.B. 1987. Keys to the Adults, Male Hypopygia, Fourth Instar Larvae and Pupae of the British Mosquitoes (Culicidae). Freshwater Biological Association Scientific Publication, 48.

Thaumaleidae

Edwards, F.W. 1929. A revision of the Thaumaleidae. Zool. Anz, 82: 121-142.

Ceratopogonidae

Boorman, J. & Rowland, C. 1988. A key to the Genera of British Ceratopogonidae (Diptera). Entomologist's Gazette, 39: 65-73.

Disney, R.H.L. 1975. A Midge (Dipt, Ceratopogonidae) new to Britain that is abundant in the limestone pavement of the Yorkshire Pennines. Entomologist's Monthly Magazine, 110: 227-8.

Edwards, F.W. 1926. On the British Biting Midges. Transactions of the Entomological Society of London, 74: 389-426.

Edwards, F.W., Oldroyd, H. & Smart, J. 1939. British Bloodsucking Flies. London, British Museum (Natural History).

Anisopodidae

Brindle, A. 1962. Taxonomic Notes on the Larvae of British Diptera. 11. Trichoceridae and Anisopodidae. The Entomologist, 95: 284-288.

Coe, R.L., Freeman, P. & Mattingley, P.F. 1950. Diptera. 2. Nematocera: families Tipulidae to Chironomidae. Handbooks for the Identification of British Insects, 9(2).

Mycetophilidae (sensu lato)

Chandler, P.J. 1987. Notes on British Fungus Gnats of the smaller families and sub-families (Diptera, Mycetophiloidea). Proceedings and Transactions of the British Entomological and Natural History Society, 20: 105-118.

Edwards, F.W. 1925. British Fungus Gnats (Diptera, Mycetophilidae) with a revised Generic Classification of the Family. Transactions of the Entomological Society of London, 1924: 505-670.

Xylomyidae

Brindle, A. 1961. Taxonomic notes on the larvae of British Diptera. 3. The genus Solva Walker (Xylomyia Rondani). The Entomologist, 94: 202-5.

Rhagionidae

Brindle, A. 1962. Taxonomic notes on the larvae of British Diptera. 12. The genus Rhagio F. (Rhagionidae). The Entomologist, 95: 311-5.

Cole, J. 1981. Chrysopilus erythrophthalmus Loew (Diptera: Rhagionidae) New to Britain. Entomologists' Gazette, 32: 275-277.

Tabanidae

Brindle, A. 1961. Taxonomic notes on the larvae of British Diptera. 1. The genus Haematopota Meigen (Tabanidae). The Entomologist, 94: 121-4.

Chvala, M., Lyneborg, L. & Moucha, J. 1972. The horseflies of Europe (Diptera: Tabanidae). Copenhagen, Entomological Society of Copenhagen.

Asilidae

Brindle, A. 1962. Taxonomic notes on the larvae of British Diptera. 10. The Asilidae. The Entomologist, 95: 241-7.

Morgan, M.J. 1981. Asilidae (Dipt.) in North Wales. Entomologist's Monthly Magazine, 116: 123-125.

Skidmore, P. 1966. Asilidae (Dipt.) of Northern England. Entomologist's Record and Journal of Variation, 78: 230-235; 257-266.

Speight, M.C.D. 1987. Re-affirmation of the status of Machimus cowini, (Diptera, Asilidae), as a separate species, with a key to distinguish the male from males of some related species. Irish Naturalists' Journal, 22(7): 296-304.

Empididae (sensu lato)

Allen, A.A. 1983. Tachydromia terricola Zett. (Dipt, Empididae) new to Britain. Entomologist's Record and Journal of Variation, 95: 223-224.

Andrewes, C.H. 1966. Two species of Empididae (Diptera) new to British list, from Wiltshire. Entomologist's Monthly Magazine, 102: 1-2.

Andrewes, C.H. 1978. Platypalpus mikii Becker (Dipt, Empididae) new to Britain. Entomologist's Monthly Magazine, 113: 81.

Chandler, P.J. 1973. Rhamphomyia (Pararhamphomyia) marginata Fabricius (Dipt, Empididae), a remarkable addition to the British list. Proceedings and Transactions of the British Entomological and Natural History Society, 6: 73-76.

Chvala, M. 1970. Revision of Palaearctic species of the genus Tachydromia Meig. (= Tachista Loew) (Dipt, Empididae). Acta Entomologica-Musei Nationalis Pragae (1969), 38: 431-540.

Chvala, M. 1973a. European species of the Platypalpus albiseta group (Diptera, Empididae). Acta Entomologica Bohemoslovaca, 70: 117-136.

Chvala, M. 1973b. Notes on British Tachydromia (Dipt, Empididae) with description of a new species from Inverness-shire. Entomologist's Monthly Magazine, 108: 214-218.

Chvala, M. 1975. The Tachydromiinae (Dipt, Empididae) of Fennoscandia and Denmark. Fauna Entomologica Scandinavica, 3: 1-336.

Chvala, M. 1983. The Empidoidea (Diptera) of Fennoscandia and Denmark. II. General part. The families Hybotidae, Atelestidae and Microphoridae. Fauna Entomologica Scandinavica, 12: 1-279.

Cole, J.H. 1964. A species of Euthyneura (Diptera., Empididae) new to Britain. The Entomologist, 97: 128.

Cole, J.H. 1985. Some scarce species of Platypalpus Macquart (Dipt, Empididae) including P. pallidiseta Kovalev new to Britain. Entomologist's Monthly Magazine, 121: 241-242.

Collin, J.E. 1961. British Flies, 6: Empididae. 782 pp. Cambridge, Cambridge University Press.

Perry, I. 1986. Some Diptera from Quy Fen. Nature in Cambridgeshire, 28: 56-58.

Smith, K.G.V. 1964. Chersodromia cursitans Zetterstedt (Dipt., Empididae) reinstated as a British species. Entomologist's Monthly Magazine, 99: 127-128.

Smith, K.G.V. 1969. Platypalpus (Cleptodromia) longimana Corti new to Britain and the male of P. alter (Collin) (Dipt., Empididae). Entomologist's Monthly Magazine, 105: 108-110.

Smith, K.G.V. & Chvala, M. 1976. Notes on some British Platypalpus Macquart (Dipt., Empididae), including a species new to science, two new to Britain and new synonymy. Entomologist's Record and Journal of Variation, 88: 137-144.

Wagner, R. 1985. A revision of the genus Heleodromia (Diptera, Empididae) in Europe. Aquatic Insects, 7: 33-43.

Dolichopodidae

Fonseca, E.C.M. d' Assis. 1978. Diptera Orthorrhapha Brachycera Dolichopodidae. Handbooks for the Identification of British Insects, 9(5).

18

Speight, M.C.D. 1987. *Achalcus melanotrichus*, *Systenus leucurus* and *S. pallipes* (Diptera: Dolichopodidae) new to Ireland, bred from rot-holes in *Betula*, *Fagus* and *Acer pseudoplatanus*, with a comment on the significance of these records. *Irish Naturalists' Journal*, 22(6): 250-252.

Lonchopteridae

Smith, K.G.V. 1969. Lonchopteridae. *Handbooks for the Identification of British Insects*, 10(2).

Phoridae

Disney, R.H.L. 1983. Scuttle flies. Diptera, Phoridae (except *Megaselia*). *Handbooks for the Identification of British Insects*, 10(6).

Platypezidae

Brindle, A. 1961. Taxonomic Notes on the Larvae of British Diptera. 5. The Clythiidae (Platypezidae). *The Entomologist*, 94: 274-278.

Chandler, P.J. 1973. The flat-footed flies (Diptera, Aschiza-Platypezidae) known to occur in Kent. With a key to the genera and species so far recorded from the British Isles. *Transactions of the Kent Field Club*, 5(1): 15-44.

Chandler, P.J. 1974. Additions and corrections to the British list of Platypezidae (Diptera) incorporating a revision of the palaearctic species of *Callomyia* Meigen. *Proceedings and Transactions of the British Entomological and Natural History Society*, 7(1): 1-32.

McLean, I.F.G. & Chandler, P.J. 1982. *Microsania straeleni* Collart (Diptera: Platypezidae), a species of "smoke fly" new to Britain. *Entomologist's Gazette*, 33: 49-50.

Verrall, G.H. 1901. British Flies, 8: Platypezidae, Pipunculidae, Syrphidae. London, Gurney and Jackson. Reprinted (1969) by Classey, Faringdon.

Pipunculidae

Coe, R.L. 1966. Pipunculidae. *Handbooks for the Identification of British Insects*, 10(2b).

Stubbs, A.E. 1980. The largest pipunculid in the land: *Nephrocerus scutellata* (Macquart, 1834) (Diptera, Pipunculidae) new to Britain, with observations on its behaviour in Greece. *Proceedings and Transactions of the British Entomological and Natural History Society*, 13: 46-48.

Syrphidae

Stubbs, A.E. & Falk, S.J. 1983. British Hoverflies: an illustrated identification guide. London, BENHS.

Conopidae

Smith, K.G.V. 1969. Conopidae. *Handbooks for the Identification of British Insects*, 10(3a).

Smith, K.G.V. 1970. The identity of *Myopa polystigma* Rondani, and an additional British and continental species of the genus (Diptera: Conopidae). *The Entomologist*, 103: 186-9.

Tephritidae

White, I.M. 1987. Tephritid flies (Diptera: Tephritidae). *Handbooks for the Identification of British Insects*, 10(5a).

Otitidae

Cogan, B.H. & Dear, J.P. 1975. Additions and corrections to the list of British acalypterate Diptera. *Entomologist's Monthly Magazine*, 110: 173-81.

Hennig, W. 1939. Otitidae. In: Lindner, E. *Die Fliegen der Palaearktischen Region*, 46-47. Schwiezerbart, Stuttgart.

Hennig, W. 1940. Ulidiidae. In: Lindner, E. *Die Fliegen der Palaearktischen Region*, 45. Schwiezerbart, Stuttgart.

Speight, M.C.D. & Chandler, P.J.C. 1983. Irish Otitidae and Platystomatidae (Diptera) including a key to the genera known in Ireland and/or Great Britain. *Irish Naturalists' Journal*, 21(3): 130-6.

Micropezidae

Chandler, P.J. 1975. Notes on the British status of three unusual Acalypterate flies (Diptera). *Proceedings and Transactions of the British Entomological and Natural History Society*, 8: 66-72.

Collin, J.E. 1945. British Micropezidae (Diptera). *Entomologist's Record and Journal of Variation*, 57: 115-19.

Pseudopomyzidae

Chandler, P.J. 1983. *Pseudopomyza atrimana* (Meigen) (Diptera: Pseudopomyzidae), a fly of an acalypterate family new to the British list. *Proceedings and Transactions of the British Entomological and Natural History Society*, 16: 87-91.

Megamerinidae and Tanypezidae

Chandler, P.J. 1975. Notes on the British status of three unusual Acalypterate flies (Diptera). *Proceedings and Transactions of the British Entomological and Natural History Society*, 8: 66-72.

Chandler, P.J. 1977. Supplementary notes on Megamerina (Diptera: Megamerinidae) and Tanypeza (Diptera: Tanypezidae). Proceedings and Transactions of the British Entomological and Natural History Society, 10: 26.

Cole, J.H. 1981. Strongylophthalma ustulata (Zetterstedt) (Diptera: Tanypezidae) new to Britain. Entomologist's Gazette, 32: 47-50.

Psilidae

Chandler, P.J. 1975. Observations on Plant Associations of the Psilidae (Diptera). Entomologist's Record and Journal of Variation, 87: 13-17.

Collin, J.E. 1944. The British species of Psilidae (Diptera). Entomologist's Monthly Magazine, 80: 214-24.

Wakerley, S.B. 1959. A new species of Psila Meigen (Diptera: Psilidae) from Northern England. Proceedings of the Royal Entomological Society of London, 28: 107-108.

Winter, T.G. 1988. Larvae of Chyliza fuscipennis (Robineau-Desvoidy) (Dipt, Psilidae) in coniferous resin. Entomologist's Monthly Magazine, 124: 73-76.

Chamaemyiidae

Andrewes, C.H. 1967. Acrometopia wahlbergi (Zett.) (Diptera, Chamaemyiidae), a genus and species of fly new to Britain. Entomologist's Monthly Magazine, 103: 208.

Collin, J.E. 1966. The British species of Chamaemyia Mg. (Ochtiphila Fln) Transactions of the Society for British Entomology. 17: 121-8.

McLean, I.F.G. 1982. Three species of Leucopis Meigen (Diptera: Chamaemyiidae) new to Britain. Entomologist's Record and Journal of Variation, 94: 70-72.

Lauxaniidae

Collin, J.E. 1948. A short synopsis of the British Sapromyzidae (Diptera). Transactions of the Royal Entomological Society of London, 99: 225-42.

Collin, J.E. 1966. A new species of Minettia Desvoidy (Diptera, Sapromyzidae). The Entomologist, 99: 144-145.

Miller, R.M. 1977. Ecology of Lauxaniidae (Diptera: Acalyptratae) I. Old and New Rearing Records with Biological Notes and Discussion. Annals of The Natal Museum, 23: 215-238.

Heleomyzidae

Collin, J.E. 1943. The British species of Heleomyzidae (Diptera). Entomologist's Monthly Magazine, 79: 234-51.

Collin, J.E. 1951. British Helomyzidae (Diptera). Additions and Corrections. Journal of the Society for British Entomology, 4: 37-39.

Papp, L. 1978. Some cavernicolous Diptera of the Geneva Museum. Revue Suisse De Zoologie, 85: 99-106.

Skidmore, P. 1966. The Biology of Scoliocentra villosa (Mg.) (Dipt, Heleomyzidae). Entomologist's Monthly Magazine, 102: 94-98.

Withers, P. 1987. The British species of the genus Suillia (Diptera, Heleomyzidae), including a species new to science. Proceedings and Transactions of the British Entomological and Natural History Society, 20: 91-104.

Chyromyidae

Collin, J.E. 1949. The palaearctic species of the genus Aphaniosoma Beck. (Diptera, Chiromyidae). Annals and Magazine of Natural History, (12) 2: 127-47.

Sepsidae

Pont, A.C. 1979. Sepsidae. Diptera Cyclorrhapha, Acalyptrata. Handbooks for the Identification of British Insects, 10(5c).

Pont, A.C. 1986. Two additions to the list of British Sepsidae (Diptera). Entomologists' Monthly Magazine, 122: 91-92.

Pont, A.C. 1986. Provisional Atlas of the British Sepsidae. Monkswood, ITE.

Sciomyzidae

Ball, S.G. & McLean, I.F.G. 1986. Sciomyzidae Recording Scheme Newsletter No. 2 -Preliminary Atlas.

Cole, J. 1988. Antichaeta obliviosa Enderlein (Diptera: Sciomyzidae) new to Britain. The Entomologist, 107: 155.

Knutson, L.V. & Lyneborg, L. 1965. Danish acalyptrate flies. 3. Sciomyzidae (Diptera). Entomologiske Meddelelser, 34: 63-102.

McLean, I.F.G. (ed). 1983. Sciomyzidae Recording Scheme Newsletter No. 1.

Rozkosny, R. 1984. The Sciomyzidae (Diptera) of Fennoscandia and Denmark. Fauna Entomologica Scandinavica, 14.

Pallopteridae

Cogan, B.H. & Dear, J.P. 1975. Additions and corrections to the list of British acalypterate Diptera. Entomologist's Monthly Magazine, 110: 173-81.

Collin, J.E. 1951. The British species of the genus Palloptera Fallen (Diptera), Entomologist's Record and Journal of Variation,

Rohacek, J. 1983. Acalypterate Diptera of peat-bogs in North Moravia (Czechoslovakia), Part 4. Tephritidae, Lonchaeidae, Pallopteridae, Piophilidae. Casopis Slezskeho musea v Opave, 32: 111-123.

Lonchaeidae

Collin, J.E. 1953. A revision of the British (and notes on other) species of Lonchaeidae (Diptera). Transactions of the Society for British Entomology, 11: 181-207.

Hackman, W. 1956. The Lonchaeidae (Dipt.) of Eastern Fennoscandia. Notulae entomologicae, 36: 89-115.

Morge, C. 1963. Die Lonchaeidae und Pallopteridae Osterreichs und der angrenzenden Gebiete. 1. Die Lonchaeidae. Naturkundliches Jahrbuch der Stadt Linz, 1963: 123-312.

Neottiophilidae and Piophilidae

Cogan, B.H. & Dear, J.P. 1975. Additions and corrections to the list of British acalypterate Diptera. Entomologist's Monthly Magazine, 110: 173-81.

Collin, J.E. 1910. Additions and corrections to the British List of Muscidae Acalyptratae. Piophila. Entomologist's Monthly Magazine, 46: 177-8.

Czerny, L. 1930. Neottiophilidae. In: Lindner, E. Die Fliegen der Palaearktischen Region, 38b. Schweizerbart, Stuttgart.

Opomyzidae

Collin, J.E. 1945. The British species of Opomyzidae (Diptera). Entomologist's Record and Journal of Variation, 57: 13-16.

Clusiidae

Stubbs, A.E. 1982. An identification guide to British Clusiidae. Proceedings and Transactions of the British Entomological and Natural History Society, 15: 89-93.

Withers, P. 1985. Notes on some British Clusiidae and reduction of Clusiodes facialis (Coll.) to synonymy. Proceedings and Transactions of the British Entomological and Natural History Society, 18: 63-64.

Odiniidae

Allen, A.A. 1987. Odinia maculata Mg. (Dipt.) at Windsor; with a note on two other species in SE London. Entomologist's Record and Journal of Variation, 99: 42-43.

Cogan, B.H. 1969. Two species of the genus Odinia R.-D. (Dipt, Odiniidae) new to Britain, one of which is new to science. Entomologist's Monthly Magazine, 104: 252-254.

Collin, J.E. 1952. On the European species of the genus Odinia R.-D. (Diptera: Odiniidae). Proceedings of the Royal Entomological Society of London, 21: 110-116.

Lewis, D.C. 1979. The larva and puparium of Odinia meijerei Collin (Dipt., Odiniidae). Entomologist's Monthly Magazine, 114: 233-235.

Carnidae

Collin, J.E. 1930. Some species of the genus Meoneura (Diptera). Entomologist's Monthly Magazine, 66: 82-9.

Collin, J.E. 1937. Two new species of the genus Meoneura (Diptera, Carnidae). Entomologist's Monthly Magazine, 73: 250-2.

Acartophthalmidae

Chandler, P.J. 1976. A note on the habits of Acartophthalmus nigrinus (Zetterstedt) (Dipt., Acartophthalmidae). Entomologist's Monthly Magazine, 112: 103.

Czerny, L. 1928.Clusiidae. In: Lindner, E. Die Fliegen der Palaearktischen Region, 54a. Schweizerbart, Stuttgart.

Irwin, A.G. 1983. Acartophthalmus bicolor Oldenberg (Dipt., Acartophthalmidae) in Suffolk. Entomologist's Monthly Magazine, 119: 54.

Periscelididae

Duda, O. 1934. Periscelididae. In: Lindner, E. Die Fliegen der Palaearktischen Region, 58a. Schweizerbart, Stuttgart.

Aulacigastridae

Cogan, B.H. & Dear, J.P. 1975. Additions and corrections to the list of British acalypterate Diptera. Entomologist's Monthly Magazine, 110: 173-81.

Collin, J.E. 1944. The British species of Anthomyzidae (Diptera). Entomologist's Monthly Magazine, 80: 265-272.

Irwin, A.G. 1982. A new species of Stenomicra Cocquillet (Diptera, Aulacigastridae) from Anglesey, North Wales. Entomologist's Monthly Magazine, 118: 235-238.

Anthomyzidae

Collin, J.E. 1944. The British species of Anthomyzidae (Diptera). Entomologist's Monthly Magazine, 80: 265-72.

Asteiidae

Chandler, P.J. 1978. A revision of the British Asteiidae (Diptera) including two additions to the British List. Proceedings and Transactions of the British Entomological and Natural History Society, 11: 23-34.

Cogan, B.H. & Dear, J.P. 1975. Additions and corrections to the list of British acalypterate Diptera. Entomologist's Monthly Magazine, 110: 173-81.

Agromyzidae

Spencer, K.A. 1972. Agromyzidae. Handbooks for the Identification of British Insects, 10 (5g).

Chloropidae

Beschovski, V.L. & Lansbury, I. 1987. Two new Rhopalopterum species from England (UK) and Hungary (Insecta, Diptera, Chloropidae). Reichenbachia, 25: 91-95.

Cogan, B.H. & Dear, J.P. 1975. Additions and corrections to the list of British acalypterate Diptera. Entomologist's Monthly Magazine, 110: 173-81.

Collin, J.E. 1946. The British genera and species of Oscinellinae (Diptera, Chloropidae). Transactions of the Royal Entomological Society of London, 97: 117-48.

Collin, J.E. 1966. A revision of the British species of Cetema Hendel (Diptera, Chloropidae) with two species new to science. The Entomologist, 99: 116-20.

Deeming, J.C. 1980. A new Gaurax Loew (Dipt, Chloropidae) from England. Entomologist's Monthly Magazine, 116: 93-94.

Drake, C.M. 1987. Meromyza hispanica Fedoseeva 1971 (Dipt., Chloropidae) new to Britain. Entomologist's Monthly Magazine, 123: 217-218.

Duda, O. 1932-3. Chloropidae. In: Lindner, E. Die Fliegen der Palaearktischen Region, 61. Schweizerbart, Stuttgart.

Ismay, J.W. 1976. A revision of Oscinisoma (Diptera, Chloropidae) in Britain. Entomologist's Gazette, 27: 107-112.

Ismay, J.W. 1980. Two Brachypterous Chloropidae (Dipt.) new to Britain. Entomologist's Monthly Magazine, 115: 225-227.

Ismay, J.W. 1981. British Meromyza (Dipt., Chloropidae). Entomologist's Monthly Magazine, 116: 177-197.

Ismay, J.W. 1985. The identity of Cetema elongata (Meigen) (Dipt., Chloropidae). Entomologist's Monthly Magazine, 121: 35-38.

Smith, K.G.V. 1965. The immature stages of Gaurax (= Botanobia) dubi (Macquart) (Dipt., Chloropidae), with notes on the specific status of G. fascipes Becker. Entomologist's Monthly Magazine, 100: 237-39.

Ephydridae

Becker, T. 1926. Ephydridae. In: Lindner, E. Die Fliegen der Palaearktischen Region, 56a. Schweizerbart, Stuttgart.

Cogan, B.H. & Dear, J.P. 1975. Additions and corrections to the list of British acalypterate Diptera. Entomologist's Monthly Magazine, 110: 173-81.

Collin, J.E. 1930. Some new species of the Dipterous Genus, Scatella Dsv., and the differentiation of Stictoscatella gen. nov. Entomologist's Monthly Magazine, 66: 133-9.

Collin, J.E. 1943. The British species of Psilopa Fln. and Discocerina Mcq. (Dipt, Ephydridae). Entomologist's Monthly Magazine, 79: 145-51.

Irwin, A.G. 1985. British Ochthera (Diptera, Ephydridae). Entomologist's Monthly Magazine, 121: 151-4.

Diastatidae

Chandler, P.J. 1986. The British species of Diastata Meigen and Campichoeta Macquart (Diptera: Drosophiloidea). Proceedings and Transactions of the British Entomological and Natural History Society, 19: 9-18.

Drosophilidae

Basden, E.B. 1954. The distribution and biology of Drosophilidae (Diptera) in Scotland, including a new species of 'Drosophila'. Transactions of the Royal Society of Edinburgh, 62: 603-54.

Chandler, P.J. 1987. The British species of Stegana Meigen (Diptera: Drosophilidae) -deletion of S. furta (Linnaeus) and addition of four species of the coleoptrata (Scopoli) group. Entomologist's Record and Journal of Variation, 99: 115-123.

Fonseca, E.C.M. d' Assis. 1965. A short key to the British Drosophilidae (Diptera) including a new species of Amiota. Transactions of the Society for British Entomology, 16: 233-244.

Milichiidae

Hennig, W. 1937. Milichiidae and Carnidae. In: Lindner, E. Die Fliegen der Palaearktischen Region, 60a. Schweizerbart, Stuttgart.

Tethinidae

Collin, J.E. 1960. British Tethinidae (Diptera). The Entomologist, 93: 191-3.

Collin, J.E. 1966. A revision of the Palaearctic species of Tethina and Rhicnoessa. Bollettino Museo Civico di Storia Naturale di Venezia, 16: 19-32.

Oestridae

Emden, F.I. van. 1954. Tachinidae and Calliphoridae. Handbooks for the Identification of British Insects, 10 (4a).

Gasterophilidae

Seguy, E. 1928. Etudes sur les Mouches Parasites, 1. Conopides, Oestrides et Calliphorines, etc. Lechevalier, Paris.

Tachinidae

Andersen, S. 1982. Revision of European species of Siphona Meigen (Diptera: Tachinidae). Entomologica Scandinavica, 13: 149-172.

Day, C.D. 1948. British Tachinid Flies. Arbroath.

Emden, F.I. van. 1954. Tachinidae and Calliphoridae. Handbooks for the Identification of British Insects, 10 (4a).

Herting, B. 1960. Biologie der westpalaarktischen Raupenfliegen. Monographien zur Angewandten Entomologie, 16.

Wainwright, C.J. 1928. The British Tachinidae. . 76: 139-254. Supplements, ibid, 1932, 80: 405-424; 1940, 90: 411-448; 1941, Proceedings of the Royal Entomological Society of London, 10: 70.

Wyatt, N.P. 1986. Thecocarcelia acutangulata (Macquart) (Diptera: Tachinidae), new to Britain. Entomologist's Monthly Magazine, 122: 203-204.

Rhinophoridae

Bedding, R. 1973. The immature stages of Rhinophorinae (Diptera: Calliphoridae) that parasitise British woodlice. Transactions of the Royal Entomological Society of London, 125: 27-44.

Emden, F.I. van. 1954. Tachinidae and Calliphoridae. Handbooks for the Identification of British Insects, 10 (4a).

Sarcophagidae

Day, C.D. & Fonseca, E.C.M. d' Assis. 1951. A key to the females of the British species of Sarcophaga (Dipt., Calliphoridae). Journal of the Society for British Entomology, 4: 36-7.

Emden, F.I. van. 1954. Tachinidae and Calliphoridae. Handbooks for the Identification of British Insects, 10 (4a).

Pape, T. 1987. The Sarcophagidae (Diptera) of Fennoscandia and Denmark. Fauna Entomologica Scandinavica, 19.

Calliphoridae

Davies, L. 1987. The distribution in Scotland and Ireland of Calliphora uralensis and its occurrence with and separation from C. vicina (Insecta: Diptera). Irish Naturalists' Journal, 22: 241-244.

Emden, F.I. van. 1954. Tachinidae and Calliphoridae. Handbooks for the Identification of British Insects, 10 (4a).

Scathophagidae

Chandler, P.J. 1970. A supplementary note on Norellia R.-D. (Dipt., Scathophagidae). Proceedings and Transactions of the British Entomological and Natural History Society, 3: 12.

Chandler, P.J. 1975. The early stages of Gimnomera tarsea Fallen (Diptera, Scatophagidae) now established to develop in the seed capsules of Pedicularis species (Scrophulariaceae). Proceedings and Transactions of the British Entomological and Natural History Society, 8: 39-41.

Chandler, P.J. & Stubbs, A.E. 1969. A species of Norellia R.-D. (Dipt., Scatophagidae) new to Britain. Proceedings and Transactions of the British Entomological and Natural History Society, 2: 120-124.

Chandler, P.J. & Stubbs, A.E. 1974. A species of the Boreal Genus Cosmetopus Becker (Dipt, Scatophagidae) New to the British Isles, taken by the River Test in Hampshire. Entomologist's Record and Journal of Variation, 86: 154-158.

Chandler, P.J. & Stubbs, A.E. 1975. A Further Note on Cosmetopus dentimanus Zetterstedt (Diptera: Scatophagidae). Entomologist's Record and Journal of Variation, 87: 147-148.

Collin, J.E. 1958. A short synopsis of the British Scatophagidae (Diptera). Transactions of the Society for British Entomology, 13: 37-56.

Hackman, W. 1956. The Scatophagidae (Dipt.) of eastern Fennoscandia. Fauna Fennica, 2: 1-67.

Nelson, J.M. 1965. Scoliaphleps ustulata Zetterstedt (Dipt., Scatophagidae) new to Britain. The Entomologist, 98: 65.

Nelson, M. 1972. Coniosternum tinctinervis Becker, a scatophagid fly new to Britain (Diptera). Entomologist's Gazette, 23: 247-248.

Anthomyiidae

Ackland, D.M. 1964. Two new British species of Anthomyiidae (Dipt.) with taxonomic notes on related pests of conifers. Entomologist's Monthly Magazine, 100: 136-44.

Ackland, D.M. 1970. Notes on the palaearctic species of Egle R.-D. (Dipt., Anthomyiidae) with descriptions of two new species. Entomologist's Monthly Magazine, 105: 185-192.

Collin, J.E. 1955. Genera and species of Anthomyiidae allied to Chirosia (Diptera). Journal of the Society for British Entomology, 5: 94-100.

Collin, J.E. 1967. Notes on some British species of Pegohylemyia (Dipt., Anthomyiidae) with descriptions of four new species. Entomologist's Monthly Magazine, 102: 181-91.

Fonseca, E.C.M. d' A. 1956. A review of the British sub-families and genera of the family Muscidae. Transactions of the Society for British Entomology, 12: 113-28.

Fonseca, E.C.M. d'A. 1966. Eight undescribed species of Muscidae (Diptera) from Britain. Entomologist's Monthly Magazine, 101: 269-78.

Hennig, W. 1966-76. Anthomyiidae. Die Fliegen der Palaearktischen Region, 7 (63a).

Smith, K.G.V. 1971. Eustalomyia hilaris Fallen (Diptera: Anthomyiidae) confirmed as British, with notes on other species in the genus. Entomologist's Gazette, 22: 55-60.

Fanniidae

Fonseca, E.C.M. d'A. 1968. Muscidae. Handbooks for the Identification of British Insects, 10 (4b).

Pont, A.C. 1983. Fannia lineata (Stein, 1895), new to Britain (Diptera, Fanniidae). Entomologist's Monthly Magazine, 119: 229-31.

Muscidae

Fonseca, E.C.M. d'A. 1968. Muscidae. Handbooks for the Identification of British Insects, 10 (4b).

Pont, A.C. 1973. Phaonia mediterranea Hennig (Dipt. Muscidae), new to Britain. Entomologist's Monthly Magazine, 108: 238-9.

Skidmore, P. 1985. The biology of the Muscidae of the world. Series Entomologica, 29.

Hippoboscidae

Hutson, A.M. 1984. Keds, flat-flies and bat-flies (Diptera, Hippoboscidae and Nycteribiidae). Handbooks for the Identification of British Insects, 10 (7).

OGCODES GIBBOSUS (Linnaeus)

DISTRIBUTION Scattered records in southern England as far north as Herefordshire, Oxfordshire and Suffolk. Particularly well recorded in the Hampshire area.

HABITAT Rather unclear, records include heathy areas in broadleaved woodland, grassland and marshland. Adults often sit on isolated bushes.

ECOLOGY Eggs are probably laid on twigs and the very mobile young larva attaches itself to wolf spiders such as Pardosa pullata and Trichosa species. The larvae then develop internally as parasitoids. Adults are recorded from June to August.

STATUS Comparatively regular in the New Forest and on the Hampshire Downs with about half a dozen known post 1960 sites. Infrequent elsewhere with little recent information other than isolated sites in Oxfordshire and Somerset. Old records are comparatively numerous and widespread suggesting a decline, though the elusive adults are perhaps prone to some under recording.

THREAT Afforestation and agricultural reclamation of sites. Overgrazing of the New Forest area by ponies with a loss of ground vegetation. Scrub invasion through the cessation of grazing.

MANAGEMENT Maintain a mosaic of vegetation types using rotational grazing or cutting policies, retaining some limited scrub or bushes, though do not allow scrub invasion. Maintain open rides and clearings within woods.

OGCODES PALLIPES Latreille

DISTRIBUTION Scattered records in southern England as far north as Glamorganshire, Herefordshire and Northamptonshire.

HABITAT Rather unclear; records include chalk grassland and scrub, heathy areas in broadleaved woodland, commons and marshes.

ECOLOGY Eggs are probably laid on twigs and the very mobile young larva attaches itself to spiders such as Alopecosa accentuata and Clubiona species. The larvae then develop internally as parasitoids. Adults recorded from June to August and have been observed in numbers (including copulating pairs) on the undersides of a birch twig on an isolated bush in an area of bracken/heath.

STATUS Known post 1960 records confined to Box Hill (1987) and Mitcham Common (1975), Surrey; Long Running, Epping Forest, Essex (1985) and Oxfordshire where it is apparently not infrequent on chalk grassland. It is probably under recorded to some extent through the elusiveness of the adults, though old records are comparatively numerous and a decline seems to have occurred.

THREAT Afforestation and agricultural reclamation of sites. Scrub invasion through lack of management.

MANAGEMENT Maintain a mosaic of vegetation types using rotational grazing or cutting policies, keeping some limited areas of scrub or bracken. Maintain open rides and clearings in woods.

ASILUS CRABRONIFORMIS Linnaeus

NOTABLE
ASILIDAE

DISTRIBUTION Recorded widely in southern England as far north as
Lincolnshire and Cheshire and throughout Wales. Records are most frequent
in Hampshire and the south-west including south Wales.

HABITAT Dry heathland, chalk downland and rough, unimproved pastureland.

ECOLOGY The larvae are probably predatory on the larvae of dung beetles
(probably Geotrupes). Eggs are said to be laid in cow dung but adults
also occur about horse dung. Adults recorded from late July to early
October and are predators of other insects including calypterate flies,
grasshoppers, staphylinid beetles and small scarabaeid beetles.

STATUS About 40 known post 1960 sites, mainly within Hampshire,
south-west England and south Wales. It seems to have declined greatly
away from these areas. Even in its strongholds its numbers can vary
considerably from year to year.

THREAT Habitat loss or degradation through changes in management such as
conversion to intensive agriculture and forestry and the loss of dung and
appropriate dung beetles through removal of grazing animals.

MANAGEMENT Maintain rotational grazing policies at sites to provide a
continuous supply of dung, produce a range of vegetation types and prevent
scrub invasion.

DASYPOGON DIADEMA Fabricius

ENDANGERED
ASILIDAE

DISTRIBUTION Recorded in the last century from coastal sites at Barmouth,
Merionethshire (apparently seen but not caught), near Swansea,
Glamorganshire, and near Bristol, Gloucestershire. In 1947 it was
recorded from Monton in Lancashire and probably at about this time it was
claimed to have been seen on Welsh coastal dunes.

HABITAT Coastal dunes.

ECOLOGY Life history unknown. Larvae possibly develop in sand at the
base of vegetation. Adults recorded in June and July and are predatory on
other insects.

STATUS Poorly known with most of the old records lacking voucher material
and the last acceptable record being for 1947. Most of the known sites
are probably now degraded and the lack of recent information on this very
large and striking fly strongly suggests it is extinct. Despite the above
records, there is still some doubt as to whether this large spectacular
species is or ever has been truly resident. Status revised from Appendix
(Shirt 1987) due to the post 1900 information.

THREAT Coastal development and recreational pressure on dunes.

MANAGEMENT Maintain a full range of vegetation types on dunes and prevent
dune erosion through excessive trampling or vehicle use.

DIOCTRIA COTHURNATA Meigen

RARE
ASILIDAE

DISTRIBUTION A rather disjunct distribution is apparent with most records
for either the Central Highlands of Scotland (Perthshire, Elgin,
Easterness and especially within the Spey Valley) or the south of England
(Hampshire, Dorset, Sussex, Surrey, Essex, Oxfordshire, Gloucestershire,
Herefordshire and especially the New Forest). Recent records also exists
for Yorkshire and for Radnorshire in Wales.

HABITAT Records include heathy woodlands, the margins of wet meadows
beside woods and recorded in the past as common in cornfields along
Speyside in Scotland.

ECOLOGY The life history is unknown. Adults recorded from May to
September and are predators of small insects.

STATUS Infrequent and apparently declined with few modern records, though
once frequent in the Scottish Highlands and the New Forest. Records from
three grassland localities in West Dorset during 1987 and a further Dorset
site in 1989 suggest it may be under recorded in this part of its range
and it was also reported from Skenfrith, Herefordshire in 1987. Not
listed in Shirt (1987).

THREAT Loss of heathland and grassland through agricultural reclamation,
intensive forestry and mis-management of sites such as excessive grazing
by ponies in the New Forest or under grazing and subsequent scrub
invasion.

MANAGEMENT Maintain a mosaic of vegetation types using traditional heath
management such as rotational grazing, cutting or burning and prevent
scrub invasion.

26

DIOCTRIA OELANDICA Meigen

DISTRIBUTION Records widely dispersed in England, Wales and as far north as Perthshire in Scotland, predominating in southern England.

HABITAT There seems to be a preference for oak woods with small trees rather than high forest. It is usually found along the edges of rides and glades.

ECOLOGY Life history is unknown. Adults recorded from May to July and are predators of other insects. They appear to be arboreal, using tree foliage as a vantage point for hunting.

STATUS A very local and declined species. About 25 post 1960 sites are known, and the New Forest appears to be a stronghold. It appears to have disappeared from much of its former range, but may prove to be under recorded in the damp valley woods of Wales, south-west and north-west England.

THREAT Clearance of oak woodland for agriculture or intensive forestry and the shading out of rides and clearings within woodland.

MANAGEMENT Maintain a good age structure in woods ensuring regeneration of trees. Maintain open rides and clearings; also any dead wood and marshy areas as potential sites for larval development.

EPITRIPTUS ARTHRITICUS (Zeller)

DISTRIBUTION Only three known records: Merton (1907) and Breckles Heath (1934), both in the Norfolk Breckland and Berrow, Somerset (1955).

HABITAT Heathland at the Breck sites and sand dunes at the Somerset site.

ECOLOGY Life history unknown, though the larvae are probably soil-dwelling predators. Adults recorded from mid July to mid August and are predatory on other insects.

STATUS A poorly known species with no recent information, suggesting that it is very rare if not extinct in Britain.

THREAT Habitat loss from agricultural improvement, coastal development, intensive forestry or mis-management leading to overgrazing or scrub invasion.

MANAGEMENT Maintain traditional heath or sand dune management as appropriate, preventing scrub invasion, ensuring areas of bare sand on heathland and maintaining a full range of vegetation types at the sand dune site.

EPITRIPTUS COWINI Hobby

DISTRIBUTION Confirmed records from the Isle of Man: Braddon (1943), Ballaterson (1944) and Cronkbourne (1940). Records from North Wales: Morfa Harlech NNR, Merionethshire (1968, 1969) require confirmation.

HABITAT On the Isle of Man it is known mainly from lanes with hedge banks with a mixture of bracken and brambles. The Welsh record may be from coastal dunes (on which it occurs in east and south Ireland). On the continent it is said to favour the fixed vegetation on the landward side of dunes, and sandy areas inland.

ECOLOGY Life history unknown, though larvae probably develop as predators in sandy soil. Adults recorded from late June to late August and are predatory on other insects.

STATUS The inclusion of the species in this review is questionable until its status in north Wales is confirmed, hence the change of RDB status. The Isle of Man is outside the area covered by this review, though records are included to draw attention to the rare status of the species in the British Isles. The species is also present on coastal dunes in east and south Ireland and appears to be fairly widespread though very local in Central Europe. The distinct taxonomic status of this species (at least from the commoner E. cingulatus) has been confirmed by Speight (1987) (as Machimus cowini), though the group to which it belongs clearly needs a European revision. Status revised from RDB2 (Shirt 1987).

THREAT Destruction of the known sites through coastal development and recreational pressure on dunes leading to erosion and 'blow-outs'; scrub invasion through inadequate management.

MANAGEMENT Maintain sand dune management at Morfa Harlech, ensuring a full transition of vegetation types but avoiding scrub invasion, and retain sandy areas on the Isle of Man where it is likely to have populations remaining.

EUTOLMUS RUFIBARBIS (Meigen)   RARE
ASILIDAE

DISTRIBUTION A restricted southern species with strongholds in the Breck districts of East Anglia and the heaths of Surrey and West Sussex. Records also exist for Dorset, the New Forest, Berkshire, Kent and Lincolnshire.

HABITAT Open, dry heathland.

ECOLOGY The eggs are apparently laid within incisions cut by the female ovipositor in herbage, though larval development probably occurs in sandy soil. Adults recorded from late June to late August and are predatory upon other insects.

STATUS Nearly 20 known post 1960 sites, mainly within the Brecks and West Sussex Heaths, with only two recent records for Surrey (Chobham Common and Mytchett Lake). No recent records are known from the New Forest where it used to be regularly found at the turn of the century and the single records from Dorset and Lincolnshire are also very old. A considerable contraction in its range has apparently occurred, probably in response to heathland loss and degradation. Status revised from RDB2 (Shirt 1987).

THREAT The loss of heathland to agriculture or intensive forestry; scrub invasion and a loss of bare ground through mis-management; accidental fires.

MANAGEMENT Maintain open heathland with patches of bare ground, using traditional heathland management such as rotational flailing, grazing or burning policies.

LAPHRIA FLAVA (Linnaeus)   RARE
ASILIDAE

DISTRIBUTION Records appear to be entirely confined to Caledonian pine forest areas of the Central Highlands of Scotland, mainly along the Spey and Dee valleys in the drier eastern parts.

HABITAT Ancient Caledonian pine forest.

ECOLOGY The larvae live in the wood of very large, old Scots pines in association with the burrows of large cerambycid beetles. It is claimed that they suck the juices of recently dead beetle larvae, though they may additionally predate living ones. Adults recorded from mid June to September and are predatory upon other insects.

STATUS A number of post 1960 records along the River Spey from the River Feshie area to Culbin Sands, with strongholds in the Abernethy Forest NNR, Loch Garten RSPB reserve and Rothiemurchus Forest areas. Also a number of recent records from the River Dee between the Eastern Cairngorms and Glen Tanar NNR. It is, however, far more local than in the past with many of its old sites destroyed and most modern ones under threat.

THREAT Loss of Caledonian forest to modern intensive forestry (which does not provide breeding sites) or agriculture. Removal of old or diseased trees and dead wood. Excessive grazing by deer appears to be hindering the regeneration of pine in some areas.

MANAGEMENT Retain all very old large pines and ensure continuity of these in future. Encourage pine regeneration, whilst also retaining open structured woodland to allow trees to grow and age unimpeded.

LAPHRIA GILVA (Linnaeus)   INSUFFICIENTLY KNOWN
ASILIDAE

DISTRIBUTION A handful of sites in southern England: Englemere, Ascot (1938) Frensham (1951) and Silchester (1951), Berkshire; Oxshott (1946) and Ash Vale (1945), Surrey and near Midhurst, Sussex (old, undated).

HABITAT Coniferous woodland or heaths containing Scots pine.

ECOLOGY Larvae were found at Ash Vale in thick corky bark of an old pine stump, where they were probably feeding on beetle larvae. It is assumed development takes several years. Adults recorded in June and July and are predatory upon other insects.

STATUS The Berkshire and Surrey records were for a short period between 1938 and 1951 during which time it is assumed to have undergone a short period of residence in Britain following an influx or introduction from the continent and the Silchester record may represent the tail-end of this residence. It is almost certainly now extinct, and its former status as a native remains questionable since pine was not established in southern England until relatively recently. Status revised from RDB1 (Shirt 1987).

THREAT Uncertain as it is probably extinct. The continuity of pine is no problem on the southern heathland belt but its needs may be more exacting than simply the presence of pine stumps.

MANAGEMENT Retain any old pine trees and dead stumps.

LAPHRIA MARGINATA (Linnaeus)
NOTABLE
ASILIDAE

DISTRIBUTION .Southern England, becoming scarcer north of the Thames beyond Oxfordshire and considered a rarity in the midlands, reaching Cheshire and Nottinghamshire. It is relatively frequent in counties such as Hampshire.

HABITAT Ancient oak forests are favoured.

ECOLOGY The larvae probably develop in beetle burrows beneath the bark or within dead wood, stumps and logs of oak. They are assumed to be predatory. Adults recorded from June to August.

STATUS Widespread and regular in older woods in Wealden Hampshire with additional post 1960 sites within Somerset, Wiltshire, Surrey, Oxfordshire, Berkshire, Middlesex and the Wyre Forest.

THREAT The loss of old oak woodland to agriculture or intensive forestry; also the removal of dead wood and old or diseased trees; the shading out of woodland rides through lack of sufficient management.

MANAGEMENT Retain any dead wood and old or diseased trees ensuring continuity of these in future; also maintain open rides and clearings.

LASIOPOGON CINCTUS (Fabricius)
NOTABLE
ASILIDAE

DISTRIBUTION An essentially southern heathland species extending north to Yorkshire amd westwards into south Wales.

HABITAT Dry sandy soils as found on heaths and sand dunes usually in the proximity of trees such as Scots pine.

ECOLOGY Life history unknown. The larvae are probably predators in soil. Adults recorded from mid April to late July and are predatory on other insects.

STATUS A rather local heathland species with about 20 known post 1960 sites, mainly in southern England. Old records are comparatively numerous and a distinct decline and contraction of its range seems to have occurred.

THREAT Habitat loss to agriculture, intensive forestry and coastal development. Scrub and pine invasion on heathland and recreational pressure on dunes.

MANAGEMENT Maintain traditional heath or sand dune management as appropriate, preventing scrub invasion and maintaining the presence of bare soil on heaths, and retaining a full range of habitat types on sand dunes.

MACHIMUS RUSTICUS (Meigen)
VULNERABLE
ASILIDAE

DISTRIBUTION Widely scattered localities in southern England (Isle of Wight, Hampshire, Sussex, Kent, Berkshire, Oxfordshire, Northamptonshire, Gloucestershire), with Hampshire and Sussex providing its main strongholds.

HABITAT Chalk and limestone grassland and downs.

ECOLOGY Life history unknown. The larvae are probably predatory in soil. Adults recorded from early June to mid August and are predatory upon other insects.

STATUS A very local insect even in Hampshire and Sussex, with only a handful of post 1960 sites known. A particularly strong colony is present at Portsdown Hill, Hampshire. Another strong colony discovered at Barnack NNR, Northamptonshire in 1985, suggests that this species may be more widespread at calcareous localities away from the major downs, if looked for carefully.

THREAT The loss of calcareous grassland to agriculture and intensive forestry and changes in grazing management, either overgrazing, or the cessation of grazing and subsequent scrub invasion.

MANAGEMENT Use rotational grazing policies to provide a mosaic of vegetation types. Retain isolated trees and bushes but prevent scrub invasion.

NEOITAMUS COTHURNATUS (Meigen)
ENDANGERED
ASILIDAE

DISTRIBUTION Only two known localities: Tubney Wood, Berkshire (1901, 1906, 1919, 1921) and Stow Wood, Oxfordshire (1895).

HABITAT Broadleaved woodland, possibly only on calcareous soils.

ECOLOGY Life history unknown. Adults recorded in June and are predatory upon other insects.

STATUS Unclear with no recent information. The Tubney Wood site is now largely converted to conifers so this fly must be regarded as very rare if not extinct.

THREAT Woodland clearance for agriculture or intensive forestry.

MANAGEMENT Retain the known sites maintaining open rides and clearings for adult feeding.

PAMPONERUS GERMANICUS (Linnaeus)

RARE
ASILIDAE

DISTRIBUTION This species has its stronghold in the major sand dunes on the west coast of Britain. Records are present from north Devon extending to the north-east coast of Scotland. It can occasionally occur inland such as at Aviemore (though probably only as a stray) and abroad this is apparently quite normal.

HABITAT Sand dunes, preferring fixed dune behind the marram grass belt with coarse vegetation.

ECOLOGY Larvae possibly develop in sand as predators of other invertebrates. Adults recorded from mid May to early August and are predatory upon other insects, characteristically resting on sand in wait for a potential victim.

STATUS Fairly regular on major dune systems on the coasts of north and south Wales, and locally common. Infrequent and possibly greatly declined away from these areas due to the loss or degradation of suitable habitat. A colony still persists at Torrs Warren, Wigtownshire in Scotland (last known record, 1983). It could not be found at Braunton Burrows, Devon during a visit in 1987, though old Devon records may apply to this site. Not listed in Shirt (1987).

THREAT Loss of coastal dunes through coastal developments and their degradation through recreational pressure with resultant erosion and 'blow-outs'; scrub invasion of fixed dune through lack of grazing.

MANAGEMENT Maintain a full range of vegetation types on dunes, especially areas of fixed dune with coarser vegetation and use fences and boardwalks where necessary to reduce disturbance and allow normal dune fixation; prevent scrub invasion of open fixed dune.

RHADIURGUS VARIABILIS (Zetterstedt)

RARE
ASILIDAE

DISTRIBUTION Virtually confined to the Central Highlands of Scotland. The vast majority of records are from localities along the River Spey in Elgin and Easterness between Kincraig and Grantown, though records are also present for Fife, Perthshire and Aberdeenshire.

HABITAT Usually shingle banks of upland rivers and to a lesser extent in sandy glades of open structured Caledonian pine forest.

ECOLOGY Eggs are laid singly onto plant stems and larval development probably occurs in damp sandy soil. Adults recorded from mid June to early August. They are predatory upon other insects and characteristically sit on bare stones and sandy soil in wait for potential victims.

STATUS Fairly regular along Speyside (four post 1960 sites involved) and locally frequent at sites like Rothiemurchus. Infrequent elsewhere with single recent records for Fife and the Nairn area of Easterness. Not listed in Shirt (1987).

THREAT River improvement schemes, shingle extraction and excessive trampling of shingle banks. Clearance of Caledonian pine forest and replacement with intensive forestry or improved pastureland.

MANAGEMENT Maintain shingle banks in a natural state free from excessive disturbance. Maintain open structured Caledonian pine forest and encourage pine regeneration by protecting saplings from deer grazing.

BOMBYLIUS DISCOLOR Mikan

DISTRIBUTION Records widely dispersed in southern England as far north as Warwickshire, Huntingdonshire and Suffolk. Also recorded from south Wales (Glamorganshire).

HABITAT A variety of habitats are used, including woodland rides and margins, sandy areas and coastal locations such as landslips. Patches of bare, light soil in warm, sunny situations are required for host nesting.

ECOLOGY The larvae probably develop in cells of mining bees, feeding on both the pollen/honey store and the bee grub. Some recorders have noted a particularly close association with colonies of _Andrena flavipes_, a widespread though local species occurring in a range of habitats. Adults recorded from March to June and may be found near to colonies of mining bees or feeding on flowers such as labiates.

STATUS A local and declining species with some 20 known post 1960 sites compared to a relatively large number of older ones. Like many aculeates, its apparent decline has involved an extensive disappearance from inland sites, with a high proportion of known modern colonies on coastal landslips.

THREAT The loss of woodland and semi-natural grassland habitats to agriculture and intensive forestry.

MANAGEMENT Maintain open rides and clearings in woods and prevent scrub invasion of these and woodland edges. Retain any sandy banks and patches of soil (especially sunny, south facing ones) which may support colonies of the hosts, and maintain a rich and varied flora for adult feeding.

BOMBYLIUS CANESCENS Mikan

DISTRIBUTION A disjunct distribution is shown with records scattered widely in south-west England as far north as Worcestershire and east to Dorset and Oxfordshire and throughout the southern coast of Wales. A number of records are also present from Scotland, mainly in Perthshire, but also Fife and Midlothian. The majority of records are coastal though it can occur well inland (e.g. Radnorshire, Wiltshire, Oxfordshire). It is also known from the Isle of Man.

HABITAT A variety of habitats are used, including sand dunes, heathland and calcareous grassland. Patches of bare, light soil in warm, sunny situations are required for host nesting.

ECOLOGY The larvae develop in the cells of solitary bees in the genus Halictus (and ?Lasioglossum), probably feeding on both the pollen/honey store and the bee grub. Adults recorded from April to July and may be found near to the potential nesting sites of the host such as sandy banks and slopes, or visiting flowers such as labiates and _Geranium robertianum_.

STATUS Regular in south-west England with about 40 known post 1960 sites, and it can be locally abundant in some areas such as Carmarthenshire and Cardiganshire. The last known Scottish record is 1922 and it appears to be very rare if not extinct in this part of its range.

THREAT Loss of suitable habitat through coastal development and recreational pressure on dunes; agricultural reclamation and afforestation of heathland and grassland and their mis-management with subsequent scrub invasion.

MANAGEMENT Maintain a full range of vegetation types on dunes and employ rotational grazing management where necessary here and elsewhere to produce a mosaic of vegetation types, including short turf to encourage bee colonies. Also retain areas of bare earth or sandy banks (especially sunny, south facing ones) for the same purpose and a rich and varied flora for adult feeding.

BOMBYLIUS MINOR Linnaeus

VULNERABLE
BOMBYLIIDAE

DISTRIBUTION Scattered records from south-western England (Devon, Dorset, Hampshire, Isle of Wight), with most records for Dorset; also an old record for Barmouth, Merionethshire. A specimen from Suffolk, apparently belonging to this species, is most intriguing and will require checking.

HABITAT Heathland and probably associated sand dunes also (such as at Studland). One record is from Chalk downland (Porton Down, Hampshire) though this may refer to a stray. Patches of bare, light soil in warm, sunny situations are required for host nesting.

ECOLOGY The larvae develop in the cells of solitary bees of the genus Colletes (several records refer to C. succinctus, also one to C. daviesanus) and possibly also other bees such as Andrena clarkella, probably feeding on both the pollen/honey store and the bee grub. Adults recorded from June to September and may be found near to colonies of the hosts or visiting flowers such as sea lavender and probably a range of composites.

STATUS The Dorset heaths are very much its stronghold and post 1960 records exist for various parts of Poole Harbour, Corfe, Purbeck, Studland NNR and Stoborough Heath NNR. The only other known post 1960 site is Porton Down, Hampshire (1985). Not listed in Shirt (1987).

THREAT Loss of sites to agriculture or intensive forestry. Lack of management of sites and subsequent scrub, bracken or gorse invasion. Accidental fires and the churning effects of horses along bridleways and paths with subsequent loss of host nesting sites.

MANAGEMENT Maintain sites in an open state, with a mosaic of vegetation types, using traditional heathland management. Retain any sandy banks and areas of bare earth (especially sunny, south facing ones) to encourage bee colonies, and maintain a rich and varied flora for adult feeding.

PHTHIRIA PULICARIA (Mikan)

NOTABLE
BOMBYLIIDAE

DISTRIBUTION Recorded widely on sandy coastal areas of Britain.

HABITAT Coastal dunes, where it is usually present amongst sparsely vegetated parts of the mid and hind dune (especially along tracks and sandy slacks), but not upon the fore dune.

ECOLOGY Larvae have been reported to be parasitoids of moth caterpillars (Gelechiidae). Adults recorded from June to August and characteristically visit the flowers of various low hawkweed-type composites.

STATUS Regular and locally abundant on many sand dunes with some 25 known post 1960 sites. Possibly overlooked through its small size. The loss or degradation of sand dunes in recent decades has probably led to a substantial reduction in the number of sites.

THREAT Loss of habitat through coastal development and recreational pressure leading to erosion and 'blow-outs'. Invasion of scrub or coarse vegetation on mid and hind dunes through inadequate grazing.

MANAGEMENT Maintain a full range of vegetation types, using fences and boardwalks if necessary to allow normal dune fixation. The open structure of mid and hind dunes, with the areas of short turf and bare sand are probably essential to this species. On sites experiencing problems with scrub invasion, regular cutting or light levels of grazing by sheep may be necessary.

THYRIDANTHRAX FENESTRATUS (Fallen)

RARE
BOMBYLIIDAE

DISTRIBUTION Virtually confined to the major heathland areas of southern England, principally within Dorset, Hampshire, Surrey and Sussex, though with additional records from Cromer, Norfolk (1868 - material in BM(NH)) and Barmouth, Merionethshire (record probably very old and somewhat dubious).

HABITAT Heathland and commons.

ECOLOGY The larvae develop in the cells of sand wasps Ammophila sp., probably feeding on both the wasp grub and its food. Adults recorded from June to September and characteristically sunbathe on paths and bare patches, occasionally visiting flowers such as umbels.

STATUS Locally frequent in heathland in Dorset, the New Forest, West Sussex and a few recent records from the Surrey heaths. Many of its former sites however, are now destroyed and many of its present ones remain threatened. It appears to have disappeared from Berkshire altogether.

THREAT Loss of heathland to agriculture or intensive forestry. Mismanagement such as undergrazing and subsequent scrub invasion. Accidental fires and the churning effects of horses along bridleways and paths with a subsequent loss of host nesting sites.

MANAGEMENT Use traditional heathland management to produce a mosaic of vegetation types. Retain any sandy banks and areas of bare soil or sand (especially sunny, south facing ones) to encourage nesting wasps, also a rich and varied flora for adult feeding.

VILLA CINGULATA (Meigen)

DISTRIBUTION Largely recorded from Oxfordshire (Wormsley, 1907; Stokenchurch, 1895, 1898; Hell Coppice, 1935; Stanton St John, 1935) with additional records for Devon (Lustleigh, 1931 and Holne, 1896), Wiltshire (Marlborough, 1914), Hampshire (New Forest, 1910) and Kent (Soakham Down, 1937).

HABITAT Calcareous grassland or woodland edge grassland, especially that on Chalk, though occasionally on other soils.

ECOLOGY Life history unknown. The larvae are possibly parasitoids of lepidopterous or aculeate larvae. Adults recorded in July and August.

STATUS No known records after 1937. It had been reported as being not uncommon at some of its old Oxfordshire haunts but the lack of recent information suggests it may now be very rare or extinct. Many of its former sites are now afforested or otherwise unsuitable. Status revised from RDB2 (Shirt 1987).

THREAT Habitat loss to agriculture and intensive forestry. Mis-management such as overgrazing, or scrub invasion through undergrazing.

MANAGEMENT Maintain rotational grazing policies to produce a mosaic of vegetation types (including patches of bare soil) and prevent scrub invasion.

VILLA CIRCUMDATA (Meigen)

DISTRIBUTION Mainly recorded from the Dorset heaths and to a lesser extent the New Forest and Surrey heaths. Purported records are also present from Cornwall, a site near Bangor, Caernarvonshire and St Helens, Isle of Wight.

HABITAT Heathland (the questionable St Helens locality refers to sand dune).

ECOLOGY Life history unknown. The larvae are possibly parasitoids of lepidopterous or aculeate larvae. Adults recorded in July and August and may be found sunning themselves on bare patches of sandy ground.

STATUS Very few if any records since 1958 (Studland, Dorset). It had been reported as not uncommon at some of its Dorset localities and a genuine decline must have occurred through the loss and fragmentation of habitat in recent decades. Status revised from RDB2 (Shirt 1987).

THREAT The loss of heathland to agriculture and intensive forestry. Mis-management and subsequent scrub or bracken invasion. Accidental fires.

MANAGEMENT Employ traditional heath management to produce a mosaic of vegetation types (including patches of bare soil) and prevent scrub invasion.

33

LEOPOLDIUS BREVIROSTRIS (Germar)

DISTRIBUTION Only eight known localities in southern England: Totton, New Forest (1952) and Mopley Ponds, Calshot (1935), Hampshire; Sydenham Hill Woods, Kent (1987); Windsor Forest, Berkshire (1930); Hell Copse, Oxfordshire (1937); Chippenham Fen NNR, Cambridgeshire (1941); near Pinbury Park, Gloucestershire (1983) and Abberley Hill, Worcestershire (1936).

HABITAT Preferences unclear, possibly woodland with the 1983 record referring to a ride in broadleaved woodland and the 1987 record to a specimen taken in a water trap set amongst lush herbaceous vegetation in the clearing of an old broadleaved wood.

ECOLOGY The larvae probably develop as parasitoids in the abdomen of social wasps (Vespula or Dolichovespula) though precise hosts unknown. Adults recorded from July to September, though it seems to peak a month or so earlier than the related L. signatus on the basis of our limited records.

STATUS A rare and elusive species with most records for the period between 1930 and 1941. It had not been recorded for over 30 years prior to the discovery of the two recent localities.

THREAT Unclear other than general woodland clearance for agriculture or intensive forestry.

MANAGEMENT Maintain woodland rides and clearings in an open condition using rotational management, ensuring a rich supply of flowers for adult feeding and host interception.

CONOPS STRIGATA Viedemann

DISTRIBUTION Records predominantly for southern England and especially for Hampshire and the west country though extending as far north as Lancashire; also Carmarthenshire in Wales.

HABITAT Preferences unclear, records include heathland, pastureland or in and around woodland.

ECOLOGY Probably a parasitoid of bees and wasps though exact hosts unknown. Adults recorded from July to September and visit flowers such as ragwort and thistles.

STATUS Widespread but local in southern England, becoming increasingly less frequent towards the north. About 25 known post 1960 sites.

THREAT Habitat loss to agriculture and intensive forestry. Mismanagement of heathland and grassland, either overgrazing or the cessation of grazing with subsequent scrub invasion.

MANAGEMENT Maintain traditional management regimes on heathland and grassland, such as rotational grazing, burning or flailing. Retain rides and clearings in woods and prevent these scrubbing over. Encourage stands of flowers such as ragworts and thistles for adult feeding and host interception and retain any banks and sandy areas (especially those in sunny, south facing situations) to encourage a rich aculeate fauna.

CONOPS VESICULARIS Linnaeus

DISTRIBUTION Recorded widely in England as far north as Cheshire and Lincolnshire and also for Carmarthenshire and Cardiganshire in Wales.

HABITAT Usually recorded from dry heathland and adjacent broadleaved woodland and parkland.

ECOLOGY Larvae are believed to develop as parasitoids in the abdomen of bees. The bumble bee Bombus muscorum is quoted as a host although the habitats do not coincide well. Other commoner bumble bees or hornets Vespa crabro are more likely hosts. Adults recorded from April to August and visit flowers such as umbels and a range of spring blossom.

STATUS Regular in the main ancient woodlands of southern England with about 30 known post 1960 sites. Records predominate in Hampshire (the New Forest) and Surrey. The close association with old woodland suggests hornets may eventually prove to be a major host.

THREAT Clearance of heathland, broadleaved woodland and parkland for agriculture or coniferisation. Removal of large old trees, stumps etc which provide nesting sites for hornets.

MANAGEMENT Retain rides and clearings in woods, preventing scrub invasion of these and ensuring the presence of blossoms and flowers here and along woodland margins for adult feeding and host interception. Retain any large old trees, hollow stumps etc. which are potential nesting sites for hornets.

LEOPOLDIUS SIGNATUS (Wiedemann)

NOTABLE
CONOPIDAE

DISTRIBUTION Recorded widely in England and Wales as far north as Northumberland with records predominating in southern counties.

HABITAT Records include woodlands, commons and gardens, probably requiring the presence of ivy to provide flowers for the wasp hosts in the autumn.

ECOLOGY The larvae probably develop as parasitoids in the abdomen of social wasps (Vespula or Dolichovespula) and adults characteristically may be found around ivy blossoms in the autumn together with large numbers of wasps. The full flight period of the adult is late July to early October with most records for September.

STATUS Very local though possibly increasing in the south with in excess of 30 post 1960 sites. It may prove to be somewhat under recorded due to its particularly late flight period when many dipterists have given up recording for the year. Its apparent increase in recent decades could in part be due to increased awareness of its autumn flight period.

THREAT Habitat loss to agriculture, intensive forestry and urban development. Removal of old trees, walls, fences etc. with good amounts of ivy, especially south-facing ones receiving most sunshine.

MANAGEMENT Retain ivy-clad walls and trees and maintain rides and clearings in woods in an open condition through rotational management.

MYOPA CURTIROSTRIS Krober

RARE
CONOPIDAE

DISTRIBUTION The very few records of this species are to be found within Cambridgeshire, Norfolk, Oxfordshire, Wiltshire and West Sussex.

HABITAT Preferences unclear, records include dry grassland and probably open-structured woodland.

ECOLOGY Probably a parasitoid of adult aculeate Hymenoptera though exact hosts unknown. Adults recorded in July and August.

STATUS Rare and declining with only two known post 1960 sites: Fouldon Common, Norfolk (1983) and a site in Sussex.

THREAT Habitat loss to agriculture and intensive forestry. Mis-management of grassland, either through overgrazing or the cessation of grazing and subsequent scrub invasion, a loss of floristic richness and diversity, and a loss of bare ground.

MANAGEMENT Maintain rotational grazing regimes on grassland to produce a mosaic of vegetation types and discourage scrub invasion. Provide open rides and clearings in woods. Retain any banks and areas of bare soil (especially those in sunny, south facing situations) to support a rich aculeate fauna, and encourage plenty of flowers for adult feeding and host interception.

MYOPA EXTRICATA Collin

RARE
CONOPIDAE

DISTRIBUTION Scattered localities in southern England (Cornwall, Devon, Somerset, Isle of Wight, Sussex, Surrey). Records from Berkshire and Dorset require checking.

HABITAT Most records refer to chalk grassland, often at coastal locations, occasionally well inland.

ECOLOGY Probably a parasitoid of adult aculeate Hymenoptera though exact hosts unknown. Adults recorded from April to June and may be found visiting flowers such as dandelion.

STATUS Rare and declining with only two known post 1960 sites: St Catherines Point, Isle of White (numerous records from 1972 to 1975) and Bolberry Down, Devon (1978).

THREAT Habitat loss to agriculture, intensive forestry and coastal development. Mis-management of grassland through overgrazing, or the cessation of grazing with subsequent scrub invasion, a loss of floristic richness and diversity, and a loss of bare ground.

MANAGEMENT Maintain rotational grazing regimes on grassland to produce a mosaic of vegetation types and prevent scrub invasion. Retain banks and areas of bare soil (especially those in sunny, south facing situations) to support a rich aculeate fauna, and encourage plenty of flowers for adult feeding and host interception.

MANAGEMENT Use traditional management such as rotational grazing to produce a range of vegetation types and discourage scrub invasion. Retain banks and areas of bare soil (especially those in sunny, south facing situations) to support a rich aculeate fauna, and encourage plenty of flowers for adult feeding and host interception.

MYOPA FASCIATA Meigen

RARE
CONOPIDAE

DISTRIBUTION Scattered localities in southern England (Devon, Dorset, Hampshire, Isle of Wight, Surrey, ?Hertfordshire, Berkshire, Oxfordshire, Suffolk, Norfolk, Gloucestershire).

HABITAT Calluna heathland.

ECOLOGY Probably a parasitoid of adult aculeate Hymenoptera, at least two observation relating to an association with colonies of the local mining bee Andrena fuscipes which is very much associated with ericaceous heathland. Adults recorded from July to September and have been seen hovering around the tips of heather shoots.

STATUS Rare and declining with only a handful of known post 1960 sites: Pitbright Common (1989), Wisley Common (1965, 1969) and Thursley Common (1960), Ambersham, Common and possibly some other sites in Sussex; Weavers Down and possibly another site in Hampshire; Talbot Heath, Dorset (1988). It was a frequent insect of the Dorset heaths in the first half of this century and the lack of recent information may be due to the lack of recent recording. This species is not listed in Shirt (1987).

THREAT Habitat loss to agriculture and intensive forestry. Mis-management of heathland, especially through the cessation of grazing or disturbance, with subsequent bracken, pine and scrub invasion, a loss of floristic richness and diversity, and a loss of bare ground. Accidental fires.

MANAGEMENT Maintain traditional heathland management to produce a mosaic of vegetation types and discourage scrub invasion. Retain banks and areas of bare soil (especially those in sunny, south facing situations) to support a rich aculeate fauna and encourage plenty of flowers (especially ericaceous ones) for adult feeding and host interception. A mosaic of vegetation types and Calluna age classes combined with firebreaks will reduce the risk of accidental fires and produce ideal conditions for this species.

MYOPA OCCULTA Viedemann

ENDANGERED
CONOPIDAE

DISTRIBUTION Only two old records from Breamore and Bordean (both in Hampshire).

HABITAT Unclear possibly chalk grassland.

ECOLOGY Probably a parasitoid of adult aculeate Hymenoptera though exact hosts unknown. Adults recorded in July and August.

STATUS Only two old records, exact dates unknown. It must now be extremely rare if not extinct. Status revised from RDB2 (Shirt 1987).

THREAT Habitat loss to agriculture, intensive forestry etc. Mis-management of grassland, either through overgrazing, or through the cessation of grazing with subsequent scrub invasion, a loss of floristic richness and diversity, and a loss of bare ground.

MYOPA POLYSTIGMA Rondani

RARE
CONOPIDAE

DISTRIBUTION The true M. polystigma may be confined to East Anglia (Cambridgeshire, Suffolk, Norfolk).

HABITAT Probably heathland and dry grassland, though it has been recorded from a garden in Norwich,

ECOLOGY Probably a parasitoid of adult aculeate Hymenoptera though exact hosts unknown. Adults recorded in May and June and visit a range of spring blossoms.

STATUS A poorly understood species which prior to 1970 was considered conspecific with the more frequent M. tessellatipennis. Reliable records include about half a dozen sites including three post 1960 ones: Cambridge Botanical Gardens and Anglesey Abbey, Cambridgeshire; Norwich, Norfolk. Recent records from Hampshire and Kent require confirmation. This species is not listed in Shirt (1987).

THREAT Habitat loss to agriculture, intensive forestry and urban development. Mis-management of heathland and grassland, either through overgrazing, or the cessation of grazing with subsequent scrub invasion and loss of floristic richness and diversity, and bare ground.

MANAGEMENT Use traditional management such as rotational grazing to produce a mosaic of vegetation types and discourage scrub invasion. Retain banks and areas of bare soil (especially those in sunny, south facing situations) to support a rich aculeate fauna, and encourage plenty of flowers for adult feeding and host interception.

MYOPA STRANDI Duda

DISTRIBUTION Scattered localities in southern England (Devon, Somerset, Kent, Suffolk, Norfolk, Cambridgeshire). Records from Worcestershire and Middlesex require checking.

HABITAT Records include heaths, grassland, fen and woodland edge.

ECOLOGY Probably a parasitoid of adult aculeate Hymenoptera though exact hosts unknown. Adults recorded in April and May and visit various spring blossom and flowers.

STATUS Extremely local with 10 known post 1960 sites, all in the East Anglia and Cambridgeshire area.

THREAT Habitat loss to agriculture and coniferisation. Mis-management of sites through overgrazing, or the cessation of grazing with subsequent scrub invasion and a loss of floristic richness and diversity, and bare ground.

MANAGEMENT Maintain traditional management of open habitats such as rotational grazing to produce a mosaic of vegetation types and discourage scrub invasion. Retain any banks and areas of bare soil (especially those in sunny, south facing situations) to support a rich aculeate fauna, and encourage plenty of flowers for adult feeding and host interception.

MYOPA VICARIA Walker

DISTRIBUTION Eight widely scattered localities: Burrator, Devon (1971); Barton Mills (1956), Cavenham and Tuddenham Heath NNR (1982 and 1984), Suffolk; Foulden Common, Norfolk (1984); Hatfield Lings (1971), Skipwith Common (1974), Strensall Common (1972) and Holme House (1971), Yorkshire.

HABITAT Heathland or dry grassland.

ECOLOGY Probably a parasitoid of adult aculeate Hymenoptera though exact hosts unknown. Adults recorded in April and May at visit various spring blossoms and flowers.

STATUS Very restricted though with a number of recent records. There have been taxonomic difficulties in the past. Its absence from apparently suitable habitat in the extreme south of England should be noted. Status revised from RDB1 (Shirt 1987).

THREAT Habitat loss to agriculture and afforestation. Mis-management of heathland, either through overgrazing, or the cessation of grazing with subsequent invasion by scrub and bracken, loss of floristic richness and diversity, and a loss of bare ground. Accidental fires.

MANAGEMENT Maintain traditional heathland management to produce a mosaic of vegetation types and discourage scrub invasion. Retain banks and areas of bare soil (especially those in sunny, south facing situations) to support a rich aculeate fauna, and encourage plenty of flowers for adult feeding and host interception.

PHYSOCEPHALA NIGRA Degeer

DISTRIBUTION A disjunct distribution is shown with northern records for various parts of Scotland (Dumfriesshire, Perthshire, Aberdeenshire, Elgin, Easterness, Argyllshire, East Ross, Sutherland) and southern records largely from the Dorset and New Forest heaths, and also Kent. Two records are also present from Yorkshire though neither appear recent.

HABITAT Heathland and moorland.

ECOLOGY A known parasitoid of adults of the bumble bee Bombus muscorum. Adults recorded from May to August and feed on flowers such as heather and rhododendron.

STATUS Widespread but very local in the Scottish Highlands with about 10 known post 1960 sites scattered widely. Very rare in southern England with records for Studland (1986) and Godlingston Heath (1984), Dorset being the only known recent ones. It has undoubtedly declined at its Dorset and New Forest strongholds where it was formerly frequent, and it is probably extinct in the Yorkshire area.

THREAT The loss of heathland and moorland through conversion to agriculture, afforestation or through scrub invasion resulting from mis-management.

MANAGEMENT Maintain a mosaic of vegetation types on moors and heaths using traditional management techniques. Encourage plenty of flowers for adult feeding and host interception. If Bombus muscorum or related moss-nesting species prove to be its main hosts, the need for damp heathland with Sphagnum will need to be taken into account, especially at its southern sites where lower precipitation makes this habitat more vulnerable.

SICUS ABDOMINALIS Kröber

ENDANGERED
CONOPIDAE

DISTRIBUTION Until recently only known as British from Barton Mills, Suffolk (9 August 1906). However, it has recently been discovered at Wicken Fen, Cambridgeshire (8 July 1989) and confirmed from Chobham Common, Surrey (2 September 1962).

HABITAT Probably unimproved grassland or heathland, though all known sites have a wetland component, eg valley bog at Chobham, fen at Wicken and Barton Mills.

ECOLOGY Probably a parasitoid of adult bumble bees Bombus.

STATUS The recent discovery of a second and third British site suggests this species may be under-recorded. Its separation from the common S. ferrugineus can be difficult.

THREAT Habitat loss to agriculture or afforestation. Mis-management of sites, through either overgrazing, or the cessation of grazing with subsequent invasion by scrub, pine or bracken and a loss of floristic richness and diversity.

MANAGEMENT Use traditional management techniques such as rotational grazing to retain sites in an open state and produce a mosaic of vegetation types whilst discouraging scrub invasion. Encourage plenty of flowers such as thistles, knapweeds and ragwort for adult feeding and host interception.

THECOPHORA FULVIPES (Desvoidy)

NOTABLE
CONOPIDAE

DISTRIBUTION Records widely dispersed in England, Scotland, North Wales and islands such as the Scillies and Arran. A rather wesern bias is shown.

HABITAT Preferences unclear, records include heathland and moorland.

ECOLOGY Probably a parasitoid of adult solitary bees of the genera Halictus and Lasioglossum. Adults recorded from June to September and may be found visiting a range of flowers or near to colonies of the host bees.

STATUS Infrequent with few recent records, though possibly overlooked to some extent due to confusion with the commoner T. atra.

THREAT Loss of habitat to agriculture, afforestation and coastal development. Mis-management of sites, through either overgrazing or the cessation of grazing with subsequent scrub invasion, loss of floristic richness and diversity, and loss of bare soil.

MANAGEMENT Use traditional management techniques such as rotational grazing to produce a mosaic of vegetation types and discourage scrub invasion. Retain any banks and areas of bare ground (especially those in sunny, south facing situations) to support a rich aculeate fauna, and encourage plenty of flowers for adult feeding and host interception.

ZODION CINEREUM (Fabricius)

NOTABLE
CONOPIDAE

DISTRIBUTION Recorded widely in England as far north as Durham, with a strong southerly bias; also Wales (Glamorganshire, Radnorshire).

HABITAT Heathland, grassland and open structured woodland.

ECOLOGY Larvae parasitoids on adult solitary bees of the genera Hylaeus and Halictus. Adults recorded from May to August and may be found visiting a range of flowers or near to colonies of the hosts.

STATUS Presently a very local species of the south with about 10 known post 1960 sites. Old records are comparatively numerous and a decline seems to have occurred.

THREAT Habitat loss to agriculture, afforestation and coastal development of some sites. Mis-management of sites, through either overgrazing or the cessation of grazing with subsequent scrub invasion, a loss of floristic richness and diversity, and a loss of bare soil.

MANAGEMENT Use traditional management techniques such as rotational grazing to produce a mosaic of vegetation types and discourage scrub. Retain open rides and clearings in woods. Retain any banks and areas of bare ground (especially those in sunny, south facing situations) to support a rich aculeate fauna, and encourage plenty of flowers for adult feeding and host interception.

ZODION NOTATUM Meigen

RARE
CONOPIDAE

DISTRIBUTION Relatively few records scattered in southern England (Dorset, Hampshire, Hertfordshire, Surrey, possibly Essex); also Wales (Carmarthenshire, Denbighshire).

HABITAT Preferences unclear, records include heathland and dry grassland.

ECOLOGY Larvae probably parasitoids of certain adult solitary bees, though precise hosts unknown. Adults recorded in June and July.

STATUS Extremely scarce with only four known post 1960 sites: Oxenbourne Down, Hampshire (1972); Sheep Leas, Surrey (1968); Rhyd-y-creuau, Denbighshire (1970) and Llangeitho, Cardiganshire (1986). Status revised from RDB2 (Shirt 1987).

THREAT Habitat loss to agriculture, afforestation and coastal development. Mis-management of sites, through either overgrazing or the cessation of grazing with subsequent scrub invasion, a loss of floristic richness and diversity, and a loss of bare ground.

MANAGEMENT Use traditional management techniques such as rotational grazing to produce a mosaic of vegetation types and discourage scrub. Retain any banks and areas of bare ground (especially those in sunny, south facing situations) to support a rich aculeate fauna, and encourage plenty of flowers for adult feeding and host interception.

STATUS A poorly known species only recently added to the British list (Cole, 1981) and possibly overlooked through confusion with the common C. cristatus. The Herefordshire site is now largely planted with conifers.

THREAT The ditching of upland streams, excessive disturbance through adjacent afforestation or trampling of banks, and pollution such as agricultural run-off.

MANAGEMENT Maintain upland streams in a natural, disturbance-free state.

CHRYSOPILUS LAETUS (Zetterstedt)   ENDANGERED
                                                    RHAGIONIDAE

DISTRIBUTION Until recently only known from a single site in southern England : Windsor Forest/Great Park, Berkshire, where it has a long history between 1939 and 1972. In 1988 it was additionally recorded from Bottisham Park, Cambridgeshire.

HABITAT Ancient broadleaved woodland, with a requirement for old or diseased beech, also dead stumps and possibly logs.

ECOLOGY Larvae develop in rotting wood in a range of situations including rot holes, aerial logs and porridge-like wood mould in old stumps. In 1939 a specimen was bred from a puparium said to have been found in mud but this information may be erroneous or the circumstances misleading. Adults recorded in April and May, usually near the breeding sites.

STATUS A very restricted species with no Windsor records for over a decade. Most records from this site apply to reared females and the only adult found in the field was an individual sitting on a log in July 1972. This site belongs to the Crown Estate and there has been removal of dead wood and old or diseased trees and afforestation of some areas. The Cambridgeshire record also applies to a reared individual found as a larva in a beech rot hole. This site is a small remnant of old parkland in an extensively arable setting and provides hope that the species may yet prove more widespread.

THREAT Removal of old and diseased trees and dead wood.

MANAGEMENT Retain any dead wood and old or diseased trees, ensuring continuity of these in future.

ATRICHOPS CRASSIPES (Meigen)   RARE
                                                    RHAGIONIDAE

DISTRIBUTION A clumped distribution in southern England (Hampshire, Sussex, Kent, Surrey, Berkshire) and the southern Welsh Borders (Herefordshire, Monmouthshire). Records are most numerous for the River Rother and its tributaries in Sussex and Kent.

HABITAT Associated with rivers, though a range of conditions seem to be tolerated. Most records are derived from meandering middle sections of rivers with a moderate flow pattern, though it has been taken in a deep fast flowing river just above the tidal limits (R. Rye at Redbrook, Monmouthshire) and also in a chalk stream (R. Trent near Romsey, Hampshire). The rivers can be on clay, sand, shingle and boulders, but there is usually abundant macrophyte vegetation. Moderate silt loading can be tolerated, but most the sites are free from serious pollutants. Some tree shading is also tolerated but not at all essential.

ECOLOGY Larvae aquatic, developing amongst the vegetation of the above situations. They are likely to be carnivorous. Adults recorded in June and July, usually on riverside vegetation.

STATUS Formerly regarded as a great rarity with only old records confined to a few localities in Hampshire and the R. Rother in Sussex. Since 1973 it has proved to be considerably more widespread and work by the Freshwater Biological Association has clearly demonstrated that searching for larvae is the most efficient way of recording this species. Some 10 post 1960 sites are now known, five from the R. Rother and its tributaries, others from near Romsey, Hampshire; R. Wey, Surrey; Burfield, Berkshire; Redbrook; Monmouthshire and Skenfrith, Herefordshire.

THREAT Despite the range of conditions used, the need for unpolluted rivers is strongly evident. Agricultural run-off, sewage and industrial effluent could prove to be harmful in even the smallest amounts. Disturbance through river improvement schemes and excessive disturbance of banks by cattle could also render stretches of river unsuitable.

MANAGEMENT Maintain rivers in a natural and unpolluted state with a healthy macrophyte flora.

CHRYSOPILUS ERYTHROPHTHALMUS Loew   VULNERABLE
                                                    RHAGIONIDAE

DISTRIBUTION Only two records: Stoke Plantation, Herefordshire (1 July 1896) and Rake Beck, Yorkshire (3 July 1979).

HABITAT Upland streams, and abroad it has been found in such streams at altitudes between 300 and 1000m, with a flow rate of 30 - 70cm per second and at water temperatures not exceeding 13-14°C. Both British localities experience a calcareous influence.

ECOLOGY Abroad, larvae have been found under stones and among aquatic bryophytes in the cool water of the above locations. Adults recorded in July.

PTIOLINA ATRA (Staeger)
NOTABLE
RHAGIONIDAE

DISTRIBUTION A mainly northern and western species with records for England, (Devon), Hampshire, Westmorland, Yorkshire, Durham), South Wales (Glamorganshire) and Scotland (East Lothian, Perthshire, Aberdeenshire, Elgin, Easterness, Dunbartonshire).

HABITAT Records include bogs, dune slacks and damp woods in both coastal and highland areas, with records from above 750m in Perthshire.

ECOLOGY Biology unknown. The larvae possibly develop as predators in the wet peat, soil or moss of the above situations. Adults recorded in May and June but appear to have a short flight period at any given site.

STATUS Widespread but very local with three known post 1960 sites in Westmorland, Durham and Aberdeenshire. Possibly overlooked because of the short flight period. During these periods it can be quite numerous.

THREAT Drainage of bogs and marshy areas for intensive forestry or agriculture; mis-management of water levels with a possible loss of breeding sites and subsequent scrub invasion.

MANAGEMENT Retain bogs and marshy areas, ensuring a high, stable water level and minimising levels of disturbance, especially on coastal dune sites. Prevent scrub invasion.

PTIOLINA OBSCURA (Fallen)
NOTABLE
RHAGIONIDAE

DISTURBANCE Records widely dispersed in England, Wales and Scotland.

HABITAT Damp broadleaved woodland, especially besides streams and rivers.

ECOLOGY Reports of bright green Ptiolina larvae from mosses such as Hypnum on stones and trees would seem to be P. obscura. Adults have been observed flying about the trunks of beech and on a colony of the common bracket fungus Bjerkandera adusta on fallen branches and are recorded from May to July.

STATUS A widespread but local species with about a dozen known post 1960 sites. Old records are comparatively numerous and a decline seems to have occurred.

THREAT Clearance of damp woodland for agriculture or intensive forestry. Removal of larger moss-covered trees and dead wood.

MANAGEMENT Ensure a good age structure of trees, especially retain larger examples with a richer moss flora and additionally retain fallen trunks or stumps.

RHAGIO ANNULATUS (Degeer)
RARE
RHAGIONIDAE

DISTRIBUTION Records few and scattered over southern England, especially the Chalk down areas of Oxfordshire and Berkshire, with additional sites in Dorset, Surrey, Gloucestershire and Herefordshire.

HABITAT Broadleaved woodland, usually on Chalk, occasionally dry woodland on other soils.

ECOLOGY Larvae probably develop as predators in damp decayed wood or soil. Adults recorded in May and June.

STATUS Apparently rare though possibly overlooked to some extent through confusion with the common R. tringaria and records are becoming more frequent with the better understanding of this species. Post 1960 sites include the Moors, Wool, Dorset (1978); three sites in Oxfordshire: Bix Bottom (1975-80), Coneyberry Hill (1956-65), Cothill NNR (1962) and Sheep Leas, Surrey (1968).

THREAT Clearance of woodland on Chalk for agriculture or intensive forestry.

MANAGEMENT Retain any damp areas and rotting wood as potential breeding sites.

RHAGIO STRIGOSUS (Meigen)
RARE
RHAGIONIDAE

DISTRIBUTION Mainly recorded from the Chalk downs of Surrey, Oxfordshire and Berkshire, with additional records from Dorset and Herefordshire.

HABITAT Dry broadleaved woods on Chalk.

ECOLOGY Larvae probably developing as predators in damp decayed wood or soil. Adults recorded in June and July and characteristically sit headdownwards on tree trunks, like the commoner R. scolopaceus.

STATUS A very restricted species, though possibly overlooked to some extent through confusion with the common R. scolopaceus from which it is still not satisfactorily distinguished in some keys. Some four post 1960 sites known: Bix Bottom (1975-81), Goring Heath (1966) and Crowsley (1971-80), Oxfordshire; Lardon Chase/Streatley Hill, Berkshire (1957-65) and probably still persisting in the Box Hill area of Surrey where it has a good history up to 1957.

THREAT Clearance of woodland on Chalk for agriculture or intensive forestry.

MANAGEMENT Retain any damp areas and rotting wood as potential breeding sites.

SPANIA NIGRA Meigen

DISTRIBUTION .Recorded widely in England, Wales and Scotland including the Isle of Bute and Arran.

HABITAT Damp broadleaved woods, meadows and coastal landslips.

ECOLOGY The larvae have been found in the thallus of _Pellia_ (a liverwort). Adults recorded from late May to early June.

STATUS Very widespread though local, with a fair number of records from the Scottish Highlands and numerous old ones from the New Forest. About 20 known post 1960 sites and occasionally locally numerous.

THREAT Clearance of damp woodland and drainage of marshy areas for agriculture and intensive forestry. Drainage and stabilisation of landslips, including construction of sea defences.

MANAGEMENT Maintain a good age structure of trees in woods; especially retain larger individuals with a rich Bryophyte community, and also retain dead wood and boulders here and elsewhere, again to encourage a rich and varied bryophyte flora.

SYMPHOROMYIA IMMACULATA Meigen

DISTRIBUTION Records widely dispersed in southern England as far north as Yorkshire.

HABITAT Grassland on calcareous soils, especially Chalk downland in the south, and Magnesium Limestone in northern England. Fairly long grassland, such as _Bromus erectus_ is usually preferred.

ECOLOGY Larvae probably develop as predators in damp soil or moss. Adults recorded from May to August.

STATUS Fairly regular on the North and South Downs and sometimes locally frequent. Otherwise fairly local and closely associated with calcareous areas, apparently predominating in climatically warmer localities and avoiding districts with late frosts. About 30 post 1960 sites are known.

THREAT Habitat loss to arable agriculture or intensive forestry. Changes in grazing management of calcareous grassland, either overgrazing with a loss of tall vegetation or undergrazing and subsequent invasion by scrub or coarse vegetation.

MANAGEMENT Maintain a mosaic of vegetation types using rotational grazing policies if necessary.

41

SCENOPINUS NIGER (Degeer)

NOTABLE
SCENOPINIDAE

DISTRIBUTION Records widely dispersed in southern England (Devon, Hampshire, Surrey, Berkshire, Suffolk, Cambridgeshire, Gloucestershire, Herefordshire) and also Denbighshire in Wales and Elgin in Scotland.

HABITAT Broadleaved woodland, occasionally other habitats, but probably requiring dead wood or old trees.

ECOLOGY The puparium has been found under the bark of a diseased oak, suggesting that dead wood or old trees are a requirement. Adults recorded from May to July and are occasionally recorded hovering, shining brightly in the sunlight.

STATUS Rather infrequent though possibly overlooked, with post 1960 records for Berkshire, Cambridgeshire and Denbighshire.

THREAT Clearance of old woods and removal of the old or diseased trees and dead wood.

MANAGEMENT Retain any dead wood and old or diseased trees, ensuring continuity of these in the future.

42

==============================
ANTICHAETA ANALIS (Meigen)   RARE
                                                   SCIOMYZIDAE

DISTRIBUTION About nine sites in all, scattered widely throughout Great Britain: Cambridgeshire and Northumberland in England, Glamorganshire in Wales and Easterness, Elgin, Angus, Sutherland and East Ross in Scotland.

HABITAT Fens and marshes. In Scotland adults have been found associated with Carex emergent from shallow pools. At Chippenham Fen they have been found at the margin of a Phragmites swamp and in a wet meadow; at Laugharne Burrows a specimen was taken from a densely vegetated, wet dune slack dominated by Juncus acutus. Other records refer to wet ditches.

ECOLOGY In Denmark, eggs and feeding larvae were found on and in the gelatinous egg capsules of the snail Lymnaea truncatula and it is unlikely that adult snails are used. The species overwinters in the pupal stage and 2-4 generations probably occur per year. Adults recorded from late May to late August.

STATUS Exceedingly local with nine post 1960 sites as follows: Thurley Fen, Lincolnshire (1989); Chippenham Fen NNR, Cambridgeshire (1982, 1983 and 1985); Newham Fen, Northumberland (1986); Crymlyn Bog NNR, Glamorganshire (1979); Laugharne Burrows MOD, Carmarthenshire (1988); Insh (RSPB), Easterness (1982); Braelangwell, East Ross (1976); Loch Ness shore, Easterness (1984) and Rescobie Marsh, Angus (1977). Status revised from RDB2 (Shirt 1987).

THREAT The drainage of wetlands for agriculture or intensive forestry; complete or extensive clearance of marginal vegetation from water edges; pollution such as agricultural run-off; mis-management of water levels with a loss of breeding sites and subsequent scrub invasion.

MANAGEMENT Prevent any drainage of sites and ensure a range of vegetation types including ditches, ponds and their marginal vegetation. Seasonally fluctuating water levels may be of importance. Avoid scrub invasion though isolated shrubs or areas of carr may be beneficial.

==============================
ANTICHAETA BREVIPENNIS (Zetterstedt)   VULNERABLE
                                                   SCIOMYZIDAE

DISTRIBUTION About a dozen sites in total, dispersed widely in England (Devon, Dorset, Berkshire, Suffolk, Norfolk, Yorkshire) and Scotland (Elgin).

HABITAT Usually associated with lush vegetation beside water bodies in wetlands, the Suffolk records refer to ditches in unimproved grazing marsh.

ECOLOGY In Denmark, eggs and larvae found on and in the egg masses of snails such as Succinea sp and may possibly also use Lymnaea truncatula (at least in the laboratory). Adults recorded from June to August.

STATUS Very rare with seven post 1960 sites: Lower Abbey Farm Marshes (1983), Sizewell (1989) and Castle Abbey (1983), Suffolk; Whitwell Common, Norfolk (1974); Southfield Farm Marsh, Kettering, Northamptonshire (1980s) Denaby Ings, Yorkshire (1967) and Bere Stream, Dorset (1984).

THREAT Clearance of damp woodland and drainage of wetlands for agriculture or intensive forestry; pollution such as agricultural run-off; complete or extensive clearance of marginal vegetation from water edges such as through river improvement schemes and ditch improvement; mis-management of water levels with a loss of breeding sites and subsequent scrub invasion.

MANAGEMENT Prevent any drainage of sites, ensuring a range of vegetation types including ditches, ponds and their marginal vegetation. From the observations recently made in Northamptonshire and Suffolk it seems likely that this species prefers situations which have not been intensively managed by grazing or cutting. On grazing marshes it apparently prefers those ditches which have not been recently cleared and have reached the later stages of the seral succession. Seasonally fluctuating water levels may be of importance.

==============================
ANTICHAETA OBLIVIOSA (Enderlein)   VULNERABLE
                                                   SCIOMYZIDAE

DISTRIBUTION Presently only known from four sites in Huntingdonshire: Brampton Wood (1987), Port Holme (1988), Great Raveley Wood (1988) and Woodwalton Fen NNR (1985, 1989).

HABITAT The Brampton Wood and Great Raveley Wood records refer to specimens taken from woodland ponds, upon clay substrate. The recorded situation at Port Holme was the margin of a Glyceria choked ditch at the edge of grassland, beneath mature willows. The Woodwalton capture probably refers to a lush dyke margin within this large peat fen. From this limited information it may be tenuously suggested that small, shaded, seasonal, or at least fluctuating, water bodies may be the preferred habitat.

ECOLOGY Biology unknown, though other species of the genus have larvae feeding on the egg clusters of semi-aquatic snails. Adults recorded in May (England) and from late April to late June (on the Continent), though by all accounts it has a rather early flight period for a Sciomyzid.

STATUS Only recently recognised in England and rapidly found at three further sites, suggesting that it may not be infrequent, at least in the Huntingdonshire area. The rather early flight period may have led to some under recording although it is a rather distinctive species. In Europe it is a rare species with records confined to Denmark, Belgium, Germany (Berlin district) and Hungary (Rozkosny, 1984). Brampton Wood and Port Holme are SSSIs; Great Raveley Wood is a Trust Reserve. This species is not listed in Shirt (1987).

THREATS The drainage of wetlands and associated carr or wet woodland for agriculture, intensive forestry etc; pollution such as agricultural run-off; complete or extensive clearance of marginal vegetation from pond or ditch edges; mis-management of water levels with a permanent drying out of water bodies and invasion by scrub.

MANAGEMENT Prevent any drainage of sites and ensure a range of vegetation types including ditches, ponds and their marginal vegetation. Seasonal water bodies, or those with seasonally fluctuating water levels may be of particular importance. Prevent scrub invasion, though established carr and wet woodland at sites may suit this species.

COLOBAEA BIFASCIELLA (Fallen)

DISTRIBUTION Records dispersed widely in England and Wales reaching Durham and Cheviot in the north though not yet known from Scotland. Records are most numerous for East Anglia and the East Midlands.

HABITAT Lush marginal vegetation around ponds, ditches and lakes.

ECOLOGY Larvae develop in the respiratory chamber of aquatic snails such as *Lymnaea palustris* or *L. truncatula*, selecting snails that are stranded, aestivating or otherwise exposed. Adults recorded from late May to mid August probably as two or three generations.

STATUS Widespread but very local with in excess of 20 known post 1960 sites. Status revised from RDB3 (Shirt 1987).

THREAT The drainage of wetlands for agriculture or intensive forestry; complete or extensive clearance of marginal vegetation from water edges such as through river improvement schemes and ditching of streams; pollution such as agricultural run-off; mis-management of water levels with a loss of breeding sites and subsequent scrub invasion.

MANAGEMENT Prevent any drainage of sites and ensure a range of vegetaton types including ditches, ponds and their marginal vegetation. Seasonally fluctuating water levels may be of importance. Avoid scrub invasion though isolated shrubs or areas of carr may be beneficial.

COLOBAEA DISTINCTA (Meigen)

DISTRIBUTION Records dispersed widely in England and Wales reaching Westmorland in the north. Records comparatively numerous for East Anglia and the East Midlands.

HABITAT Marshy areas and marginal vegetation of ponds, ditches and lakes.

ECOLOGY The larvae develop as parasitoids of aquatic snails such as *Anisus leucostoma*. Adults recorded from late May to early August.

STATUS Widespread but very local with about 20 known post 1960 sites. Not quite as rare as formerly believed. Status revised from RDB3 (Shirt 1987).

THREAT The drainage of wetlands for agriculture or intensive forestry; pollution such as agricultural run-off; complete or extensive clearance of marginal vegetation from water edges such as through river improvement schemes and ditching of streams; mis-management of water levels with a loss of breeding sites and subsequent scrub invasion.

MANAGEMENT Prevent any drainage of sites and ensure a range of vegetation types including ditches, ponds and their marginal vegetation. Seasonally fluctuating water levels may be of importance. Prevent scrub invasion though isolated shrubs or areas of carr may be beneficial.

COLOBAEA PECTORALIS (Zetterstedt)

DISTRIBUTION Only five certain localities: Gordano Valley, Somerset (1984); Thompson Common (1984) and Fowl Mere (1962? both in Norfolk; Kenfig Pool, Glamorganshire (pre 1960) and Felden, Hertfordshire (very old). An old record for St Merryn, Cornwall will require further investigation.

HABITAT Wetlands, probably with a requirement for rich marginal, vegetation around lakes, ponds and ditches.

ECOLOGY The larvae develop as parasitoids of aquatic snails such as *Anisus vortex*. Adults probably present from June to September though few English dates available.

STATUS Only the two post 1960 records as outlined above. Gordano Valley is an NNR; Thompson Common is a Norfolk Trust reserve.

THREAT The drainage of wetlands for agriculture or intensive forestry; pollution such as agricultural run off; complete or extensive clearance of marginal vegetation from water edges such as through river improvement schemes and the ditching of streams; mis-management of water levels with a loss of breeding sites and subsequent scrub invasion.

MANAGEMENT Prevent any drainage of sites and ensure a range of vegetation types including ditches, ponds and their marginal vegetation. Seasonally fluctuating water levels may be of importance. Prevent scrub invasion though isolated shrubs or areas of carr may be beneficial.

COLOBAEA PUNCTATA (Lundbeck) NOTABLE SCIOMYZIDAE

DISTRIBUTION Records dispersed widely in England as far north as Yorkshire and also extending into South Wales (Monmouthshire, Glamorganshire).

HABITAT Lush marginal vegetation beside rivers, lakes, ponds and ditches. The adults are characteristically found where lower summer water levels leave their snail hosts stranded beside ditches and ponds.

ECOLOGY The larvae are highly specialised parasitoids, feeding on terrestrial and aestivating aquatic snails. Each consumes one snail only and pupates within the shell of that host. Known hosts include Planorbarius corneus, Planorbis planorbis and Lymnaea peregra. Adults recorded from mid May to mid August.

STATUS Widespread but very local with about 15 known post 1960 sites.

THREAT The drainage of wetlands for agriculture or intensive forestry; pollution such as agricultural run-off; complete or extensive clearance of marginal vegetation from water edge such as through river improvement schemes and the ditching of streams; mis-management of water levels or grazing with a loss of breeding sites and subsequent scrub invasion.

MANAGEMENT Prevent any drainage of sites and ensure a range of vegetation types including ditches, ponds and their marginal vegetation. Seasonally fluctuating water levels appear to be an important feature of sites and this feature should be maintained without allowing any long-term drop in water levels. Prevent scrub invasion, though isolated shrubs or areas of carr may be beneficial.

DICHAETOPHORA FINLANDICA Verbeke RARE SCIOMYZIDAE

DISTRIBUTION Records dispersed widely in England (Oxfordshire, Cambridgeshire, Huntingdonshire, Suffolk, Norfolk, Westmorland, Yorkshire, Cheviot) and Wales (Glamorganshire and a possible recent record for Anglesey). The vast majority of records are for the fens and heaths of East Anglia and the East Midlands.

HABITAT Fenlands including damper parts of the breckland heaths, and also recorded on a couple of occasions from sand dunes (Whitford Burrows, Glamorganshire and Witherslack, Westmorland). Shaded areas at the edges of woods or the edges of streams are particularly favoured.

ECOLOGY Larvae probably feed as parasitoids on aquatic pulmonate snails. Adults recorded from late June to late September.

STATUS Widespread but very local with about a dozen post 1960 sites. This species has only recently been recognised as distinct from the commoner D. obliterata and its known range is being extended every year. Status revised from RDB1 (Shirt 1987).

THREAT The drainage of wetlands for agriculture or intensive forestry; pollution such as agricultural run-off; complete or extensive clearance of marginal vegetation from water edge such as through river improvement

---

schemes and the ditching of streams; recreational pressure on dunes; mis-management of water levels with a loss of breeding sites and subsequent scrub invasion.

MANAGEMENT Prevent any drainage of sites and ensure a range of vegetation types including ditches, ponds and their marginal vegetation. Prevent scrub invasion though isolated shrubs or areas of carr may be beneficial.

DICTYA UMBRARUM (Linnaeus) NOTABLE SCIOMYZIDAE

DISTRIBUTION Records widely dispersed in upland areas in the north of England and Scotland extending to North Wales and isolated records from the south west, especially the New Forest and Dorset bogs.

HABITAT Marshes, bogs and vegetation around ponds and lakes; also dune slacks in North Wales and at Culbin Sands, Elgin. Most localities are on peat, where adults are typically found in association with flushes.

ECOLOGY Larvae probably parasitoids of aquatic pulmonate snails and have been reared in laboratory conditions using Lymnaea palustris and L. tomentosa. Adults recorded from May to September.

STATUS About 50 post 1960 sites, mainly from northern upland areas, though still present in small numbers in the New Forest.

THREAT The drainage of wetlands for agriculture or intensive forestry; pollution such as agricultural run-off; complete or extensive clearance of marginal vegetation from water edges such as through river improvement schemes and the ditching of streams; recreational pressure on dunes; mis-management of water levels with a loss of breeding sites and subsequent scrub invasion.

MANAGEMENT Prevent any drainage of sites and ensure a range of vegetation types including ditches, ponds and their marginal vegetation. Prevent scrub invasion though isolated shrubs or areas of carr may be beneficial.

ECTINOCERA BOREALIS Zetterstedt   RARE
                                                  SCIOMYZIDAE

DISTRIBUTION Mainly recorded from Scotland (Dumfriesshire, Perthshire, Aberdeenshire, Elgin, Easterness, East Ross, Sutherland) with additional localities from Yorkshire, Cumbria? (on border with Yorkshire), Denbighshire and recently from Devon. Regarded as a boreo-montane species in Europe as a whole.

HABITAT Scottish records usually refer to densely shaded coniferous woodland especially in highland areas. However it has been taken from limestone pavement on a number of occasions and the Devon record is from a sandy shore overhung by oak woodland.

ECOLOGY Life history unknown, but larvae probably parasitoids on terrestrial snails or slugs. Adults recorded from late May to July.

STATUS Very local in Scotland and northern England, very rare elsewhere and with about a dozen post 1960 sites in total. The Devon record provides a very intriguing extension to its range and habitat.

THREAT Habitat loss through intensive forestry in Caledonian pine forests, the afforestation of upland areas and the destruction of limestone pavement by removal as rockery stone.

MANAGEMENT Uncertain other than maintaining the natural/semi-natural habitat at known sites.

PELIDNOPTERA NIGRIPENNIS Fabricius   NOTABLE
                                                  SCIOMYZIDAE

DISTRIBUTION Records are from three areas of Great Britain. Most are for Scotland where it is very local but widespread especially in the valleys of highland areas. It occurs at lower levels in the major fen and Breck areas of East Anglia and Cambridgeshire, and a few records are present for the south-west in Glamorganshire and Devon.

HABITAT Damp woods (both broadleaved and coniferous) and shaded parts of fens and damp heathland, especially in montane and submontane situations in Scotland, but also well known from some lowland fens in England.

ECOLOGY Biology unknown. Sciomyzids characteristically develop as parasitoids of snails, though this species belongs to a distinct and isolated taxonomic group and it may have an entirely different life history, millipedes being possible hosts according to some sources. Adults recorded from mid May to late July.

STATUS Widespread but local in Scotland with about 25 post 1960 sites and especially regular along the Spey Valley. Recent English records are very few and include Wangford Warren, Suffolk (1982) and Yarner Wood, Devon (1978). Status revised from RDB3 (Shirt 1987).

THREAT The drainage and clearance of damp woodland and wetlands for agriculture and intensive forestry; scrub invasion and a loss of breeding sites through mis-management of water levels.

MANAGEMENT Prevent any drainage of wetland sites and ensure a range of vegetation types, preventing scrub invasion, though isolated shrubs or areas of carr may be beneficial.

PHERBELLIA ANNULIPES (Zetterstedt)   NOTABLE
                                                  SCIOMYZIDAE

DISTRIBUTION Scattered localities in southern England (Somerset, Surrey, Kent, Berkshire, Buckinghamshire, Oxfordshire, Gloucestershire, Herefordshire) and South Wales (Monmouthshire).

HABITAT Old broadleaved woodlands, especially beech and an association with calcareous soils, both limestone and chalk seems apparent. The adults are typically observed in shaded rather than open situations.

ECOLOGY In the laboratory the larvae have been reared from the snail Discus rotundatus and behaved as parasitoids. Adults recorded from early June to early August and have been observed walking on moss-covered fallen beech trunks on several occasions, suggesting this may be a site for host snails.

STATUS Post 1960 records from about 15 sites with numerous records for Windsor Forest, Berkshire. Only added to the British list in 1965 and possibly still somewhat under recorded.

THREAT The clearance of old broadleaved woodlands in southern England for agriculture or intensive forestry; removal of dead wood.

MANAGEMENT Retain any dead wood such as fallen trunks at sites, allowing their natural decomposition and ensure future continuity of this resource.

PHERBELLIA ARGYRA Verbeke

DISTRIBUTION Most records are for East Anglia: Mildenhall (1911), Barton Mills (1909, 1912), West Stow (1921) and Lopham Fen (1970), Suffolk; Thompson Common (1973, 1983) and Ringmere (1953), Norfolk; additionally Cambridge, Cambridgeshire (1918); 3 sites near Romney Marsh, Kent (1982); Askrigg (1937) and Bentley Common, Yorkshire (1976).

HABITAT Wetlands and grazing levels marshes especially at the margins of pools and ditches. Both inland and coastal sites are used.

ECOLOGY Larvae develop as parasitoids in aquatic pulmonate snails such as Planorbis planorbis and Anisus vortex. Adults recorded from early May to late September, probably as 4-6 generations.

STATUS Known from six post 1960 sites, though the choice of sites probably places it in a vulnerable position.

THREAT The drainage of wetland areas for agriculture coastal development or intensive forestry; complete or extensive clearance of marginal vegetation from ditches; pollution such as agricultural run-off; mis-management of water levels with a loss of breeding sites and subsequent scrub invasion.

MANAGEMENT Prevent any drainage of sites; ensure a range of vegetation types including ditches, ponds and their marginal vegetation using rotational management where necessary. Seasonally fluctuating water levels may be of importance. Prevent scrub invasion.

PHERBELLIA BRUNNIPES Meigen

DISTRIBUTION Records scattered widely in England, Wales and Scotland. Perhaps most frequent in highland areas of Scotland and Westmorland and also the Thames and Severn estuaries.

HABITAT A range of wetlands are used including fen, acid bog, dune slack, coastal levels, gravel pits and damp woods. Standing water may be a requirement.

ECOLOGY Larvae probably develop as parasitoids of aquatic pulmonate snails, though exact hosts are unknown. Adults recorded from early May to mid September.

STATUS Widespread though local with about 40 known post 1960 sites. Formerly regarded as a rarity, and the apparent increase probably marks an increase in recording levels in recent years. Status revised from RDB3 (Shirt 1987).

THREAT The drainage of wetland areas for agriculture, coastal development or intensive forestry; complete or extensive clearance of marginal vegetation from water edges such as through river improvement schemes and the ditching of streams; pollution such as agricultural run-off; recreational pressure on dunes; mis-management of water levels with a loss of breeding sites and subsequent scrub invasion.

MANAGEMENT Prevent any drainage of sites and ensure a range of vegetation types including ditches, ponds and their marginal vegetation using rotational management where necessary. Seasonally fluctuating water levels may be of importance. Prevent scrub invasion.

PHERBELLIA DORSATA (Zetterstedt)

DISTRIBUTION Records scattered widely in southern England as north as Lincolnshire and the southern half of Wales. It is perhaps most frequent on the fens and commons of East Anglia and the East Midlands.

HABITAT A range of wetlands are utilised, both inland and coastal and both shaded and exposed. A requirement for standing water is probably present.

ECOLOGY The larvae develop as parasitoids of the aquatic snail Planorbis planorbis (other species including terrestrial ones have been attacked in the laboratory). Adults recorded from late April to early October probably as four or five generations.

STATUS About 35 post 1960 sites are known, the majority being in East Anglia or the East Midlands. Status revised from RDB3 (Shirt 1987).

THREAT The drainage of wetland areas for agriculture, coastal development or intensive forestry; complete or extensive clearance of marginal vegetation from water edges such as through river improvement schemes and the ditching of streams; pollution such as agricultural run-off; mis-management of water levels with a loss of breeding sites and subsequent scrub invasion.

MANAGEMENT Prevent any drainage of sites and ensure a range of vegetation types including ditches, ponds and their marginal vegetation using rotational management where necessary. Seasonally fluctuating water levels may be of importance. Prevent scrub invasion.

NOTABLE
SCIOMYZIDAE

PHERBELLIA GRISEOLA (Fallen)

DISTRIBUTION Recorded widely in England, Wales, and Scotland including a number of sites in Rhum.

HABITAT A wide range of wetlands are used including fens, bogs, dune slacks and damp woods and a requirement for standing water is present.

ECOLOGY The larvae develop as parasitoids of aquatic snails such as Lymnaea palustris (a wide range of hosts have been used in the laboratory). Adults recorded from early May to early September probably as four to six generations.

STATUS Widespread but very local in most areas with about 30 known post 1960 sites. Status revised from RDB3 (Shirt 1987).

THREAT The drainage of wetland areas for agriculture, coastal development or intensive forestry; complete or extensive clearance of marginal vegetation from water edges such as through river improvement schemes and the ditching of streams; pollution such as agricultural run-off; mismanagement of water levels with a loss of breeding sites and subsequent scrub invasion.

MANAGEMENT Prevent any drainage of sites and ensure a range of vegetation types including ponds, ditches and their marginal vegetation using rotational management where necessary. Seasonally fluctuating water levels may be of importance. Prevent scrub invasion.

NOTABLE
SCIOMYZIDAE

PHERBELLIA GRISESCENS (Meigen)

DISTRIBUTION Records scattered widely in England and Wales as far north as Durham, and with a single record from Kinrara, Elgin in Scotland (1982).

HABITAT The majority of records are from coastal situations such as grazing marsh and levels, suggesting that mildly brackish conditions are preferred. It is occasionally reported inland.

ECOLOGY The larvae develop as parasitoids of snails, a wide variety of both aquatic and terrestrial species being attacked in the laboratory though brackish water species such as Hydrobia ventrosa (Hydrobiidae) may prove to be more typical hosts in natural circumstances. Adults recorded from late May to early September, probably as 5-7 broods.

STATUS About 20 known post 1960 sites scattered throughout the known range. Status revised from RDB3 (Shirt 1987).

THREAT The drainage of wetland areas for agriculture, coastal development or intensive forestry; complete or extensive clearance of marginal vegetation from water edges such as through river improvement schemes and the ditching of streams; pollution such as agricultural run off; mismanagement of water levels with a loss of breeding sites and subsequent scrub invasion.

MANAGEMENT Prevent any drainage of sites and ensure a range of vegetation types including ditches, ponds and their marginal vegetation using rotational management where necessary. Seasonally fluctuating water levels may be of importance. Prevent scrub invasion.

RARE
SCIOMYZIDAE

PHERBELLIA KNUTSONI Verbeke

DISTRIBUTION Widely recorded in southern England (Devon, Suffolk, Norfolk, Cambridgeshire, Herefordshire) and South Wales (Glamorganshire, Pembrokeshire).

HABITAT Adults found in dry habitats, recent records apply to dry sand dune, breck heath or chalk grassland.

ECOLOGY The larvae probably develp as parasitoids of snails. Although it is unknown whether aquatic or terrestrial species are preferred, the situations where adults have been recorded indicate that terrestrial snails are probably used. Adults recorded from June to September, presumably as several generations.

STATUS About half a dozen post 1960 sites known. However the relatively recent description of this species as new to science (1966) may have led to specimens being overlooked in some old collections. This species is not listed in Shirt (1987).

THREAT Habitat loss to agriculture, afforestation, coastal development etc.; overgrazing or the cessation of grazing followed by scrub invasion and a loss of certain vegetation elements.

MANAGEMENT Maintain a range of vegetation types at sites, using policies such as rotational grazing where necessary and prevent scrub invasion.

PHERBELLIA NANA (Fallen)

DISTRIBUTION Recorded widely in England as far north as Yorkshire; also Wales (Glamorganshire, Anglesey) and Scotland (Sutherland).

HABITAT A wide range of wetland are used including open marshes and deeply shaded forest pools, margins of lakes and dune slacks. Permanent or temporary water bodies both appear to be used; there are indications that pools and ditches which dry out in summer and have sparse emergent Phragmites may be preferred.

ECOLOGY The larvae develop as parasitoids in a range of aquatic snails (Aplexa, Lymnaea, Physa, Planorbis) and terrestrial species (Helicella, Hygromia, Succinea). Adults recorded from mid May to mid September probably as 4-8 generations.

STATUS Widespread but very local with about 20 known post 1960 sites.

THREAT The drainage of wetland areas for agriculture or intensive forestry; complete or extensive clearance of marginal vegetation from water edges such as through river improvement schemes and the ditching of streams; pollution such as agricultural run-off; recreational pressure on dunes leading to blow-outs; mis-management of water levels with a loss of breeding sites and subsequent scrub invasion.

MANAGEMENT Prevent any drainage of sites and ensure a range of vegetation types including temporary ponds, ditches and their marginal vegetation using rotational management where necessary. Seasonally fluctuating water levels may be of importance. Prevent scrub invasion.

PSACADINA VERBEKEI Rozkosny

DISTRIBUTION Recorded widely in England as far north as Yorkshire and Wales (Merionethshire and Pembrokeshire).

HABITAT A range of wetland are used including fens, damp heaths, riversides and dune slacks. Standing water is probably a requirement, though records seem to relate to both bog and base rich conditions.

ECOLOGY The larvae develop as parasitoids of aquatic snails such as Lymnaea (a wide range of aquatic and terrestrial species have been attacked in the laboratory) and appear to be adapted for life at the margins of aquatic environments. Adults recorded from early April to mid October.

STATUS Widespread but very local with about 25 known post 1960 sites.

THREAT The drainage of wetland areas for agriculture, coastal development or intensive forestry; complete or extensive clearance of marginal vegetation from water edges such as through river improvement schemes and the ditching of streams; pollution such as agricultural run-off; recreational pressures on dunes; mis-management of water levels with a loss of breeding sites and subsequent scrub invasion.

MANAGEMENT Prevent any drainage of sites, ensuring a range of vegetation types including ponds, ditches and their marginal vegetation using rotational management where necessary. Seasonally fluctuating water levels may be of importance. Prevent scrub invasion.

PSACADINA VITTIGERA (Schiner)

DISTRIBUTION Only six known sites: Beeston Common (1985) and Catfield Fen (1977) both in Norfolk; Chippenham Fen NNR (up to 1982) and Wicken Fen (1946) both in Cambridgeshire; Cothill NNR, Oxfordshire (1985); and Foxhall Pond, Suffolk (numerous dates from 1896 to 1904).

HABITAT Wetlands, especially fens, with standing water probably being a requirement.

ECOLOGY The larvae are probably parasitoids on aquatic snails at the margins of water bodies. Adults recorded from late March to mid September.

STATUS An extremely rare southern species with the four known post 1960 sites.

THREAT The drainage of wetlands for agriculture or intensive forestry; complete or extensive clearance of marginal vegetation from water edges such as through river improvement schemes and the ditching of streams; pollution such as agricultural run-off; mis-management of water levels with a loss of breeding sites and subsequent scrub invasion.

MANAGEMENT Prevent any drainage of sites, ensuring a range of vegetation types including ponds, ditches and their marginal vegetation using rotational management where necessary. Seasonally fluctuating water levels may be of importance. Prevent scrub invasion.

PTEROMICRA LEUCOPEZA (Meigen)

DISTRIBUTION Only three certain localities: Larkrigg Spring, Westmorland (1982); Westhay Moor, Somerset (1983); Cliffe, Kent (1980). A record for Wicken Fen, Cambridgeshire (1904) requires confirmation.

HABITAT Wetlands and abroad particularly associated with densely shaded ponds, marshes and swamps.

ECOLOGY The larvae develop as parasitoids in aquatic snails such as Bathyomphalus contortus with Anisus vortex being attacked in the laboratory. Adults recorded from June to August.

STATUS The three certain records are all post 1960 and widely scattered, suggesting it may be more widespread but too scarce to be readily detected.

THREAT The drainage of wetlands for agriculture, coastal development or intensive forestry; complete or extensive clearance of marginal vegetation from water edges such as through river improvement schemes and the ditching of streams; pollution such as agricultural run-off; the removal of shading trees and shrubs; mis-management of water levels with a loss of breeding sites.

MANAGEMENT Prevent any drainage of sites, ensuring a range of vegetation types including ponds, ditches and their marginal vegetation, also the presence of some trees or shrubs for shading. Seasonal water bodies, or those with seasonally changing water levels may be of particular importance.

PSACADINA ZERNYI Mayer

DISTRIBUTION Only eight known sites: Thompson Common (1983), Foulden Common (1982), East Walton Common (1983), Catfield Fen (1977) and West Harling Common (1970) all in Norfolk; Wisley Common, Surrey (1973); Pevensey Levels (1988) and Three Bridges (1876), Sussex.

HABITAT Wetlands especially fens (or breckland sites with 'pingo' hollows) with standing water probably being a requirement.

ECOLOGY The larvae probably develop as parasitoids on aquatic snails such as Lymnaea and Physa. Adults recorded from May to October.

STATUS An extremely rare southern species with only six post 1960 sites.

THREAT The drainage of wetlands for agriculture or intensive forestry; complete or extensive clearance of marginal vegetation from water edges such as through river improvement schemes and the ditching of streams; pollution such as agricultural run-off; mis-management of water levels with a loss of breeding sites and subsequent scrub invasion.

MANAGEMENT Prevent any drainage of sites ensuring a range of vegetation types including ponds, ditches and their marginal vegetation using rotational management where necessary. Seasonally fluctuating water levels may be of importance. Prevent scrub invasion.

PTEROMICRA GLABRICULA (Fallen)

DISTRIBUTION Records scattered widely in England, Wales and Scotland including Barra and the Orkneys.

HABITAT A wide range of wetlands including fens, bogs, dune slacks, moorland pools and woodland pools. Standing water is probably a requirement.

ECOLOGY The larvae develop as parasitoids in aquatic snails such as Lymnaea with Planorbis, Physa, Discus and Succinea being attacked in the laboratory. Adults recorded from May to September.

STATUS Widespread but very local with about 20 post 1960 sites. Status revised from RDB2 (Shirt 1987).

THREAT The drainage of wetlands for agriculture, coastal development or intensive forestry; complete or extensive clearance of marginal vegetation from water edges such as through river improvement schemes and the ditching of streams; pollution such as agricultural run-off; recreational pressure on dunes; mis-management of water levels with a loss of breeding sites and subsequent scrub invasion.

MANAGEMENT Prevent any drainage of sites, ensuring a range of vegetation types including ponds, ditches and their marginal vegetation and use rotational management of these where necessary. Seasonally fluctuating water levels may be of importance. Prevent scrub invasion though some isolated shrubs or areas of carr may be useful.

PTEROMICRA PECTOROSA (Hendel)

VULNERABLE
SCIOMYZIDAE

DISTRIBUTION Only two confirmed records: Wicken Fen, Cambridgeshire (1985) and a site in Essex (recent). Records for Pembrey Forest, Carmarthenshire (1986) and Braunton Burrows NNR, Devon (1989) require confirmation based on genitalia.

HABITAT Wetlands, standing water probably being a requirement. The two unconfirmed records are from pools or slacks on large coastal dune systems.

ECOLOGY The larvae develop as parasitoids of aquatic snails, Segmentina nitida and Anisus vortex being attacked in the laboratory. Adults probably recorded from May to August.

STATUS A very poorly known species, with details of some older presumed records not currently available. Wicken Fen is managed by the National Trust but has suffered from substantial scrub invasion in recent years.

THREAT The drainage of wetlands for agriculture, coastal development or intensive forestry; complete or extensive clearance of marginal vegetation from water edges such as through river improvement schemes and the ditching of streams; pollution such as agricultural run-off; mis-management of water levels with a loss of breeding sites and subsequent scrub invasion.

MANAGEMENT Prevent any drainage of sites, ensuring a range of vegetation types including ponds, ditches and their marginal vegetation using rotational management of these where necessary. Seasonally fluctuating water levels may be of importance. Prevent scrub invasion, though some isolated shrubs or areas of carr may be useful.

RENOCERA STRIATA (Meigen)

NOTABLE
SCIOMYZIDAE

DISTRIBUTION Most records apply to sites along the River Spey in Elgin and Easterness between Insh and Grantown. It has also been recorded from Rather Heath, Westmorland (1984); Aberithan Turbary, Radnorshire (1987), and records from Whixall Moss, Shropshire (1957) and a site in Westmorland require checking.

HABITAT Riverside fen and marsh, mainly in upland areas.

ECOLOGY Biology unknown, larvae possibly develop as parasitoids of aquatic molluscs such as pea mussels (Sphaeriidae). Adults recorded from May to August.

STATUS Highly restricted, though locally frequent along the Spey Valley with about 15 known post 1960 sites. The Westmorland and Radnorshire records are also recent.

THREAT The drainage of wetland areas for agriculture or intensive forestry; complete or extensive clearance of marginal vegetation from water edges such as through river improvement schemes and the ditching of streams; pollution such as agricultural run-off; mis-management of water levels with a loss of breeding sites and subsequent scrub invasion.

MANAGEMENT Prevent any drainage of sites, ensuring a range of vegetation types including ponds, ditches and their marginal vegetation. Prevent scrub invasion, though some isolated shrubs or areas of carr may be useful.

SALTICELLA FASCIATA (Meigen)

VULNERABLE
SCIOMYZIDAE

DISTRIBUTION Recorded from 11 coastal dunes in Britain within Cornwall, Somerset, Dorset, Suffolk, Norfolk, Lincolnshire, Yorkshire, Glamorgansire, Pembrokeshire and the Scilly Isles. Often a very limited distribution within these sites, occurring in areas of only a few square metres and not nearby in apparently identical habitats.

HABITAT Confined to coastal areas and adults typically found in Elymus fore-dunes, but also from fixed dune grassland at Tenby, Pembrokeshire and a sparsely vegetated shingle beach at Snettisham, Norfolk.

ECOLOGY The larvae are recorded feeding on living or dead terrestrial snails of the family Helicidae and also behave as general scavengers of dead invertebrates. Adults recorded from June to September, probably as two or three generations. A detailed account of the biology, habitat and world distribution is provided by Knutson, Stephenson and Berg (1970, Trans. R. ent. Soc. Lond 122 : 81-100).

STATUS Only five post 1960 sites: Holme Dunes (1985), Brancaster Dunes (1987) and Snettisham (1986), Norfolk; Gibralter Point, Lincolnshire (1987); Tenby, Pembrokeshire (1963 and 1967). Likely to be vulnerable through habitat loss and the apparently small size of the colonies.

THREAT Coastal development and recreational pressure on dunes and beaches.

MANAGEMENT Maintain a succession or mosaic of vegetation types and use fences and boardwalks where necessary to discourage disturbance.

SCIOMYZA DRYOMYZINA Zetterstedt
VULNERABLE
SCIOMYZIDAE

DISTRIBUTION Known from only eight sites: Dolgarrog Marsh, Caernarvonshire (1969); a site in Gwynedd (1920s); Port Meadow, Oxfordshire (1962); Sudbury (1921), Henny (1921) and Lowestoft (1898) all in Suffolk; Bubwith, Yorkshire (1924); Charterhouse Alderholt, Surrey (1968). A record for Thursley Common NNR, Surrey (1967) requires checking.

HABITAT Wetlands, exact preferences are unclear. It usually occurs inland, occasionally on the coast and standing water may be a requirement.

ECOLOGY The larvae have been recorded as parasitoids of the snail Oxyloma in North America, (Oxyloma pfeifferi is a frequent terrestrial species in fens and marshes in Britain, but S. dromyzina has not yet been reared here). Adults recorded from June to August.

STATUS Probably declining due to habitat loss, the drainage and agricultural improvement of its marsh and wet meadow habitats, and only three post 1960 records are present. It tends to occur at very low population levels at sites.

THREAT The drainage of wetlands for agriculture, intensive forestry and coastal development; complete or extensive clearance of marginal vegetation from water edges such as through river improvement schemes and the ditching of streams; pollution such as agricultural run-off; mis-management of water levels with a loss of breeding sites and subsequent scrub invasion.

MANAGEMENT Prevent any drainage of sites, ensuring a range of vegetation types including ponds, ditches and their marginal vegetation. Use rotational pond or ditch management where necessary and prevent scrub invasion, though some isolated shrubs or areas of carr may be useful.

SCIOMYZA SIMPLEX Fallen
NOTABLE
SCIOMYZIDAE

DISTRIBUTION Records widely dispersed in England (Hampshire, Sussex, Kent, Essex, Hertfordshire, Suffolk, Norfolk, Huntingdonshire, Westmorland Yorkshire, Durham), South Wales (Glamorganshire, Carmarthenshire) and Scotland (Aberdeenshire, Elgin, Easterness).

HABITAT A wide range of wetlands are used including coastal levels, inland fens and damp woods, with standing water possibly being required.

ECOLOGY The larvae probably develop as parasitoids or predators of terrestrial snails of the family Succineidae according to one authority and may use other terrestrial and aquatic species in addition. Adults recorded from mid May to mid September.

STATUS Widespread but very local with about 25 known post 1960 sites. It was not infrequent in Carmarthenshire in 1988 and may be under recorded in the Welsh part of its range. Status revised from RDB3 (Shirt 1987).

THREAT The drainage of wetlands for agriculture, coastal development or intensive forestry; complete or extensive clearance of marginal vegetation from water edges such as through river improvement schemes and the ditching of streams, pollution such as agricultural run-off; mis-management of water levels with a loss of breeding sites and subsequent scrub invasion.

MANAGEMENT Prevent any drainage of sites, ensuring a range of vegetation types including ponds, ditches and their marginal vegetation. Use rotational pond or ditch management of these where necessary and prevent scrub invasion, though some isolated shrubs or areas of carr may be useful. Seasonally fluctuating water levels may be of importance.

TETANOCERA FREYI Stackelberg
RARE
SCIOMYZIDAE

DISTRIBUTION Eleven widely dispersed sites, in Scotland: Rossie Moor, Perthshire (1981); Culbin Sands (Loch Loy), Easterness (1981); Taynish NNR, Argyllshire (1976); Migdale Wood, Sutherland (1984); England: Rather Heather (1984) and Larkrigg Spring (1982), Westmorland; Sutton Broad (1985) and Thompson Common (1983), Norfolk; Crockford Stream, Hampshire (1981, 1988) and Wales: Crymlyn Bog NNR, Glamorganshire (1980s?) and Cors Goch, Anglesey (1987).

HABITAT Wetlands; exact preferences unclear, though some base enrichment may be required.

ECOLOGY Larvae probably develop as predators or parasitoids of gastropod molluscs, but it is unclear whether aquatic or terrestrial species are used, or snails or slugs. Adults recorded from early June to late August.

STATUS Widespread but exceedingly local with all known records recent.

THREAT The drainage of wetlands for agriculture, coastal development or intensive forestry; complete or extensive clearance of marginal vegetation from water edges such as through river improvement schemes and the ditching of streams; pollution such as agricultural run-off; mis-management of water levels with a loss of breeding sites and subsequent scrub invasion.

MANAGEMENT Prevent any drainage of sites, ensuring a range of vegetation types including ponds, ditches and their marginal vegetation. Prevent scrub invasion.

TETANOCERA PHYLLOPHORA Melander

DISTRIBUTION Records scattered widely in England, Wales and Scotland, predominating in upland areas of Scotland and northern England.

HABITAT Usually recorded from woodland, often that adjacent to wetlands and carr, though it may not be confined to damp woodland. Some Scottish records relate to Caledonian pine forest and it is recorded from both calcareous areas and base deficient granite areas (though possibly influenced by localised base enrichment such as that of the Moine Schists along the Spey Valley.

ECOLOGY The larvae develop as predators or parasitoids of various terrestrial snails such as Discus rotundatus, Cochlicopa, Helix and Hygromia. Adults recorded from mid May to mid August.

STATUS A widespread but local species with about 45 known post 1960 sites. It is locally frequent in some parts of the Central Highlands.

THREAT Woodland clearance for agriculture or intensive forestry and drainage of associated wetlands.

MANAGEMENT Prevent any drainage within woodlands and maintain the presence of some areas of carr on wetland sites, ensuring a range of vegetation including rides and clearings in woods.

TETANOCERA PUNCTIFRONS Rondani

DISTRIBUTION Records scattered widely in England (Cornwall, Isle of Wight, Hampshire, Sussex, Surrey, Gloucestershire, Worcestershire, Shropshire, Durham), Wales Monmouthshire, Carmarthenshire) and Scotland (Aberdeenshire, Elgin, Dunbartonshire).

HABITAT Wetlands, especially damp woodland, also riverside situations, damp heathland and coastal marshes.

ECOLOGY Larvae probably develop as predators or parasitoids of gastropod molluscs, but it is unclear whether aquatic or terrestrial species, or slugs or snails are used. Adults recorded from June to August.

STATUS Widespread but local with about 20 post 1960 sites known.

THREAT The drainage of wetlands and clearance of damp woods for agriculture or intensive forestry; complete or extensive clearance of marginal vegetation from water edges such as through river improvement schemes and the ditching of streams; pollution such as agricultural run-off; mis-management of water levels with a loss of breeding sites and subsequent scrub invasion.

MANAGEMENT Prevent any drainage of sites, ensuring a range of vegetation types including rides and clearings in woods. Prevent scrub invasion on open sites though isolated shrubs or areas of carr may be beneficial.

53

BERIS CLAVIPES (Linnaeus)

DISTRIBUTION Widely scattered records in England, Wales and Scotland as far north as Nethy Bridge (Elgin). Possibly more frequent in western parts of Britain.

HABITAT Marshes and fens, often beside streams and standing water.

ECOLOGY Larvae probably develop in moss and decaying vegetable matter on moist or wet soils. On the continent, a puparium was found in wet moss near a spring (Rozkosny, 1982). Adults recorded from May to July (peaking in late May and early June) and may be found resting on herbage near water margins.

STATUS A local but widespread species with about 30 known post 1960 sites. It is also said to be locally common in Radnorshire. The relatively early flight period may account for some under recording.

THREAT The drainage of wetlands for agriculture or intensive forestry and mis-management of water levels with a subsequent loss of breeding sites and scrub invasion.

MANAGEMENT Maintain a high stable water level in wetlands, preventing drying out or scrub invasion.

BERIS FUSCIPES Meigen

DISTRIBUTION Records widely dispersed in southern England excluding the south east, and extending up the west coast, Wales, north-west England and Scotland as far north as Argyllshire.

HABITAT Damp woodland and adjacent fens and marshes especially on calcareous soil.

ECOLOGY On the continent, larvae have been found under the bark of a tree trunk lying in a spring. Adults recorded from May to September.

STATUS A local but widespread species with about a dozen known post 1960 sites. The accuracy of many determinations is questionable, as this species has been difficult to identify with past keys and its true status rather unclear.

THREAT The destruction of damp woodland and drainage of adjacent marshes for agriculture or intensive forestry.

MANAGEMENT Maintain a high, stable water level in damp areas and encourage a full succession of marginal vegetation beside ponds and streams, retaining any dead wood in such situations. Prevent any drying out of wetlands with subsequent scrub invasion.

CHORISOPS NAGATOMII Rozkosny

DISTRIBUTION Records widely dispersed in southern England, extending as far north as Yorkshire and also widely in Wales.

HABITAT Preferences far from clear, though usually taken in broadleaved woodland and parkland; also wetlands and near to rivers.

ECOLOGY Life history unknown, though a puparium was found in flood refuse on the muddy bank on a chalk stream running through fenland water meadows, suggesting that damp leaf litter could be the larval situation. Adults recorded from July to early September and males have been observed swarming around large trees.

STATUS A local but widespread southern species with about 25 known post 1960 sites. Only recently separated from the commoner C. tibialis. It can be common at some sites in certain years.

THREAT Clearance of woods and areas of parkland and drainage of marshy areas for agriculture or intensive forestry.

MANAGEMENT Maintain a varied structure in woodland including open rides and clearings and any marshy areas, streams or ponds.

CLITELLARIA EPHIPPIUM (Fabricius)

DISTRIBUTION Two very old records (about 1850): possibly Darenth Woods and Coombe Wood (? near Deal), Kent.

HABITAT Unclear, probably the edges of woods or nearby meadows.

ECOLOGY The larvae are known abroad to develop in ant nests possibly including Lasius fuliginosus and development lasts about three years. Mature larvae leave the ant's nest and pupariate nearby. Adults recorded in June.

STATUS Seemingly extinct and with some doubt over the authenticity of the British records.

THREAT Unclear.

MANAGEMENT Unclear.

EUPACHYGASTER TARSALIS (Zetterstedt)   NOTABLE
                                        STRATIOMYIDAE

DISTRIBUTION Records widely dispersed in southern England (Somerset, Dorset, Hampshire, Kent, Middlesex, Berkshire, Cambridgeshire, Northamptonshire) and also from Nethy Bridge, Elgin in Scotland.

HABITAT Probably broadleaved woodland and parkland, with a requirement for dead wood and perhaps more specifically that in rot holes of old or diseased trees.

ECOLOGY Larvae have been reported either in rot holes, under the bark, or within the decaying wood of a wide range of trees including white poplar Populus alba, beech, ash, balsam poplar Populus ? trichocarpa and maple; abroad also from oaks and apple. A rearing record from pine in Scotland has been questioned by some workers. At least four recent records of larvae are from small, shallow rot holes in trunks, one to two metres or more above ground, and this may prove to be a more typical situation than just beneath bark. Adults recorded from May to July.

STATUS Six known post 1960 sites within Dorset, Middlesex, Berkshire, Cambridgeshire and Northamptonshire with most old records from the New Forest. Perhaps somewhat overlooked and more easily recorded through rearing.

THREAT The clearance of old woods for agriculture or intensive forestry and removal of old or diseased trees and dead wood within such sites.

MANAGEMENT Retain any old or diseased trees and dead wood and ensure continuity of these in the future.

NEOPACHYGASTER MEROMELAENA (Austen)   NOTABLE
                                       STRATIOMYIDAE

DISTRIBUTION Records widely dispersed in England as far north as Yorkshire; also Scotland: Nethy Bridge (Elgin).

HABITAT Broadleaved woodland and parkland with a requirement for dead wood such as standing dead trees, stumps or fallen trunks and large limbs.

ECOLOGY Larvae have been found beneath the bark of a range of dead (either standing or fallen) broadleaved trees. Poplars are perhaps the most frequent source of larvae, though records additionally exist for holly, horse chestnut, willow, beech and elm. On the continent, sycamore and hornbeam are also reported. Larvae are often associated with liquid or damp debris in such situations, including the margins of wounds such as rot holes, though they can tolerate dehydration. Whilst larvae can live entirely on detritus, they also eat dead insects should these be present. Adults recorded from May to July.

STATUS A widespread but local species with about 15 known post 1960 sites and with a long history from the New Forest. Searching for puparia under bark and then rearing adults is probably the best way of recording this species.

THREAT The clearance of old woods for agriculture or intensive forestry and removal of old or diseased trees and dead wood.

MANAGEMENT Retain any old or diseased trees and dead wood and ensure continuity of these in the future.

ODONTOMYIA ANGULATA (Panzer)   ENDANGERED
                                STRATIOMYIDAE

DISTRIBUTION Records restricted to three sites in the Somerset Levels: Edington (1947), Chilton Polden (1951), Street Heath (1951); three sites in Norfolk: East Walton Common (1989), Thompson Common (1982, 1985), Sutton Broad (1905); 'Whittlesea Mere', Huntingdonshire (last century, Dale Collection); Wicken Fen (1906 and 1915), Cambridgeshire and an unconfirmed sighting at Tuddenham, Suffolk (1880).

HABITAT Fens and shallow ponds. Thompson Common and East Walton Common are both large 'pingo' systems.

ECOLOGY The species has been reared twice from Thompson Common and the 1982 record refers to larvae in an area of winter-flooded grassland around pond 64a. Abroad, the larvae are also known from the margin of a lake. Adults recorded from June to August, usually on herbage or flowers near the breeding site.

STATUS Very infrequent and declining with only two post 1960 sites. Thompson Common is a county trust reserve, East Walton Common is a SSSI. It was particularly frequent and widespread at the latter site in 1989.

THREAT Drainage of wetlands for agriculture or intensive forestry, scrub invasion and pollution such as agricultural run-off.

MANAGEMENT Maintain natural water levels in wetland accepting any natural seasonal fluctuations in water level, and retain areas of standing water with a full succession of surrounding vegetation. Use rotational ditch/pond management if necessary (but note probable need for shallow margins) and prevent scrub invasion.

ODONTOMYIA ARGENTATA (Fabricius)

VULNERABLE
STRATIOMYIDAE

DISTRIBUTION Scattered localities in southern England from Kent to Somerset to Cambridgeshire to Suffolk.

HABITAT Wetlands including fen and carr. It seems to be associated with well vegetated ditches at a number of its modern sites.

ECOLOGY On the continent the larvae have been found in flood refuse, in moss and also on a moist rotting alder. Adults recorded from April to June (peak in May). Adults are reported as visiting the catkins of sallows, hawthorn and resting on foliage whilst males sometimes hover, either individually or in small swarms, at heights of 3 - 4.5 metres.

STATUS Very infrequent and declining with six known post 1960 sites: Bishops Waltham (1989) and Leckford, (1947 and 1970), Hampshire; Avington, Berkshire (1985); Brampton Flood Meadow, Huntingdonshire (1968); Sizewell, Suffolk (1989) and Chippenham Fen NNR, Cambridgeshire (1982, 1983, 1985, 1988). Older records are comparatively frequent, involving nearly 30 sites. The early flight period may have led to some under recording in recent years.

THREAT Drainage of wetlands for agriculture or intensive forestry, scrub invasion and pollution such as agricultural run-off; also excessive clearance of vegetation beside ponds and ditches.

MANAGEMENT Maintain a high, stable water level in wetland and provide areas standing water with a full succession of surrounding vegetation. Use rotational ditch/pond management where clearance is necessary, attempting to produce banks with shallow margins. Prevent scrub invasion of wetlands.

ODONTOMYIA HYDROLEON (Linnaeus)

ENDANGERED
STRATIOMYIDAE

DISTRIBUTION The only known sites are Banc y Mwldan, Cardiganshire (July 1986 and 1987) and Seive Dale Fen SSSI, Yorkshire (17 July 1988), though a number of older, doubtful records exist.

HABITAT The Cardinganshire site is a floristically diverse meadow containing base-rich seepages, the seepage apparently most favoured being one with Carex paniculata. The Yorkshire site is a spring fed poor fen.

ECOLOGY A larva was found in weed in a Carex paniculata seepage at Banc y Mwldan. Adults frequent flowers of hogweed Heracleum sphondylium.

STATUS Long regarded as doubtfully British but recently confirmed. Verrall (1909) included it in a list of reputed British species, noting reference to British records in publications dated 1829, 1837 and 1851. In the absence of voucher material these records remain doubtful. Reports included the London area, Somerset and Ireland, whilst a specimen labelled 'Berkshire' taken about 1840 had a typical markings. It is now a confirmed British species and clearly falling within the endangered category, though the Welsh colony seems reasonably strong with several dozen individuals being observed in both years. Not listed in Shirt (1987).

THREAT The Welsh site is under threat of being used as a dump by a sand and gravel extraction company at the time of writing and adjacent quarrying threatens the hydrology of the seepages. The Yorkshire site is owned by the Forestry Commission and is a SSSI.

MANAGEMENT Maintain the natural hydrological state of the sites, preventing drying out of damp areas and invasion by scrub or dominating grasses. Further clarify the exact requirements of this species so the appropriate conditions can be maintained.

ODONTOMYIA TIGRINA (Fabricius)

DISTRIBUTION Recorded widely in the southern half of England, Wales and with an isolated Scottish record from Aviemore, Elgin (pre 1909). The vast majority of records are for southern England.

HABITAT Wetlands, including fens, ponds, canals and ditches in coastal levels. It seems to prefer water bodies with a rich flora and where both emergent and floating vegetation is present. On the Gwent and Somerset Levels it was found to prefer the narrower ditches with much emergent vegetation and to be least frequent in the large drainage ditches, in ditches that were especially choked with vegetation or where cleared in the previous year.

ECOLOGY The larvae have been found in shallow water at the margins of ponds, ditches and in marshes (both freshwater and slightly brackish) amongst vegetable matter. Adults recorded from May to July and occur on flowers such as umbels or vegetation near the breeding sites. Larvae tend to be more elusive than adults.

STATUS Regular though very local in many southern counties becoming infrequent in the north. About 60 known post 1960 sites with particularly strong populations on the coastal marshes of Monmouthshire, Somerset and the Thames estuary.

THREAT The loss of wetlands through drainage for agriculture or intensive forestry. Pollution such as agricultural run-off and mis-management of water levels with a subsequent loss of breeding sites and possible scrub invasion.

MANAGEMENT Maintain a high, stable water level ensuring the presence of some standing water, using rotational pond/ditch management if necessary. Retain reasonable levels of the ditch-type described under habitat. Prevent scrub invasion.

ODONTOMYIA ORNATA (Meigen)

DISTRIBUTION Scattered localities in southern England as far north as Wiltshire, Middlesex and Norfolk and for south Wales. Many sites are coastal though it can occur well inland with several records for the London suburbs up until the 1950's.

HABITAT Mainly ditches on coastal levels. Sites on peat are preferred at least on the Somerset/Gwent levels. The preferred ditches are those at earlier stages of hydroseral succession, with floating cover and rich submergent vegetation, rather than ditches which are choked with emergent plants. Even ditches cleared the previous year have yielded larvae providing some floating or emergent vegetation was present. Ditches more than 1 metre wide seem preferred to narrower ones.

ECOLOGY The larvae develop in shallow water in ditches and at the margin of ponds and probably canals. Larvae are free floating or more often occur amongst surface Lemna or other aquatic vegetation and puparia have been found in flood refuse or floating on the water surface. Despite its mainly coastal distribution, the larvae seem to favour freshwater or only very weakly brackish conditions. Adults are recorded from May to July and occur on flowers such as umbels, and herbage near the breeding sites. They do not appear to fly very far from their breeding locations and can be localised within a site. Larvae are perhaps easier to find.

STATUS Regular and locally frequent on the coastal levels of Sussex (such as Pevensey) and Somerset and Gwent, but elsewhere a very dramatic decline has taken place with no known post 1960 records other than those from two sites on the Essex marshes (Hadleigh Marsh and Fobbing Marsh, both 1987); a single locality just inland from the North Kent Marshes (1988) and the marshes to the south of Minsmere RSPB reserve, E. Suffolk (1988). Most of its present localities are under some degree of threat.

THREAT The loss of wetlands, especially existing coastal level sites through drainage for agricultural reclamation, coastal developments and pollution such as agricultural run-off. Also mis-management of water levels with a loss of breeding sites and possible scrub invasion.

MANAGEMENT Maintain a high, stable water level ensuring the presence of some standing water, using rotational pond/ditch management if necessary. Undertake some management each year to ensure continuity of the presence of the early stages of the hydroseral succession. Retain or create a gentle profile at the sides of ditches; some cattle trampling can be beneficial for sustaining suitable margins. Prevent scrub invasion beside ditches or ponds.

===============
VULNERABLE
STRATIOMYIDAE
OXYCERA ANALIS Meigen

DISTRIBUTION Records widely dispersed in southern England (Somerset, Dorset, Hampshire, Kent, Berkshire, Oxfordshire, Cambridgeshire, Bedfordshire, Gloucestershire, Herefordshire).

HABITAT Fens, seepage marshes and streamside situations in carr, woodland or at woodland edge. A strong calcareous influence seems to be required, with many sites lying on chalk and limestone.

ECOLOGY Larvae probably develop in shallow water or among moss or wet vegetation at the edges of ponds and streams. Adults recorded from May to July.

STATUS Formerly a fairly widespread species especially in Herefordshire, but apparently declining since and only 4 post 1960 localities records are known: West Milton, Dorset (1987); Ashford Hangers, Hampshire (1988); Moor Copse, Berkshire (1963) and Arpinge Ranges, Kent (1986). It is a rare and little known species in Europe as a whole.

THREAT The loss of wetlands through drainage for agriculture or intensive forestry; the loss or alteration of marginal vegetation beside water through ditching of streams or pond clearance; pollution such as agricultural run-off. Also mis-management of water levels with a loss of breeding sites and possible scrub invasion.

MANAGEMENT Maintain a high stable water level ensuring the presence of some standing water. Any clearance of ditches, ponds or streams needs great care to ensure continuity of very gently shelving marginal habitat. Prevent scrub invasion.

===============
RARE
STRATIOMYIDAE
OXYCERA DIVES Loew

DISTRIBUTION Recorded from Selkirkshire, Roxburghshire, Perthshire, Lanarkshire and Dunbartonshire in Scotland, Yorkshire and Northumberland in England.

HABITAT Mossy springs, seepages, flushes, wet rock faces and small streams in partially shaded situations. In one case on moorland at the edge of a plantation. A calcareous influence is usually apparent.

ECOLOGY Larvae probably living in the wet moss of the above situations. Adults recorded from June to September, usually sunning themselves on foliage in wooded areas close to wet rock faces and by mossy waterfalls.

STATUS Very rare though widespread in the north with seven known post 1960 sites up to 1988: Cotherstone (1981), Hubberholme (1975) and Ashberry Pasture (1980s), Yorkshire; near Harwood, Northumberland (1986); Port Clair (1965), Dunalastair Reservoir (post 1960) and Pass of Killiecrankie (post 1960), Perthshire. In July 1988 it was recorded from 6 separate 10 km squares within Selkirkshire and Roxburghshire, highlighting its under recording in this part of Britain. It was also

recorded from an extra Yorkshire site, Low Dalby (Sieve Dale Fen SSSI). It may additionally persist at some of its old sites if carefully searched for. This species is also rare in Europe with the majority of records from the Alps. Status revised from RDB2 (Shirt 1987).

THREAT The ditching of springs and streams, drainage of mossy seepages or flushes; disturbance such as excessive trampling or adjacent forestry or agriculture; removal of shading influences and pollution such as agricultural run-off; changes in local hydrology such as quarrying or water abstration with a loss of springs, seepages, etc.

MANAGEMENT Maintain water supply to springs, seepages and flushes and retain a rich moss flora and shading influence.

===============
NOTIBLE
STRATIOMYIDAE
OXYCERA MORRISII Curtis

DISTRIBUTION Records widely dispersed in England as far north as Durham; also north-west Wales and recently Kirkcudbrightshire in Scotland.

HABITAT Perhaps most frequently recorded at sparsely vegetated open seepages on coastal landslips, about seepages associated with springs and more rarely those in fens and calcareous meadows. Larvae have also been reported from coastal levels, though this would appear to be unusual.

ECOLOGY Larvae probably typically developing in shallow water or wet vegetation of the above situations, and at one muddy landslip seepage they were found on moss at the edge of trickling water; also reared from larvae taken in ditches of coastal levels marsh in Suffolk. Adults recorded from June to August usually on sparse herbage or the foliage of bushes around seepages.

STATUS Widespread but very local with about 20 known post 1960 sites. It can be common at some sites, but only very locally. Status revised from RDB2 (Shirt 1987).

THREAT The loss of seepages and springs through drainage for agriculture or intensive forestry, stream improvement schemes, coastal development and changes in hydrology associated with local water abstraction, quarrying etc; pollution such as agricultural run-off; mis-management of water levels with a loss of breeding sites and possible scrub invasion.

MANAGEMENT Maintain water supplies to springs and seepages and a stable water level in associated marshes. Prevent open, sparsely vegetated areas becoming choked with herbage and scrub.

THREAT The drainage or ditching of seepages and associated marshland for intensive forestry or pastures; changes in local hydrology through water abstration, nearby quarrying etc; coastal development and recreational pressure on dunes.

MANAGEMENT Maintain water supplies to springs and seepages and a stable water level in associated marsh, preventing drying out with a loss of potential breeding sites and subsequent scrub invasion.

OXYCERA TERMINATA Meigen   VULNERABLE
STRATIOMYIDAE

DISTRIBUTION Records widely dispersed in southern England (Somerset, Dorset, Bedfordshire, Herefordshire, Gloucestershire, Monmouthshire, Northamptonshire), a western bias being apparent and with records predominating in the southern Welsh borders.

HABITAT Small, partly shaded streams in hilly calcareous areas seem to be preferred.

ECOLOGY Larvae unknown but possibly developing in the moss, sand or shingle beside streams. Adults recorded in June and July.

STATUS A rare and declining species with only 6 known post 1960 sites: Afon Honddu, Monmouthshire (1981); four sites along the Monnow Valley, Herefordshire (1985 and 1987) and Fineshades Abbey, Northamptonshire (1985).

THREAT Loss of sites through river improvement schemes and ditching of streams; excessive trampling of banks; loss of adjacent woodland through the encroachment of agriculture or intensive forestry; pollution such as agricultural run-off.

MANAGEMENT Maintain water supply and clean water quality for streams and springs, with margins free from excessive disturbance and with an emphasis on keeping a full range of bank vegetation, also retaining any sand or shingle banks and shading influences.

OXYCERA PARDALINA Meigen   NOTABLE
STRATIOMYIDAE

DISTRIBUTION Records widely dispersed in England, Wales and Scotland as far north as Banffshire. A substantial proportion of the records are from the southern Welsh Borders in Herefordshire and also Lancashire.

HABITAT Associated with small calcareous springs and streams, especially those in wooded or extensively scrubbed valleys of hilly areas, with moss or algae covered boulders. Some sites are coastal cliffs and landslips and it has also been found at springs in open grassland.

ECOLOGY Larvae develop amongst algae and in wet moss cushions, preferring the clear water of calcareous springs and streams. Adults recorded from June to August, occurring on vegetation and flowers near the breeding sites.

STATUS A widely distributed though extremely local species with about 20 known post 1960 sites. It has clearly been under recorded in the past and its choice of habitat means it may still prove to be locally frequent in some areas. Status revised from RDB2 (Shirt 1987).

THREAT The ditching of springs and streams and disturbance such as that from excessive trampling, adjacent forestry or agriculture; removal of shading influences and pollution such as agricultural run-off; changes in local hydrology through water abstration, nearby quarrying etc.

MANAGEMENT Maintain water supply to springs and retain a rich moss flora and shading influence.

OXYCERA PYGMAEA (Fallen)   NOTABLE
STRATIOMYIDAE

DISTRIBUTION Records widely dispersed in England, Wales and Scotland with a north-western bias, and absent over most of south-east England and areas such as the Spey Valley in Scotland.

HABITAT Small base-rich seepages with short herbage or sparse herbage on hillsides or coastal cliff grassland provide the most typical habitat. Sites are usually open in character, though it can tolerate partial shade in woodland glades. In north-west Wales it is associated with open seepages feeding fen, and this was probably the habitat for old records from Tuddenham Fen, Suffolk. Other habitats include wet fen and seepages on limestone grassland.

ECOLOGY Larvae occur amongst saturated moss in seepages and beside tiny trickles, often in clumps of moss which protrude above water level. Adults recorded in June and July and are best recorded by sweeping herbage around seepages.

STATUS Widespread but very local, with about 30 known post 1960 sites, though sometimes occurring in good numbers.

STRATIOMYS CHAMAELEON (Linnaeus)
ENDANGERED
STRATIOMYIDAE

DISTRIBUTION Old records scattered thinly but widely in England as far north as Cheshire in the west and Lincolnshire in the east. Recent records restricted to Oxfordshire and Anglesey.

HABITAT Wetlands, including seepages in fens, carr and damp woods.

ECOLOGY Larvae assumed to develop in pools and seepages where they probably take three or four years to develop. Abroad eggs are said to be laid in neat batches on the underside of leaves of Alisma plantago-aquatica, Butomus and Sagittaria. Adults recorded from June to September and visit flowers such as umbels.

STATUS Only four post 1960 sites: Cors Erddreiniog NNR (1980, 1987) and Pentraeth (1987), Anglesey and two adjacent sites in Oxfordshire: Cothill NNR (1978) and Dry Sandford Pit (1979, 1980). Previous records are virtually restricted to the turn of the century.

THREAT Destruction of the four known modern sites through drainage for agriculture or intensive forestry; clearance of the marginal vegetation from ditches and pools; pollution such as agricultural run-off and mis-management of water levels with a loss of breeding sites and possible scrub invasion.

MANAGEMENT Maintain the natural hydrology of seepages and pools. Prevent drying out and scrub invasion.

STRATIOMYS LONGICORNIS (Scopoli)
VULNERABLE
STRATIOMYIDAE

DISTRIBUTION Scattered records mainly in south-east England (especially the Thames Marshes) and north to Lincolnshire. Most records are coastal though it can occur well inland, probably as strays from the coast.

HABITAT Almost exclusively coastal saltmarshes and highly brackish pools and ditches on coastal levels.

ECOLOGY Larvae have been found on a few occasions in mud at the edge of brackish ditches and crawling over blanket weed algae in a shallow saline lake. There is some evidence that this species breeds in very shallow, strongly brackish ditches. On the continent larvae have been found in water among aquatic vegetation, in saline pools near the sea shore and in saltmarshes, though the species is not confined to saline habitats. The possibility that it may successfully breed in freshwater habitats in Britain seems unlikely. Larvae probably take three or four years to develop. Adults recorded from May to August and occur on vegetation and flowers such as Matricaria and umbels near to the breeding sites.

STATUS Infrequent and probably declining with about a dozen known post 1960 sites, mainly for the Thames Marshes. Most of the remaining sites are under some degree of threat, especially the Thames Marshes, where strongly brackish pools and ditches are increasingly becoming lost following seawall construction.

THREAT Drainage and agricultural improvement of sites, especially coastal marshes; coastal development schemes such as flood barriers and harbours; reduced salinity levels behind improved flood defences; recreational pressure on coasts; pollution such as agricultural run-off and industrial effluent; mis-management of water levels with a loss of breeding sites and subsequent scrub invasion.

MANAGEMENT Maintain a high, stable water level in coastal levels with an emphasis on retaining any highly brackish pools and ditches. Ensure unimpeded tidal patterns in salt marshes and a full succession of vegetation types. Use rotational ditch/pond management where necessary on levels, to retain some open water, and prevent scrub invasion.

STRATIOMYS POTAMIDA (Meigen)
NOTABLE
STRATIOMYIDAE

DISTRIBUTION Records widely dispersed in England as far north as Northumberland and also into south Wales.

HABITAT Wetlands, including fens, damp heaths, damp woodlands, alder carr and coastal landslips and ravines. A Lancashire locality, from which it was reared, is described as a moorland marsh, though this is not typical. It can occur on coastal sites, but usually avoids saline areas. Adults are occasionally seen well away from water and have been recorded at nearly 300m on top of the south downs.

ECOLOGY Larvae develop in the mud of seepage marsh, and away from seepages, in the mud and standing water amongst vegetation at the edge of ponds and ditches. They probably take three or four years to develop and seem able to tolerate quite severe drying out of sites in summer droughts. On the continent larvae have been found at the margins of standing water, in marshes by springs and alongside streams. Adults recorded from June to August and occur on vegetation and flowers such as umbels, near the breeding sites.

STATUS A widespread but local species which actually appears to have undergone an increase in recent decades. Old records are relatively few but about 80 post 1960 sites are now known and the 1980s have been especially favourable.

THREAT The drainage of wetlands for agriculture or intensive forestry; clearance of marginal vegetation from ditches and pools; pollution such as agricultural run-off; mis-management of water levels with a loss of breeding sites and subsequent scrub invasion.

MANAGEMENT Maintain a high stable water level in wetlands, retaining some standing water and its marginal vegetation, using rotational ditch/pond management if necessary (noting the probable need for shallow margins); prevent any drying out and scrub invasion.

STATUS Formerly regarded as a rarity, but in recent years it has proved to be a local but widespread species, not uncommon at some sites. A more precise understanding of the adult habits (resting on the foliage of shrubs and bushes is preferred) may partly account for this. Some 30 post 1960 sites are now known and most of these are post 1980. It is confined to western Europe with few continental records.

THREAT Drainage of wetlands for agriculture or intensive forestry; pollution such as agricultural run-off; coastal development schemes; mis-management of water levels with a loss of breeding sites and possible scrub invasion.

MANAGEMENT Maintain a high stable water level, providing a mosaic or succession of vegetation types including some standing water and its marginal vegetation, using rotational ditch/pond management if necessary. Prevent scrub invasion, though isolated shrubs may be beneficial.

ZABRACHIA MINUTISSIMA (Zetterstedt)

DISTRIBUTION Records widely dispersed in England (Somerset, Wiltshire, Hampshire, Buckinghamshire, Cheshire, Lancashire, Yorkshire) and Scotland (Aberdeenshire, Elgin).

HABITAT Records refer to a range of situations, including native pine woodland, heath and dunes with pine and artificial pine plantations.

ECOLOGY The main and possibly the only true larval development site is under the bark of conifers such as Pinus. Recently dead, pole-sized pines, where bark beetles have loosened the bark, seem to be especially favoured. Abroad it has also been reported from other conifers, including Abies, Larix and Picea. There are also reports of larvae occurring occasionally in the galleries of bark beetles on birch, though this would seem to be a much less important development site.

STATUS A widespread but very local species with only two known post 1960 sites: Delamere, Cheshire (1960) and Sandall Beat, Yorkshire (1967). It may be under recorded and more easily located by rearing larvae which can be abundant when found. It has been suggested that the species is indigenous to the Scottish Highlands, where it has been found in areas of relict pine forest and may have spread to other parts of Britain in association with forestry operations.

THREAT Uncertain other than the loss of pine trees.

MANAGEMENT Retain any dead wood of pine and old or diseased pine trees, ensuring a continuity of these in the future, but do not allow the invasion of pine onto good quality open habitats.

STRATIOMYS SINGULARIOR (Harris)

DISTRIBUTION Records widely dispersed in England, south Wales and Scotland as far north as Edinburgh. Most records are coastal though a few are well inland.

HABITAT Wetlands, especially on brackish coastal marshes, though occasionally on inland fens and marshes.

ECOLOGY Larvae develop in a variety of mildly brackish ponds and ditches, especially those with plants such as Scirpus maritimus. They have been found both in mud (including beneath cracked mud at the bottom of a small dried up pool) and crawling over blanket weed (algae) in a shallow brackish lagoon, and probably take three or four years to develop. Adults recorded from June to August, occuring on flowers such as umbels near to the breeding sites.

STATUS A local but widespread species, not infrequent on some coastal levels, especially in the south-east, rather more rarely inland where historically there has been brackish influence. About 60 post 1960 sites are known, though many of these are experiencing some degree of threat.

THREAT The drainage of wetland sites, especially coastal marshes for agricultural reclamation; coastal development schemes such as flood barriers, sea wall and harbour constructions (including situations where the salinity is lost from coastal marshes through sea wall construction, with a subsequent loss of brackish ponds and ditches); pollution such as agricultural run-off and industrial effluent; mis-management of water levels with a loss of breeding sites and possible scrub invasion.

MANAGEMENT Maintain a high, stable water level in wetlands and ensure the continued presence of brackish pools and ditches on coastal marshes. Use rotational ditch/pond management if necessary (noting the probable need for shallow margins) and prevent scrub invasion.

VANOYIA TENUICORNIS (Macquart)

DISTRIBUTION Records widely dispersed in England as far north as Norfolk and Northamptonshire and also into south Wales. Records apply equally to inland and coastal sites.

HABITAT Most localities are fens and seepage meadows, with additional records for coastal landslips, coastal marshes and dune slacks. It is unclear if the presence of some shrubs and bushes is an obligatory requirement for the adults.

ECOLOGY E.B. Basden reared a larva from the nest of a Mute Swan in Buckinghamshire (1931) though it probably develops more generally in damp soil or litter, possibly including that away from standing water. Adults recorded from June to August and especially favour sitting on the foliage of shrubs and bushes. Males apparently dance in large compact swarms above shrubs and bushes.

THREAT The drainage of bogs through agricultural reclamation and for afforestation. A fall in water level will also encourage scrub invasion. Clearance of marginal vegetation from water edges.

MANAGEMENT Maintain a high, stable water level in bogs with pools and ditches and prevent scrub invasion.

BLERA FALLAX (Linnaeus)

DISTRIBUTION Records are restricted to the major native pine forests of the Eastern Highlands of Scotland, almost exclusively along Speyside between Kingussie and Grantown on Spey, though with old records from Forres and Logie, Elgin (both 1902) and Braemar, Aberdeenshire (1873). The Loch Garten and surrounding areas of Abernethy forest may be its only surviving site today.

HABITAT Ancient coniferous woodland, as found in Caledonian pine forests.

ECOLOGY The larvae appear to develop in the dead wood of large post mature native pines and adults have been observed flying at the bases of such pines especially those with a thick mass of flaky bark exposed edge-on at ground level. A syrphid pupa, probably of this species was found beneath the loose bark of a fallen pine trunk at Loch Garten. Verrall (1901) cites a dubious observation of a female laying eggs in sap runs of oak and beech. Adults recorded from June to August and are said to be attracted to the flowers of wild raspberry and the stumps of cut pines.

STATUS Declining. Abernethy Forest is perhaps its only remaining population. This site is an NNR in part and the Loch Garten area is owned by the RSPB. There is no recent information from the Rothiemurchus or the Glen Feshie area, and the Grantown area where it was last recorded in 1943 is unlikely to support suitable habitat today.

THREAT Clearance of ancient Caledonian pine forest and especially of the old trees and dead wood within and replacement with modern forestry plantations which do not provide the old stumps or trees for larval development.

MANAGEMENT Ensure a future continuity of the dead wood resource required by this species by maximising the number of post mature trees within a site and retaining all stumps. Excessive deer grazing seems to be seriously hindering pine regeneration at some sites so that fencing areas or protection of young trees may be required. The maintainance of open glades may be necessary.

ANASIMYIA INTERPUNCTA (Harris)

DISTRIBUTION Scattered records in southeast England from Hampshire to Norfolk, most frequent in the Thames estuary and the Nene/Ouse washes of the fens.

HABITAT Known equally from coastal and inland marshes. Associated with tall emergent vegetation such as Glyceria maxima at margins of standing water and there is some indication that nutrient-rich winter flooded sites are preferred. Some of the Essex sites are slightly stagnant in places.

ECOLOGY Larvae aquatic, possibly developing in the sheaths of partly submerged water plants such as G. maxima. Adults recorded from May to July.

STATUS Only separated from the very local A. lunulata in recent years, since when it has shown itself to be the more restricted of the two with an entirely different habitat requirement and about a dozen known post 1960 sites. Status revised from RDB2 (Shirt 1987).

THREAT The drainage of wetlands for agricultural reclamation or afforestation. A fall in the water level can lead to a loss of pools, ditches and their marginal vegetation and subsequent scrub invasion. Complete or extensive clearance of marginal vegetation from water edges (e.g. canal restoration, pond management, ditch clearance). Pollution such as agricultural run-off or that from industry or sewage, especially at sites in the Thames estuary, could be a problem although it clearly seems to tolerate sites of high fertility.

MANAGEMENT Maintain a high, stable water level with pools, ditches and a rich marginal vegetation. Use rotational ditch management if necessary.

ANASIMYIA LUNULATA (Meigen)

DISTRIBUTION Records widely scattered in England, Wales and Scotland (including the Outer Hebrides). Not recorded in south east England (apart from Thursley Common NNR) where it seems to be replaced by A. interpuncta (reflecting the comparative lack of bogs in this region).

HABITAT Closely associated with boggy pools and ditches, including those on damp lowland heathland.

ECOLOGY The larvae are aquatic, possibly developing amongst the marginal vegetation of pools. Adults recorded from May to August.

STATUS Exceedingly local with about 20 known post 1960 sites scattered throughout Britain. A decline seems apparent, especially in areas such as the New Forest, though recent recording efforts in South Wales have demonstrated it is not infrequent in some parts, such as Carmarthenshire and it may be under recorded in Wales generally.

BRACHYOPA BICOLOR (Fallen)

DISTRIBUTION Records widely scattered in Southern England (Wiltshire, Hampshire, Sussex, Hertfordshire, Berkshire, Gloucestershire, Staffordshire) also Breconshire in Wales, with most records for the New Forest and Windsor Forest.

HABITAT Ancient broadleaved woodland. Closely associated with beech, requiring old diseased trees.

ECOLOGY The larvae probably develop under the dead bark of beech, favouring old diseased trees. Adults visit spring blossom such as that of cherry and hawthorn and are recorded from early May to mid June.

STATUS A very local and possibly declining species with about 10 known post 1960 sites, six within the New Forest (Mark Ash, Ober Water, Queens Bower, Bolderford Bridge, Millyford Bridge Heath, Bramshaw) and additional sites in Wiltshire (Chickengrove Bottom, late 1960's), Berkshire (Windsor Forest, not a strong population with relatively few records in relation to recording effort), Herefordshire (Cusop Dingle - 1977) and Breconshire (Ystradfellte - 1964). Status revised from RDB2 (Shirt 1987).

THREAT Clearance of old broadleaved woodland and old beech trees for agriculture or intensive forestry. The shading out of rides and clearings within woods.

MANAGEMENT Retain any old diseased beech trees especially those with obvious sap runs or diseased limbs. A continuity of old diseased trees with suitable sap runs is crucial and requires large areas of woodland to ensure reasonably stable levels of the breeding resource. Maintain rides and clearings with spring blossom for adult feeding.

BRACHYOPA INSENSILIS (Collin)

DISTRIBUTION Mainly recorded in southern England, but extending sporadically to the north Midlands, Wales and recent, very isolated records from Sutherland and Easterness in Scotland.

HABITAT Broadleaved woodland, parkland and even isolated old trees in hedgerows and along road sides. There is a requirement for old or diseased trees with sap runs and elms are especially favoured.

ECOLOGY The larvae probably develop in sap runs, mainly in elm and also on horse chestnut and occasionally beech. Adults may be observed hovering near such sites or visiting spring blossom such as cherry and hawthorn and are recorded from early May to late June.

STATUS Dutch elm disease must have had a detrimental effect on this species as elm appears to provide the main breeding site. However, it seems to be able to use other species, especially horse chestnut in place of elm. It is not a species restricted to ancient woodland (though it can occur there) and seems to possess some ability to colonise new areas. About 20 post 1960 sites are known.

THREAT Loss of old broadleaved woodland for agriculture or intensive forestry; Dutch elm disease and removal of old living elms in woods and hedgerows. Removal of trees for assumed hygene purposes in parks and roadsides. The shading out of rides and clearings within woods.

MANAGEMENT Retain old or diseased trees especially elms with oozing sap runs, which may be detected by the brown staining of the bark and ensure their continuity in future. In woodland, maintain rides and clearings with blossoms for adult feeding.

BRACHYOPA PILOSA Collin

DISTRIBUTION Mainly recorded in southern England with strong populations in parts of the New Forest, Windsor Forest and beechwoods on the North Downs of Surrey. Also recently from Northants and East Ross in Scotland.

HABITAT Ancient broadleaved woodland. Closely associated with beech.

ECOLOGY The larvae probably develop under the bark of dying or recently dead large beech trees, especially recent windfalls, though some observations suggest that other trees such as oak and birch may also be used. Adults may be found at such sites or visiting spring blossom such as cherry and hawthorn and are recorded from late April to early June.

STATUS Widespread but very local, with about 20 known post 1960 sites and often locally abundant at Windsor Forest, the New Forest and the North Downs, but only occasionally recorded elsewhere in recent years, suggesting a loss of suitable sites. The Northants record was at a relatively young beech wood suggesting some ability to colonize new sites. However, the main strongholds at Windsor and the New Forests are under pressure through dead wood removal and lack of suitable tree regeneration. Status revised from RDB3 (Shirt 1987).

THREAT Clearance of beech woodland and especially of the large post-mature or recently dead trees. The shading out of rides and clearings within woods. Intensive forestry and the removal of dead wood is a major problem at Windsor and the New Forest.

MANAGEMENT Retain large post mature or recently dead trees ensuring their continuity in future. This requires large areas of woodland to ensure reasonably stable levels of the resource for larval development. Maintain rides and clearings with blossoms for adult feeding.

BRACHYPALPUS LAPHRIFORMIS (Fallen)

DISTRIBUTION Recorded widely in southern Westmorland (1988), England, especially in Hampshire, though occurring sporadically as far north as Yorkshire (1984), into South Wales (Glamorganshire 1952 1982) and even a reputed record from Argyllshire (1982).

HABITAT Ancient broadleaved woodland and parkland. Closely associated with dead hollow trunks of beech and much more rarely with ash and oak.

ECOLOGY The larvae develop in the rotten wood of hollow trunks, preferring those broken off two to four metres above the ground. Stumps in both shaded woodland and open parkland seem to be used. Adults may be seen sunbathing or hovering around such stumps or living trees nearby and are recorded from late April to early August. They occasionally visit flowers such as hawthorn but seem less reliant upon a source of nectar than many other hoverflies.

STATUS Very local with about 40 known post 1960 sites. Many of its old sites are now destroyed and no colonization of new sites seems to occur. However, it is still widespread and locally frequent over much of Hampshire and Windsor Forest, Berkshire with other post 1960 records for Devon, Wiltshire, Sussex, Dorset, Oxfordshire, Glamorganshire and Yorkshire. Status revised from RDB3 (Shirt 1987).

THREAT Clearance of ancient beech woods for agriculture or intensive forestry and removal of hollow trunks or stumps.

MANAGEMENT Retain and ensure continuity of tall dead stumps, especially self pollarding trunks, in the future, maximising the number of diseased and post mature trees within a site.

CALIPROBOLA SPECIOSA (Rossi)

DISTRIBUTION Recent records are known only from the Windsor Forest area of Berkshire and the New Forest, Hampshire, though old records exist for Derbyshire and Yorkshire. A recent sight record is also reported from a site in Nottinghamshire.

HABITAT Ancient broadleaved woodland and parkland. Associated mainly with hollow stumps of beech and more rarely oaks and elm.

ECOLOGY The larvae have been reared from wet wood pulp in the base of a hollow beech stump and a female has been observed ovipositing in the wood mould of a hollow stump during which she completely buried herself, reappearing after about half a minute. Other more casual observations suggest that rot holes in between buttress roots of large stumps or post mature trees, which lead to a rotten interior are also oviposition sites. Adults may be found sunbathing on or near such stumps, or flying in their vicinity, in both dense and open woodlands and occasionally at the blossom of hawthorn or at sap runs. Males are said to be accomplished hoverers, though this is rarely observed. They are recorded in May and June.

STATUS Highly restricted though regularly recorded and even occasionally locally frequent in parts of the New Forest (Denny Wood, Mark Ash, Bramshaw Wood) and parts of Windsor, though populations seem to fluctuate markedly from year to year.

THREAT Clearance of ancient forests and parkland for conversion to agriculture or intensive forestry and removal of the dead stumps.

MANAGEMENT Retain any dead stumps within a site, maximising the number of diseased and post mature trees to ensure a continuous supply of this resource. Maintain the presence of rides and clearings to provide flowering shrubs, especially hawthorn, for adult feeding.

CALLICERA AENEA (Fabricius)

DISTRIBUTION Mainly recorded from southern England, with scattered old records as far north as Yorkshire and a recent one from Carmarthenshire (1986).

HABITAT Preferences rather unclear; there seems to be some bias towards heathland, though many records apply to old broadleaved woodland. In 1988, it was remarkably recorded from a garden in Wolverhampton. Old trees are probably a requirement.

ECOLOGY The larvae probably develop in water filled cavities and pot holes of broadleaved trees. An adult has been seen about birch logs on a common in north Hampshire, and a preference for dead or old birch on commons and heaths seems feasible. Adults recorded from June to August.

STATUS Infrequent and perhaps declining with about 15 known post 1960 sites. Records are very unpredictable and there seems to be very little attachment to individual sites, suggesting a species with a mobile and adventive nature. Status revised from RDB2 (Shirt 1987).

THREAT Removal of dead wood and post mature trees.

MANAGEMENT Retain any old trees and dead wood and ensure a continuity of these in the future.

CALLICERA RUFA (Schummel)

DISTRIBUTION Records widely dispersed in the Scottish Highlands (Perthshire, Argyllshire, Aberdeenshire, Elgin, Easterness, West Ross, East Ross).

HABITAT Native pine woods and old Pinus sylvestris plantations. There is a requirement for living trees of at least 100 years age, with rot holes, for larval development.

ECOLOGY Larvae develop in water-filled rot holes as outlined above and may take five years or more before being ready to pupate. The rot holes in which they live are most common on trees with branches that grow upwards at sharp angles to the trunk, and in twin-trunked trees at the point where the two trunks meet. A few are formed where a branch breaks off at its extreme base. Rot holes are common in many pine woods but are inconspicuous. There can be in excess of 30 larvae per rot hole. Trees have to be at least 100 years old before they contain enough timber to support a rot hole. Rot holes take a long time to develop, but once formed they probably survive for many years, supporting successive generations of C. rufa. The adults are rarely seen and do not appear to visit flowers like most hoverflies. They are most frequently found sitting on the trunks of old pine trees and are recorded from June to August.

STATUS Prior to 1988 regarded as an endangered (RDB1) and declined species, almost exclusively on the basis of known adult records. Surveys by Dr G. E. Rotheray and I. MacGowan during the autumn of 1988 concentrated on finding the larvae and have demonstrated a wide distribution in the Scottish Highlands (16 out of 19 sites surveyed in 7 vice counties). This survey has also recognised the importance of old plantations in addition to native pinewoods. The species was regarded as being confined to the latter habitat until this time. The presence of C. rufa in small woods is probably due to the repeated colonisation of individual rot holes by successive generations. Status revised from RDB1 (Shirt 1987).

THREAT Clearance of native pine woodland, old pine plantations and removal of old trees. Where gaps in the age structure of trees is present at a site, the loss of rot holes for a period of time could lead to local extinction of the fly. It is unlikely that extensive commercial plantations with younger age classes of trees could support this species.

MANAGEMENT Maintain and encourage the presence of old pines, especially those that are well branched or have twin trunks. Ensure the age structure of trees at a site is suited to the continued presence of rot holes. Artificially created rot holes made by cutting into trees may help overcome this to some extent. Epiphytic growth of saplings and shrubs in rot holes can lead to their drying out and render them unsuitable to C. rufa, therefore this threat should be carefully watched for and acted against where appropriate.

65

CALLICERA SPINOLAE (Rondani)

DISTRIBUTION Recorded from some seven sites in East Anglia: Southwold (1928), Bradiston Marshes (1942), Monks Soham (1947) and Iken (late 1940's) all in Suffolk; Houghton, Norfolk (1972, 1974); Gog Magog Hills (1979, 1984) and Lode (1971, 1972, 1974, 1975, 1978), Cambridgeshire.

HABITAT Almost certainly associated with very old broadleaved trees, with adults usually occurring near woods or in parkland/garden situations.

ECOLOGY In Russia, this species has been reared from rot holes in poplars (G. Rotheray - pers. comm.). Adults are usually found at the flowers of ivy on walls in late September and October.

STATUS Rather unclear due to the highly sporadic nature of the records. The data from Lode and the Gog Magog Hills suggests that the species does breed in Britain as opposed to being a migrant, and the fluctuations in the adult population may be related to changes in the amount of the resource for larval development. It should be noted that the great storm of 1987 has destroyed most of the old trees at two of the known sites, placing the fly into an even more precarious position.

THREAT Removal of post-mature trees and lack of regeneration of suitable trees through changes in woodland management.

MANAGEMENT Retain any old broadleaved trees, especially those with obvious rot holes, and ensure a continuity of suitable trees in the future; also ivy-clad walls for adult feeding.

CHALCOSYRPHUS EUNOTUS (Loew)   VULNERABLE
SYRPHIDAE

DISTRIBUTION Only six known sites within the Welsh Borders and southern England: Knapp and Paper Mill N.R., Alfrick (1986 and 1987), Shrawley Wood, nr Stourport (1986 and 1987) and an unspecified site in the Wyre Forest (1971), all in Worcestershire; Cothill NNR, Berkshire (1953); Ledbury, Herefordshire (1899) and Bracketts Coppice, Dorset (1987).

HABITAT Old broadleaved woodlands with streams.

ECOLOGY Larvae probably develop in dead wood. Most records apply to adults sitting on partly submerged logs, strongly suggesting that the larvae live in semi-submerged wood. Adults recorded in May and June.

STATUS Four post 1960 sites. It may prove to be more widespread along the Welsh borders with more thorough searching and the Dorset record is encouraging. This species is likely to remain vulnerable through the apparently specialised choice of breeding site.

THREAT Unclear, but probably the clearance of old woodland sites and removal of dead wood, especially semi-submerged logs.

MANAGEMENT Maintain known sites as broadleaved woodland, retaining any semi-submerged logs and ensure a continuity of dead wood in future by maximising the number of diseased and post mature trees.

CHAMAESYPHUS CALEDONICUS Collin   ENDANGERED
SYRPHIDAE

DISTRIBUTION The only certain locality (according to Speight, pre 1988) is Culbin Sandhills in Scotland, where it was taken in August 1935. Further material regarded as belonging to this species by Coe came from the Central Highlands, though some of his material is now known to be misidentified. A very recent record from Rothiemurchus Forest, Easterness (1988) is said to genuinely represent this species.

HABITAT Heathland associated with Caledonian pine forest.

ECOLOGY Biology unknown. A development within dead wood or damp soil are 2 more obvious possibilities.

STATUS No recent information from Culbin Sands despite further visits to the site. Its status in the mid Spey will need closer examination.

THREAT Destruction or modification of the known site especially through afforestation.

MANAGEMENT Attempt to maintain stability of the known site, in particular by retaining any dead wood and boggy areas which may provide potential breeding sites.

CHAMAESYRPHUS SCAEVOIDES (Fallen)   RARE
SYRPHIDAE

DISTRIBUTION Widely recorded in the northern half of Scotland (Perthshire, Aberdeenshire, Elgin, Easterness, West Ross, Sutherland) with numerous records along Speyside.

HABITAT Usually associated with heather within Caledonian pine forest areas.

ECOLOGY Biology unknown. A development within dead wood or damp soil are two more obvious possibilities. Adults recorded from June to August.

STATUS Not infrequent along the Spey Valley, but very local elsewhere in the Scottish Highlands with a total of about 15 known post 1960 sites.

THREAT Afforestation and improvement of Caledonian pine forest and its heathland for pastureland, especially the drainage of boggy areas and removal of dead wood.

MANAGEMENT Maintain Caledonian pine forest in a open state with glades, and ensure the continued presence of any damp, boggy areas and dead wood which may provide potential breeding sites.

CHEILOSIA BARBATA Loew   NOTABLE
SYRPHIDAE

DISTRIBUTION A clumped distribution in southern England, extending as far north as Derbyshire. A rather strong southeast bias is shown with a number of records for Kent, the Surrey Downs and Chilterns.

HABITAT Broadleaved woodland on chalk soils, occasionally clay woods nearby.

ECOLOGY Larvae probably phytophagous though host plant is unknown. A member of the family Compositae is most probable. Adults recorded from May to September suggesting the presence of two broods.

STATUS A very local species with about 15 known post 1960 sites.

THREAT Clearance of chalk woodland for agriculture or intensive forestry. The shading out of rides and clearings within.

MANAGEMENT Maintain rides and clearings in an open state to encourage a rich and varied flora. Coppicing of the woods could also benefit both the ground flora and associated insects such as this species.

CHEILOSIA CARBONARIA (Egger)

NOTABLE
SYRPHIDAE

DISTRIBUTION A clumped distribution in southern England with records extending as far north as Derbyshire.

HABITAT Mostly associated with rides, clearings and edges of old broadleaved woodland.

ECOLOGY Larvae phytophagous though the host plant is unknown. Most likely to be composites such as thistles Cirsium and Carduus. Adults recorded from April to August, usually found feeding on umbelliferous flowers. The flight period suggests that this species has two broods.

STATUS A scarce and very restricted species with about 15 known post 1960 sites but possibly under recorded to some extent through its resemblance to commoner species such as C. vernalis. Status revised from RDB3 (Shirt 1987).

THREAT Clearance of old woodland for agriculture or intensive forestry. Shading out of rides and clearings within.

MANAGEMENT Maintain rides and clearings in an open condition to encourage a rich and varied flora and associated insects such as this species.

CHEILOSIA CHRYSOCOMA (Meigen)

RARE
SYRPHIDAE

DISTRIBUTION Records widely scattered in England, Wales and as far north as Perthshire in Scotland. Most frequent in Gloucestershire, Herefordshire and Oxfordshire.

HABITAT Broadleaved woodland. Rides and glades at edges of woods in or near marshy areas are preferred, especially where calcareous soils are present.

ECOLOGY Larvae probably phytophagous though the host plant is unknown. Adults recorded from April to August suggesting the presence of two broods.

STATUS A widespread but extremely local species with about a dozen known post 1960 sites. This species is not listed in Shirt (1987).

THREAT Clearance of woodland and drainage of marshy areas for agricultural improvement or afforestation.

MANAGEMENT Maintain rides and clearings in woods, also a high, stable water level in adjacent marshes to encourage a rich and varied flora and prevent scrub invasion. Coppicing could be beneficial.

67

CHEILOSIA CYNOCEPHALA (Loew)

NOTABLE
SYRPHIDAE

DISTRIBUTION Records widely scattered, most frequent in the south but with isolated ones as far north as East Lothian and Lanarkshire in Scotland.

HABITAT Mainly grassland and usually on chalk soils, possibly limestone soils in the north.

ECOLOGY Larvae phytophagous, reared from the musk thistle Carduus nutans, a plant most typically associated with calcareous soils. Adults recorded from May to September, suggesting the presence of two broods.

STATUS A scarce and very local species with about 20 known post 1960 sites, though possibly under recorded to some extent through a close resemblance to other commoner species, such as C. vernalis. Status revised from RDB3 (Shirt 1987).

THREAT Habitat loss to agriculture and coniferisation. Changes in the grazing management of chalk grassland leading to the invasion of scrub, coarse grasses and a subsequent fall in floristic richness and diversity, including the host plant.

MANAGEMENT This should concentrate upon maintaining a healthy thistle population, especially Carduus nutans. Rotational grazing policies are advised on grassland to produce a range of vegetation types.

CHEILOSIA MUTABILIS (Fallen)
NOTABLE SYRPHIDAE

DISTRIBUTION Old records show a very wide distribution in Britain, extending up to the Scottish Highland where it was once quite frequent. Recent records however are few, though they include North Wales.

HABITAT Records include heathland, moorland, grassland, woodland rides and clearings.

ECOLOGY Larvae phytophagous, reared from the roots of welted thistle Cardus acanthoides. Adults recorded from March to August suggesting the presence of two broods.

STATUS Very local and possibly declined with about 20 known post 1960 sites, scattered widely throughout the known range. Status revised from RDB3 (Shirt 1987).

THREAT Loss of suitable habitat to agriculture and intensive forestry; also changes in the grazing management of sites, leading to the invasion of scrub and coarse grasses and a subsequent fall in floristic richness and diversity.

MANAGEMENT This should concentrate upon maintaining a healthy thistle population. Rotational grazing policies are advised in order to produce a mosaic of vegetation types; also maintain open rides and clearings in woods.

CHEILOSIA NEBULOSA (Verrall)
RARE SYRPHIDAE

DISTRIBUTION Records widely dispersed in England, extending north to Easterness in Scotland, and also to Pembrokeshire and Merionethshire in Wales.

HABITAT Broadleaved woodland, in particular rides, clearings and woodland edge beside marshy ground.

ECOLOGY Larvae probably phytophagous though host plant unknown. Larvae probably develop in composites such as thistles Cardus and Cirsium. Adults recorded from early April to mid May and are most easily observed at sallow blossom with males often hovering nearby at heights of about 10 ft. The flight period suggests only a single brood.

STATUS Widespread but exceedingly local with about a dozen known post 1960 sites and a decline seems to have occurred. The early flight period of the adult suggests it could be under recorded to some extent especially in areas such as Wales. It used to be reasonably regular at Chippenham Fen NNR, Cambridgeshire, but recent information is sparse.

THREAT Clearance of woodland and drainage of adjacent marshes for agricultural improvement or intensive forestry. Scrub invasion of marshy areas, rides and clearings.

MANAGEMENT Maintain a high, stable water level in marshy areas, open rides and clearings in woods and ensure a rich and varied flora containing thistles.

CHEILOSIA NIGRIPES (Meigen)
RARE SYRPHIDAE

DISTRIBUTION Authentic specimens are known from about a dozen sites in the chalk areas of southern England (Hampshire, Sussex, Surrey, Oxfordshire), and a record from Gloucestershire on Cotswold limestone is probably also correct. There is also a record in the London area of Kent in a district apparently without calcareous soils.

HABITAT Broadleaved woodland on chalk and occasionally limestone. In particular woodland edges, glades or adjacent damp meadows are favoured.

ECOLOGY Larvae probably phytophagous, though host plant unknown and not easily predicted. Probably a small herb of chalk woodlands. Adults recorded from late May to mid June and may be found sunbathing on foliage or visiting buttercups.

STATUS Very local with some six known post 1960 sites: Ashford Hill, Hampshire (1979 1987); West Dean Woods, Sussex (1980); Headley (1965), White Downs (1985) and Box Hill (a comparatively strong colony with a number of recent records), Surrey; Blackheath, Kent (1961, 1964).

THREAT Loss of suitable habitat to agriculture and intensive forestry. Mis-management of sites with a loss of a rich ground flora (for example through sycamore invasion or shading out of rides and clearings). Recreational pressures at sites such as Box Hill.

MANAGEMENT Maintain open rides and clearings in woods; coppicing could be useful in encouraging floristic richness and diversity. Woodland edge meadows are known to be important on some sites, these need to remain unimproved, with Rananculus among a rich flora, and whilst the exact requirements are unclear there has tended to be little management or a late autumn cut.

CHEILOSIA PUBERA (Zetterstedt)

NOTABLE
SYRPHIDAE

DISTRIBUTION Records widely dispersed in England and Scotland as far north as the Isle of Mull.

HABITAT Fens, fen carr, wet pastures, lake margin marshes, possibly requiring base rich conditions.

ECOLOGY Larvae probably phytophagous, though host plant unknown and not easily predicted. Adults recorded from early May to late June and may be found sunbathing on foliage or visiting buttercups and marsh marigold.

STATUS About 15 known post 1960 sites, mainly from northern England (Yorkshire, Cumberland and Northumberland), Scotland (not uncommon on Mull, also recorded from Berwickshire and Midlothian) and an isolated site at Leckford, Hampshire (1947 & 1976). Status revised from RDB3 (Shirt 1987).

THREAT Drainage of wetlands for agricultural improvement and intensive forestry; pollution such as agricultural run-off and scrub invasion of wetlands through a fall in water level.

MANAGEMENT Maintain a stable water level at sites; a mosaic of vegetation types (including open rides and clearings in woods) should sustain the as yet unknown larval requirement.

CHEILOSIA SAHLBERGI Becker

VULNERABLE
SYRPHIDAE

DISTRIBUTION Restricted to a small number of sites in the Central Highlands of Scotland: Beinn A Chuallaich (post 1960), Ben Lawers (1977) and Loch Na Lairige, nr Ben Lawers (1979), Perthshire; Creag Meagaidh, Westerness (post 1980); Feshie, Easterness (1959); Carn Liath, Aberdeenshire (1964); Braeriach (1957) and Lurchers Gulley (1988) in the Cairngorms.

HABITAT Montane, well above the tree-line at altitudes of 760-915 metres, especially areas with base rich soils derived from the Moine Schist geological system.

ECOLOGY Larvae probably phytophagous though host plant unknown. Many montane herbs have a prostate and succulent rosette structure that would be ideal for larval development. Adults recorded from May to July and may be found visiting flowers such as saxifrages, buttercups and tormentil Potentilla erecta.

STATUS The montane habitat means this species may be overlooked to some extent. However if it is restricted to base rich areas the total area of suitable habitat could be rather limited. Status revised from RDB3 (Shirt 1987).

THREAT Degradation of fragile habitats from skiing and associated development, as well as trampling from hill walkers, with a resultant loss of vegetation and soil erosion. This species seems to occur too high for afforestation to be a problem.

MANAGEMENT Keep sites free from excessive disturbance and if this is impractical in areas already receiving high public pressure, then take measures to limit habitat damage including re-routing of paths. Ensure that seepages and other wet areas are not drained as part of path improvement. Resist ski developments that may have impact on base rich areas of mountains. Maintain traditional levels of deer or sheep grazing to ensure a continuity of the characteristic base rich montane flora.

CHEILOSIA SEMIFASCIATA Becker

RARE
SYRPHIDAE

DISTRIBUTION Old records widely scattered in southern England and extending into North Wales where it still persists.

HABITAT In the English part of its range it is associated with orpine Sedum telephium in broadleaved woods, especially coppice with a rich ground layer of herbs. In Wales it is associated with navelwort Umbilicus rupestris which is widespread and thrives upon stone walls, embankments and rock crevices in acid conditions. However even here it seems to require plants in cooler, shaded areas.

ECOLOGY Larvae phytophagous mining the succulent leaves of both orpine in England and navelwort in more westerly regions such as North Wales. Adults recorded in April and early May and males are said to sunbathe on the ground close to woodland margins. The larval biology is described in detail by Rotheray, G.E. (in press).

STATUS A highly declined species possibly extinct at most of its old English localities though it was discovered at Pamber Forest, Hampshire in 1989. The only known post 1960 records are from North Wales, where it seems to be not infrequent and it may prove to be under recorded in Wales generally because of the early flight period. This species is not listed in Shirt (1987).

THREAT Loss of orpine from English woods through the cessation of coppicing which this plant is largely dependant upon. Navelwort is not so much a woodland plant though the hoverfly is mainly dependent on the plant in this habitat so all forms of woodland loss, intensive forestry and other activities which may reduce the plant should be avoided.

MANAGEMENT Maintain or introduce coppicing at known orpine sites (as much for the conservation of the plant as the fly) in the hope that the fly has survived in a few such sites. In navelwort areas maintain woodland and woodland margins in a semi-shaded state to ensure survival of this plant in shaded situations.

CHEILOSIA SOROR (Zetterstedt)

DISTRIBUTION Recorded widely in chalk areas of southern England with records extending as far north as Durham and into South Wales.

HABITAT Calcareous grassland, scrub and woodland, with a very strong association with areas such as the North and South Downs, the Cotswolds and the Chilterns. Pockets of woodland nearby may be required for the larval development.

ECOLOGY Larvae developing in truffles which favour calcareous soils especially under beech. Adults recorded from July to September and are especially attracted to the flowers of umbels such as wild parsnip Pastinaca sativa and wild carrot Daucus carota.

STATUS Widespread but local in the south, with about 25 known post 1960 sites. There is some evidence to suggest a decline in this species, almost certainly attributable to the substantial loss of suitable habitat and the degradation of it through mis-management. It can still be locally abundant at some sites.

THREAT Habitat loss to agriculture or intensive forestry. Changes in the grazing management of chalk grassland with subsequent scrub invasion and a loss of floristic richness and diversity including nectar source flowers.

MANAGEMENT Maintain a mosaic of vegetation types on calcareous soils with woodland, woodland edges and adjacent grassland. On grassland use rotational grazing if necessary; limited scrub is probably acceptable. Maintain open rides and clearings in woods ensuring plenty of umbellifers for adult feeding.

CHEILOSIA SP.B. Stubbs and Falk

DISTRIBUTION Only a single specimen known from the banks of the River Dee at Ballater in Scotland in late May 1981.

HABITAT Lushly vegetated riverbanks with sweet cicely Myrrhis odorata and a range of thistles and other composites.

ECOLOGY Larvae almost certain to be phytophagous and probably on composites such as thistles Carduus and Cirsium or butterbur. The adult was taken on the flowers of sweet cicely.

STATUS The taxonomic status of this specimen should be noted. It closely resembles the European Cheilosia rufimana, but differs in a number of important features which raises the possibility of this representing an entirely new species. It has not been found on subsequent visits to the site and may have a limited flight period. Status revised from RDB3 (Shirt 1987).

THREAT River improvement schemes along parts of the Dee could destroy the lushly vegetated river banks, and the site of capture is only just outside the town and is thus vulnerable to recreational pressure or disturbance.

MANAGEMENT Maintain the richly vegetated river banks free from excessive disturbance and rich in composites and umbelliferae.

CHEILOSIA VELUTINA Loew

DISTRIBUTION Records scattered widely in England and Scotland as far north as Midlothian with a strong southerly bias.

HABITAT Calcareous grassland, scrub and woodland, particularly on southern chalk areas. Occasionally occurring on non-calcareous sites. There have been reports of it occurring commonly on waste ground in certain localities, especially in calcareous districts.

ECOLOGY Larvae phytophagous, probably on a species of thistle Carduus or Cirsium. The adults are recorded from April to August and may be found feeding on umbels. The flight period suggests that two broods occur.

STATUS An infrequently recorded species with about 15 known post 1960 sites. However, it is frequently confused for the more frequent C. proxima with which it often occurs and has probably been under recorded to some extent, both in collections and in the field. Status revised from RDB3 (Shirt 1987).

THREAT Habitat loss to agriculture or intensive forestry. Changes in the grazing management of grassland with subsequent scrub invasion and a loss of floristic richness and diversity. Waste ground can by its nature be transient when specific measures are taken.

MANAGEMENT This should concentrate upon maintaining a healthy population of thistles. Rotational grazing policies to produce a mosaic of vegetation types should be considered. Its use of waste ground may provide opportunities in some cases to link in with urban conservation management, with the need to ensure continuity of pioneer vegetation, perhaps involving rotovation or bulldozing selected parts of a site.

CHRYSOGASTER MACQUARTI Loew

DISTRIBUTION Records widely dispersed in England, Scotland and Wales, becoming more frequent towards the north.

HABITAT Boggy marshes and flushes; usually associated with acid conditions, though occasionally taken on non-acid marshes.

ECOLOGY Larvae develop in the mud at the base of aquatic plants and, being very closely related to C. hirtella, they are assumed to obtain oxygen using modified hind spiracles for penetrating air spaces within aquatic plants. Adults recorded from June to September and may be found on flowers of tormentil Potentilla erecta, buttercups and composites.

STATUS A local species with about 30 post 1960 sites, most frequent in the north and especially along the Spey Valley. Its separation from the more common Chrysogaster hirtella is difficult and could have resulted in some under recording. Status revised from RDB3 (Shirt 1987).

THREAT Drainage of bog areas for agricultural improvement or intensive forestry. A fall in water level can also encourage the invasion of scrub and coarse grasses.

MANAGEMENT Maintain open peatland habitat with a high, stable water table, preventing scrub invasion. Maintain the presence of pools and ditches and lush marginal conditions.

CHRYSOTOXUM ELEGANS Loew

DISTRIBUTION Records widely dispersed in southern England as far north as Worcestershire, Northamptonshire and Norfolk and also into South Wales. Many records are from coastal areas.

HABITAT Usually found on dry, open grassland, though it has been seen in dense woodland.

ECOLOGY Larval habits unknown though possibly predators of root aphids or in ants nests. Adults recorded from May to September and may be found visiting the flowers of umbels, shrub blossom such as elder or sunbathing on foliage. Males may be found hovering in loose swarms above grassland at a height of 3 to 4 ft.

STATUS Most regularly taken in counties such as Hampshire, Dorset, Cornwall and Devon, otherwise infrequent and declining. About 15 post 1960 sites known, though old records are numerous and often refer to its local abundance.

THREAT The loss of coastal grassland and woods to arable agriculture and intensive forestry. Recreational pressures, including building development, are a threat in the coastal belt. Vast areas of suitable habitat have been lost this way and probably account for its decline.

MANAGEMENT Prevent the invasion of scrub or coarse grasses on coastal grassland. Grazing may be necessary to produce a mosaic of short vegetation types, especially if ants are involved in the larval development. Maintain the presence of rides and clearings in woods.

CHRYSOTOXUM OCTOMACULATUM Curtis

DISTRIBUTION Reliable records few and restricted to Cornwall, Dorset, Surrey and Hampshire. Records are most numerous from the Dorset heaths.

HABITAT Most records relate to heathland.

ECOLOGY Larval habits unknown though possibly predators of root aphids or living in ant nests. Adults recorded from May to August.

STATUS Declining, with only five known post 1960 localities: Arne (1974) and Corfe (1960), Dorset; Thursley Common NNR (1966) and nearby Hankley Common (1988), Surrey; and Woolmer Heath (1974), Wealden Hampshire.

THREAT Loss of heathland to arable agriculture and intensive forestry has greatly reduced the area of suitable habitat and changes in heathland management may have resulted in its decline at existing sites. Accidental fires are a constant danger.

MANAGEMENT Maintain a pattern of traditional heath management, including rotational treatment of heather, attempting to maintain a mosaic of vegetation types and prevent scrub invasion.

CHRYSOTOXUM VERNALE Loew

DISTRIBUTION A small number of sites on the south coast of England between Hampshire and Cornwall: Penzance, Cornwall (1871); Tamerton Foliat, Devon (old); Oakers Wood (1988); Studland (1919, 1968), West Moors (1897), Parley (1942) and Wareham Heath (1917), Dorset; Lyndhurst (1869), Mudeford (1951), Hampshire and possibly some other unspecified New Forest sites.

HABITAT Heathland and possibly associated heath woodland.

ECOLOGY Larval habits unknown though possibly predators of root aphids or living in ant nests. Adults recorded from May to July and were recorded visiting the flowers of wood spurge Euphorbia amygdaloides at Oakers Wood.

STATUS Declining, with little recent information other than the two post 1960 sites from Dorset.

THREAT Clearance of heathland for arable agriculture and intensive forestry has greatly reduced the area of suitable habitat and changes in heathland management may have resulted in its decline at existing sites. Accidental fires are a constant danger.

MANAGEMENT Maintain a pattern of traditional heath management, attempting to retain a mosaic of vegetation types and prevent scrub invasion.

CRIORHINA ASILICA (Fallen)
NOTABLE SYRPHIDAE

DISTRIBUTION Records widely scattered in England as far north as Berwickshire, predominating in the south; also South Wales (Glamorganshire).

HABITAT Broadleaved woodland with a requirement for dead wood. Occasionally on fens such as Woodwalton where it can be quite common, probably reflecting a continuity of suitable dead wood.

ECOLOGY Larvae develop in dead wood and at Windsor adults are particularly frequent around well rotten, fallen beech trunks. Adults recorded from April to July and visit spring blossom such as hawthorn Crataegus and rhododendron Rhododendron.

STATUS A very local southern species with about 45 known post 1960 sites. A useful indicator of dead wood continuity. It can occur in good numbers at sites such as Windsor Forest, Woodwalton Fen and other old woods.

THREAT Clearance of old woodland for agriculture or intensive forestry and removal of dead wood. The shading out of rides and clearings within woods.

MANAGEMENT Retain any dead wood, particularly fallen trunks or large limbs in shaded conditions, and ensure continuity of these in future by maximising the number of post-mature trees. Maintain open rides and clearings in woods with blossoms for adult feeding.

CRIORHINA RANUNCULI (Panzer)
NOTABLE SYRPHIDAE

DISTRIBUTION Records scattered widely in England, Scotland and Wales, predominating in the south.

HABITAT Broadleaved woodland with a requirement for dead wood. Small pockets of woodland seem to be utilised in addition to large woods.

ECOLOGY Larvae develop in dead wood, though the precise requirements are unknown. Adults recorded from March to early June (peak April) and frequent the blossom of sallow, sloe and cherry.

STATUS A widespread but very local species with about 40 known post 1960 sites, though the particularly early flight period could have led to some under recording. It can occasionally be found in good numbers at sites such as Windsor Forest and in other old woods.

THREAT Clearance of woodland for agriculture or intensive forestry and removal of dead wood. The shading out of rides and clearings within woodland.

MANAGEMENT Retain any dead wood and ensure future continuity by maximising the number of post mature trees within a site and encourage variety in the nature of dead wood. Maintain rides and clearings in an open condition with blossoms for adult feeding.

DIDEA ALNETI (Fallen)
ENDANGERED SYRPHIDAE

DISTRIBUTION Old records for about 18 sites scattered widely in England and Scotland as far north as Easter Ross with a recent record for Trawsfynydd, Merionethshire (1979).

HABITAT Woodland, favouring rides and woodland edges. Abroad it is said to be associated with conifer plantations though some British records apply to broadleaved woods.

ECOLOGY Larvae probably aphidophagous but details unknown. Adults recorded from May to September which suggests two broods are present and abroad they have been recorded feeding on a wide range of flowers.

STATUS Only a single record since 1948 and seriously declined, as it is a large species unlikely to be overlooked. The nature of the records suggests it may possibly be migratory, with irregular influxes from the continent, though until this can be more fully demonstrated it must be regarded as an extremely rare native.

THREAT Woodland clearance for agriculture and afforestation. The shading out of rides and clearings within woodland.

MANAGEMENT Ensure a good age structure and variety of trees within a wood and maintain open rides and clearings with plenty of flowers for adult feeding.

DIDEA FASCIATA Macquart
NOTABLE SYRPHIDAE

DISTRIBUTION Records scattered widely in England, Wales and Scotland though most frequent in ancient forest areas in the southern half of England.

HABITAT Broadleaved woodland and nearby open land.

ECOLOGY Larvae probably aphidophagous specialising on those aphids found in ancient broadleaved woodland, though on the continent it has been claimed to feed on Cinara piceae upon Abies alba. Adults recorded from May to October suggesting that two broods are present. Adults visit blossom such as hawthorn in the spring and umbels and composites throughout the flight period.

STATUS A very local species, not infrequent in the south, but becoming much rarer in the north and some of the Scottish records have been assigned to a different colour form (this may require further investigation). Nearly 60 post 1960 sites are known.

THREAT The clearance of ancient broadleaved woodland for agriculture or intensive forestry. The shading out of rides and clearings within woodland.

MANAGEMENT Ensure a good age mixture of the trees within sites including mature trees. Also maintain flower rich rides, clearings and wood edges for adult feeding.

DIDEA INTERMEDIA Loew

DISTRIBUTION Records scattered widely in England and Scotland. Most frequent in Scotland but also with numerous records for Windsor Forest and the New Forest. The lack of records from Wales is interesting as much apparently suitable habitat is available there.

HABITAT Most records from coniferous woodland, especially plantations and adjacent areas and with a few records from Caledonian pine forest and it may require younger pine trees or denser stands. In southern England there seems to be some association with heathland, quite independant of conifers, although it can occur in plantations here.

ECOLOGY Larvae aphidophagous and have been found abroad on pine feeding on *Schizolachnus pineti*. Adults have also been observed taking great interest in gorse infested with an *Aphis* species in the New Forest. Adults recorded from May to September, probably as two broods and may be found on the flowers of umbels and bedstraw.

STATUS A very local but not infrequent species in afforested areas of the Scottish Highlands. It seems to be increasing here, with populations enhanced through coniferisation. In southern England there seems to be a definite decline probably through loss of heathland, though there is evidence to suggest that conifer plantations are being colonised, though whether this is by the original southern heathland populations is indeterminable. It seems likely that the species was indigenous to Caledonian forests prior to coniferisation of highland areas.

THREAT None in Scotland as conifer plantations are not a threatened resource. Loss of heathland in the south (where gorse may provide the larval habitat) to agriculture, intensive forestry, accidental fires and scrub invasion through mis-management.

MANAGEMENT Retain heathland sites in the south and maintain gorse by employing traditional management. Management probably unnecessary in Scotland other than retaining open rides and clearings in plantations with plenty of flowers for adult feeding, and encouraging pine regeneration in Caledonian forests by protecting saplings from grazing by deer.

DOROS CONOPSEUS (Fabricius)

DISTRIBUTION Records mainly from southern England, but extending to Westmorland and Caernarvonshire. Most recent records are from Sussex and Wiltshire.

HABITAT Calcareous grassland and scrub, especially near woodland edges. Brambles are usually present at known sites and most sites are on chalk.

ECOLOGY Larvae suspected of feeding on root aphids and abroad have been reported from turf. Adults recorded from late May to July usually resting on or flying around bramble. On the chalk downs in Surrey a female was observed ovipositing low down on the trunk of an isolated ash tree on chalk grassland, suggesting a more specific developmental site is the turf around tree trunks.

STATUS Decreasing with many of its old sites destroyed. About a dozen post 1960 sites as follows: Verditch Chase, (1960's; 1979), Grovel Wood (late 1960's) and Martin Down (1982), Wiltshire; Oxenbourne Down, Hampshire (1973); Friston Forest (1969, 1975, 1976), Brighton area (1986), Kingley Vale (1978), Lewes Downs (1987) and Arundel Park (1976), Sussex; Box Hill area (post 1965), Surrey; Dagnam Park (undated) and Leigh-on-Sea (1960, 1968), Essex. A reasonably strong population is present at Friston despite extensive afforestation, though it may be dependant on rides. At Leigh-on-Sea it has been found for a period of over 200 years (since mid 1700's).

THREAT Habitat loss through afforestation or agricultural improvement; also changes in grazing management with scrub invasion and a loss of floristic richness and diversity.

MANAGEMENT Maintain a mosaic of vegetation types including some limited scrub employing rotational grazing policies if necessary.

EPISTROPHE DIAPHANA (Zetterstedt)

DISTRIBUTION Records widely scattered in southern England from Kent to Cornwall and as far north as Worcestershire and Huntingdonshire.

HABITAT Broadleaved, woodland, especially margins and unimproved meadows nearby.

ECOLOGY Larvae aphidophagous though details unknown, other than that larvae of this genus are known to feed on aphids on leaves of shrubs and trees. Adults recorded from June to August.

STATUS Locally frequent in counties such as Oxfordshire, Wiltshire, East Hampshire (but not the New Forest) and Surrey, otherwise rather rare. Nearly 40 known post 1960 sites.

THREAT Clearance of old broadleaved woodland, and its afforestation. Drainage or pollution of unimproved, herb rich meadows, especially through river improvements as along one of its strongholds, the Basingstoke Canal.

MANAGEMENT Maintain known sites as deciduous woodland with herb rich rides, clearings and edges; also ensure a good age structure with old trees which may support the aphids this species feeds on.

EPISTROPHE EUCHROMA (Kowarz)

DISTRIBUTION Scattered records mainly from southern England but extending to Lancashire and an isolated record from Aviemore in Scotland.

HABITAT Broadleaved woodland, adults usually found in rides, clearings and wood edges. There seems to be a preference for old woods.

ECOLOGY Larvae aphidophagous and abroad have been recorded feeding upon aphids on Euonymus europaeus and on cherry Prunus avium. Adults recorded from April to June and have been found on the blossom of sloe and the flowers of wood spurge Euphorbia amygdaloides.

STATUS A very scarce, possibly declining species with seven known post 1960 sites in contrast to a good number of older ones. Occurence is rather unpredictable and apart from a few sites such as in the New Forest there seems to be little attachment to individual sites, suggesting a mobile and adventive species. Even at sites where formerly common, it seems to have declined and recent records usually refer to single individuals.

THREAT Clearance of woodland for agriculture and intensive forestry, and especially of the sloe at woodland edges and in rides and clearings. The shading out of rides and clearings within woods.

MANAGEMENT Maintain the presence of sloe in rides, clearings and woodland edges. Prevent the scrubbing over of rides and clearings, using rotational scrub clearance if necessary.

ERISTALIS CRYPTARUM (Fabricius)

DISTRIBUTION South-west England (Cornwall, Devon, Somerset, Dorset, Hampshire). Most records are from the New Forest and Dartmoor.

HABITAT Lush marshy spots, stream sides and pond margins with a rich boggy soil and such plants as Iris.

ECOLOGY Larvae aquatic, probably amongst the submerged parts of marginal vegetation and are of the 'rat tailed maggot' type. Adults recorded from March to September.

STATUS Heavily declined with only two known post 1960 sites within the Dartmoor area (Dartmeet 1978 and Soussons Plantation 1966) and it has always been rather sporadic in its occurence. It may be extinct in other parts of its range or overlooked among commoner Eristalis species.

THREAT Drainage of marshes, with a resultant loss of ponds, canalisation of rivers and ditching of streams with a loss of the marginal vegetation in which the larvae probably develop. Also excessive trampling of river banks at sites such as Dartmeet, Devon and pollution such as agricultural run-off.

MANAGEMENT Maintain a high stable water level in marshes, ensure a rich marginal vegetation around water bodies.

ERISTALIS RUPIUM Fabricius

DISTRIBUTION Recorded widely in the hilly areas of Wales, northern England and Scotland.

HABITAT Upland areas with a preference for lush marshy spots with plenty of flowers either in sheltered valley bottoms and forest glades or more rarely in exposed situations up to 300m.

ECOLOGY Larvae aquatic, probably in pools, but whether acidic or basic conditions are required is unknown, though pH may be an important factor. The larvae are of the 'rat tailed maggot' type. Adults recorded from June to September.

STATUS Very local, but not infrequent in upland areas with in excess of 45 known post 1960 sites. It can occur in local abundance.

THREAT The drainage of upland bogs and marshes for improved pastureland and for afforestation.

MANAGEMENT Maintain a high, stable water level in marshy areas, ensuring the presence of pools and ditches for the larvae and a rich and varied surrounding vegetation. Such sites should not be heavily grazed.

EUMERUS ORNATUS Meigen

DISTRIBUTION Records widely scattered in England and Scotland as far north as Midlothian. Little available information for Wales, though likely to occur there. Most frequent in old woodland areas of southern England.

HABITAT Broadleaved woodland. The association with old woods is particularly strong, and small pockets of woodland are used in addition to large forest areas.

ECOLOGY Unknown; other members of the genus develop in bulbs. The adults are recorded from April to August, preferring woodland rides and edges where they fly low over paths and herbage sometimes settling on sunlit ground or foliage.

STATUS A very local species with about 20 known post 1960 sites. It can be locally frequent in some areas such as Somerset, Gloucestershire, Westmorland and the New Forest.

THREAT The clearance of old woods for agriculture or intensive forestry and shading out of rides and clearings which may support the larval food plant.

MANAGEMENT Maintain rides and clearings in an open condition rotational management of these where necessary to prevent scrub invasion.

=====
NOTABLE SYRPHIDAE
=====

EUMERUS SABULONUM (Fallen)

DISTRIBUTION Mainly recorded from the coasts of south western England from Hampshire to North Cornwall, North and South Wales and additionally from Suffolk and a few sites in southwest Scotland (Ayrshire, Wigtownshire).

HABITAT Maritime cliffs, especially those with landslips and sandy head deposits. Less frequently on coastal dunes, and there is also an inland record from the southern margin of Dartmoor. In North Cornwall and Devon, where it was recently taken at five sites, it was closely associated with warm sunny cliff slopes with patches of bare soil and plants such as Sedum anglicum. There may be a requirement for Squills Scilla.

ECOLOGY The larvae are thought to be phytophagous in plant roots or bulbs, though they have yet to be discovered. A good deal of suspscion falls upon Squills Scilla. Adults recorded from June to August.

STATUS Apparently scarce but possibly under-recorded. At least 16 known post 1960 sites: Studland heath (1968) and Purbeck (1986), Dorset; a site in Carmarthenshire (1989); Morfa Harlech (1976) and Morfa Bychan (1976), Merionethshire; Newborough Warren, Anglesey (1976); Ogoff Goch (1987), Careg Wylan (1987), Davidston (1966) and Nolton Haven (1966), Pembrokeshire; a site in Wigtownshire (initialled GR; 1984) and possibly Western Gailes, Ayrshire (exact date unknown); also five sites between Millook (Cornwall) and Clovelly (Devon) in 1989, with evidence to suggest a wide distribution on this coastline. Status revised from RDB3 (Shirt 1987).

THREAT Loss of coastal sites to coastal development and the afforestation or agricultural reclamation of stabilised parts of dune systems. Recreational pressures with dune erosion and the drainage or pollution of slacks.

MANAGEMENT Maintain a full succession of vegetation types on dunes and minimise the disturbance to fore dunes using fences if necessary to allow normal dune fixation.

=====
NOTABLE SYRPHIDAE
=====

FERDINANDEA RUFICORNIS (Fabricius)

DISTRIBUTION Scattered records in southern England and the Midlands and also for East Lothian in Scotland (1918).

HABITAT Broadleaved woodland, especially old woodlands with trees infested with goat moth.

ECOLOGY Larvae probably develop in the sap runs of old, diseased trees, especially those infested with the goat moth (the association of these two species is probably indirect). Adults recorded from April to August, probably as two broods, and may be found sunbathing on the trunks of large trees.

STATUS Widespread but very local. Possibly declining at sites such as the New Forest where fairly frequent early this century though in recent years it has been regularly turning up in new counties. About 20 known post 1960 sites, scattered widely. Status revised from RDB2 (Shirt 1987).

THREAT Clearance of old woodland for agriculture or intensive forestry and removal of the old and diseased trees within.

MANAGEMENT Retain any old or diseased trees with sap runs and ensure continuity of these in the future.

=====
ENDANGERED SYRPHIDAE
=====

HAMMERSCHMIDTIA FERRUGINEA (Fallen)

DISTRIBUTION Presently known from eight definite sites (all recent) along the Spey Valley between Kingussie, Easterness and Grantown, Elgin (old records for "Aviemore", "Nethy Bridge" and "Grantown" are difficult to assign to actual sites); also three sites in E. Sutherland (Turboll, Arnaboll Wood and Achany).

HABITAT Aspen Populus tremula woodland, including birch or pine woods with an aspen component. There is a requirement for dead aspen trees.

ECOLOGY Larvae have mostly been found in fallen aspen trunks, though it is also possible that they use standing dead trees and living trees with some rot. Adults recorded from early June till mid July, resting on stumps, logs and sound trunks and also visiting flowers such as roses.

STATUS Regarded as an exceedingly rare Spey Valley speciality until 1976 when it was sighted at an E. Sutherland site. It has since been taken at two further sites in this vice county and is proving to be widespread in the mid Spey Valley, where six sites were located in 1982, plus six more in 1989. Careful searches of aspen woods throughout the Scottish Highlands may reveal an even wider distribution.

THREAT Clearance of aspen and other semi-natural woods with an aspen component in Scotland, largely for intensive forestry, and the removal of dead wood and large old trees.

MANAGEMENT Retain any dead wood, old or diseased trees and ensure continuity of these in the future.

HELOPHILUS GROENLANDICUS Loew

DISTRIBUTION In Stubbs and Falk (1983) this species is stated as being only known from single specimens from Canna (1936) and Raasay in the Inner Hebrides. However, the Royal Scottish Museum contains a Waterhouse specimen labelled Poll Duchail, I. of Eigg, 9/7/1939.

HABITAT Probably associated with boggy pools on moorland.

ECOLOGY Larvae aquatic probably developing in boggy pools and are of the 'rat-tailed maggot' type. Adults recorded in July.

STATUS A boreal species which could be resident on the Scottish Islands or windblown from northern latitudes. The low level of recording on these islands means it could have been overlooked in recent years. Status revised from RDB3 (Shirt 1987).

THREAT The destruction of bogs on the Scottish islands through peat cutting.

MANAGEMENT Retain such bogs ensuring a high, stable water level and control the amount of peat cutting on such islands.

LEJOGASTER SPLENDIDA (Meigen)

DISTRIBUTION Mainly recorded from coastal regions in southern Britain from North Wales to Suffolk and with a few Scottish records (sites in Westerness, Skye and Aberdeenshire). Also occasionally occurring inland at sites in Berkshire, Cambridgeshire and at a loch in South Aberdeenshire (Loch Kinord, Dinnet NNR).

HABITAT Coastal brackish and tidal marshes in estuaries or otherwise are preferred sites but non-brackish sites such as fens and marshes are sometimes inhabited. On the west coast of Scotland it is associated with Iris seepage marsh fringe along the shores of sea lochs.

ECOLOGY Larvae are said to have been reared from the decaying vegetation of a floating mat of Typha and other plants in an old pond. Adults recorded from May to August.

STATUS A very local, mainly coastal species with about 25 known post 1960 sites.

THREAT The destruction of coastal marshes through drainage for agriculture; the spread of coastal development; complete or extensive clearance of marginal vegetation from water edges; pollution such as agricultural run-off; mis-management of water levels with a loss of breeding sites and subsequent scrub invasion.

MANAGEMENT On inland sites maintain a high stable water level and employ rotational ditch management on grazing levels and marshes if necessary to ensure all successional stages are present every year.

LEJOPS VITTATA (Meigen)

DISTRIBUTION Scattered records from the coastal marshes of southern England from Somerset to Norfolk with most records from the Thames estuary, Sussex and Somerset. There is an old inland record from Hertfordshire but this seems very dubious.

HABITAT Coastal marshes. There seems to be a close association with Scirpus maritimus growing along ditches or in adjacent marsh, indicative of brackish conditions usually at the transition to freshwater where freshwater plants occur with the Scirpus. However, it can occur several miles from the sea on coastal levels where in the past saline influence was more direct.

ECOLOGY Larvae aquatic, probably living in the ditches or pools of coastal marshes. Adults recorded from May to September. Adults have been seen feeding on the pollen of Scirpus maritimus and are well camoflaged on the flower heads.

STATUS Rare, though it has been found to be locally frequent in a small number of sites in North Kent, Sussex and Somerset with about a dozen known post 1960 sites. However the habitat required is diminishing.

THREAT The destruction of coastal marshes through drainage for agriculture and coastal development; complete or extensive clearance of marginal vegetation from water edges. Major deepening and clearance of ditches, often with pump drainage, is associated with the eutrophication of ditches from fertilizer run-off. The Thames Barrage has resulted in extensive modification of flood embankments and ditches for many miles of coast. Saline influence is likely to weaken on most remaining sites. Nearly all sites are in areas suffering conservation problems.

MANAGEMENT Maintain a high, stable water level and employ rotational ditch management where necessary on grazing levels and marshes to ensure all successional stages are present every year. In the long term it may be necessary to take measures to top up the salinity.

MELANGYNA BARBIFRONS (Fallen)

DISTRIBUTION Records widely dispersed in southern England as far north as Lancashire, also North Wales (Merionethshire) and possibly from Aviemore in Scotland (needs confirmation).

HABITAT Broadleaved woodland, a rather loose association and often found on commons nearby.

ECOLOGY Larvae probably aphidophagous though on what species is unknown. Adults recorded from March until June (peak April) and frequent sallow blossom and wood anemone Anemone nemorosa.

STATUS Infrequent and very local with only a handful of post 1960 sites known. It is likely to be under recorded through the early flight period (peak in March and April) and males are exceedingly elusive, suggesting a canopy dwelling nature in this sex.

THREAT Clearance of broadleaved woodland for agriculture and intensive forestry. Shading out of rides and clearings within woods.

MANAGEMENT Maintain open rides and clearings, ensuring the presence of sallows and other spring flowers for adult feeding.

MELANGYNA ERICARUM (Collin)

DISTRIBUTION Mainly recorded from the Scottish Highlands (Aberdeenshire, Easterness, Elgin and Sutherland). There is also a record from Bernwood Forest in Oxfordshire (1980/81) which is quite remarkable and somewhat dubious.

HABITAT Exact requirements unclear as it has been found in Scottish pine woods and in birch carr and marshland away from conifers. Adults recorded from June to October.

ECOLOGY Larvae aphidophagous though on what species is unknown.

STATUS A poorly known species which has been somewhat misinterpreted in the past and could be under recorded. It appears to be a speciality of the Scottish Highlands and the Oxfordshire specimen (supposedly taken with the essentially Scottish Metasyrphus nielseni) should be treated with some suspicion. Post 1960 records include Morrone Birkwood NNR, Aberdeenshire (1971); Boat of Garten, Elgin (1966) and Loch an Eileen, Easterness (1981). This species is not listed in Shirt (1987).

THREAT Clearance of native woodland in the Scottish Highlands and replacement with intensive forestry. Over grazing by deer can lead to a loss of a ground vegetation which could be detrimental to this species.

MANAGEMENT Maintain an open structure of birch and pine trees in native woodland. A mosaic of ground vegetation types (using fenced enclosures to exclude deer) could benefit this species and other invertebrates.

MALLOTA CIMBICIFORMIS (Fallen)

DISTRIBUTION Records scattered widely in southern England and the Midlands as far north as Cheshire with a very recent record for Newborough Forest, Anglesey (1987).

HABITAT Broadleaved woodland and parkland with a requirement for old trees with rot holes.

ECOLOGY Larvae have been reared from wet rot holes of horse chestnut and elm and it is possible that birch and beech are also used. Pupation occurs just above the rot holes in drier detritus, and rot holes at height seem to be preferred, both in woodlands or isolated trees (as in Hyde Park). Adults recorded from May to August and visit the flowers of roses, brambles and hogweed.

STATUS Infrequent and records very unpredictable. There seems to be little attachment to individual sites suggesting a mobile and adventive nature. About 15 post 1960 sites, scattered widely. Status revised from RDB2 (Shirt 1987).

THREAT Clearance of woodland for agriculture, forestry and urban development and removal of old and diseased trees with rot holes.

MANAGEMENT Maximise the number of old and diseased trees in a site and ensure a continuity of them in the future. Maintain open rides and clearings in woods with blossoms and flowers for adult feeding.

MEGASYRPHUS ANNULIPES (Zetterstedt)

DISTRIBUTION Records widely dispersed in England, Wales and Scotland.

HABITAT Exact requirements unclear, though often found in coppiced woodland, at woodland edges and in rides.

ECOLOGY Larvae aphidophagous though on what species is unknown. Goeldin (1975) recently described the larva and reared this species almost to pupation on Aphis fabae (bean aphis) in the laboratory. The larvae are likely to be arboreal in the wild. Adults recorded from April to October.

STATUS A very local and declining species, most frequent in Scotland. About 15 known post 1960 sites with older records comparatively numerous.

THREAT Clearance of native woodland for agriculture or intensive forestry. The shading out of rides and clearings within woodland.

MANAGEMENT Maintain open rides and clearings in woods, using rotational clearance if necessary, ensuring flowers for adult feeding. Maintain a good age structure of trees including mature ones which may support suitable aphids.

MELANOSTOMA DUBIUM (Zetterstedt)

DISTRIBUTION Mainly recorded from the Scottish Highlands (Argyllshire, Perthshire, Westerness, Ross-shire) and the Pennines (Yorkshire, Durham).

HABITAT Montane and upland areas with most records for altitudes between 460 and 915 m and characteristically on boggy ground near small streams. It has also been taken at lower ground near a lake.

ECOLOGY Larvae probably aphidophagous though details unknown. Adults recorded from June to August and may be found feeding on a range of flowers, especially tormentil _Potentilla erecta_ and buttercups.

STATUS It has only been regarded as a distinct species in Britain over the last few years but recent evidence suggests it could be locally frequent in montane areas.

THREAT The drainage of upland bog areas for improved pasture and afforestation of lower slopes on mountains. Skiing could be a problem in some areas leading to soil erosion and a loss of vegetation.

MANAGEMENT Maintain the natural hydrology and vegetation communities of upland bogs and streams and ensure their freedom from excessive disturbance.

MELANOSTOMA 'Form A' Stubbs & Falk

DISTRIBUTION Known from a handful of sites in the Scottish Highlands: Derry Lodge, Aberdeenshire (1970); Glen Einich (recent) and Loch Avon (pre 1960), Easterness; Beinn Heagarnich (1992), Perthshire; Glen Shiel to Glen Quoich, Ross (1934).

HABITAT Montane bogs with most records (perhaps all) above 700m.

ECOLOGY Larvae probably aphidophagous. Adults recorded in June and July.

STATUS A very poorly known species which is exceedingly hard to identify. It may be a form of the common _M. mellinum_.

THREAT The drainage of upland bog areas, for improved pastureland or afforestation of lower slopes of mountains. Skiing could be a problem in some areas leading to soil erosion and a loss of vegetation.

MANAGEMENT Maintain the natural hydrology and vegetation communities of montane bogs ensuring their freedom from excessive disturbance.

MELANGYNA GUTTATA (Fallen)

DISTRIBUTION Records scattered widely in England, Wales and Scotland including the Inner Hebrides and the Isle of Man.

HABITAT Broadleaved woodland.

ECOLOGY Larvae aphidophagous and have been found on the leaves of sycamore. Adults recorded from June to September in woodland rides and edges, usually feeding on umbels.

STATUS Widespread but extremely local with about a dozen known post 1960 sites. Probably under recorded to some extent, though some decline seems to have occurred. It seems to occur at low population levels at a site. Status revised from RDB3 (Shirt 1987).

THREAT Clearance of broadleaved woodland for agriculture and intensive forestry. Shading out of rides and clearings within woodland.

MANAGEMENT Maintain flower rich rides, clearings and wood edges and ensure a good age structure of trees in woodland, including very old trees.

MELANGYNA TRIANGULIFERA (Zetterstedt)

DISTRIBUTION Records scattered widely in England and Scotland as far north as Edinburgh.

HABITAT Broadleaved woodland, even gardens.

ECOLOGY Larvae aphidophagous and have been found on _Prunus_ trees and bushes feeding on various species of aphids. They are black and white, closely resembling bird droppings in the field. Adults are recorded from April to September, probably as two broods and frequent the flowers of umbels although they have also been recorded from the blossom of privet.

STATUS A local but widespread species with about 25 known post 1960 sites. The adults appear to be elusive and work in Edinburgh has shown that larvae are rather more easy to find, possibly reflecting a canopy dwelling habit in the adult.

THREAT Clearance of broadleaved woodland for agriculture, intensive forestry and urban development. Shading out of rides and clearings within woodlands.

MANAGEMENT Maintain rides and clearings in an open condition, ensuring the presence of shrubs and trees such as _Prunus_ and plenty of flowers for adult feeding.

METASYRPHUS LAPPONICUS (Zetterstedt)

DISTRIBUTION The few British records are scattered in the Scottish Highlands (Perthshire, Aberdeenshire, Elgin, Sutherland).

HABITAT Probably woodland though exact requirements unkown, and it has been taken away from ancient pine woods.

ECOLOGY Larvae probably aphidophagous. Adults recorded in June and July.

STATUS On the continent this is a Scandinavian species and is felt to be somewhat migratory (which may have led to its accidental occurrence in Britain). Its separation from the closely related Metasyrphus (Lapposyrphus) species A (a migratory species probably associated with spruce plantations in Britain) is very difficult and may have resulted in some unreliable data.

THREAT Uncertain other than intensive forestry in the native woodlands in the Scottish Highlands.

MANAGEMENT Uncertain.

METASYRPHUS LATILUNULATUS (Collin)

DISTRIBUTION Records scattered widely in England as far north as Yorkshire.

HABITAT Preferences unclear, known from woods and heaths.

ECOLOGY Larvae probably aphidophagous. Adults recorded from May to September, probably as two broods.

STATUS Its close resemblance to the common M. luniger has probably led to it being largely overlooked or misidentified. About 10 post 1960 sites are known, but some specimens may require checking.

THREAT Loss of habitat to agriculture and intensive forestry. Shading out of rides and clearings within woodland.

MANAGEMENT Maintain open rides and clearings in woods with plenty of flowers for adult feeding; also a mosaic of vegetation types on heathland using traditional management techniques.

METASYRPHUS NIELSENI Dusek & Laska

DISTRIBUTION Most records are for the Scottish Highlands (Perthshire, Aberdeenshire, Elgin, Easterness) with recent records for south Northumberland and a dubious site in Oxfordshire and older ones for Cheshire and Westmorland.

HABITAT Coniferous woodland, and adjacent heathland. A strong association is shown with Caledonian pine forests though the English records are linked to conifer plantations.

ECOLOGY Larvae aphidophagous upon pines, Pinus sylvestris certainly being used and possibly non-native conifers. Adults recorded from May to October probably as two or more broods, and frequent the flowers of tormentil Potentilla erecta, dwarf sallow Salix repens and rowan Sorbus aucuparia.

STATUS Regular in some Caledonian pine forests, perhaps even locally frequent with about eight known sites and the English records suggest some powers of dispersal, though not as strong as many other pine-associated hoverflies. The close resemblance to certain other Metasyrphus species and the fact that it was only described as new to science in 1976 may have led to it being partly, overlooked. However, recent doubts about some features used for the separation of M. nielseni from M. nitens mean that English records should be treated with caution.

THREAT The clearance of open structured Caledonian pine forests in Scotland mainly for intensive forestry, and overgrazing of the ground flora by deer.

MANAGEMENT Maintain the open structure which should be typical of Caledonian pine forest, with shrubs and flowers for adult feeding.

METASYRPHUS NITENS (Zetterstedt)

DISTRIBUTION Records scattered widely in England and Wales, extending as far north as Yorkshire, but with a strong southerly bias.

HABITAT Broadleaved woodland. The association with old forests is particularly strong.

ECOLOGY Larvae probably aphidophagous. Adults recorded from May to August, probably as two broods and visit a range of flowers, especially umbels.

STATUS An extremely local species with about 15 known post 1960 sites. It can be confused with the commoner M. latifasciatus and could be under recorded to some extent.

THREAT The destruction of ancient woodland for agriculture and intensive forestry. The shading out of rides and clearings within woodland.

MANAGEMENT Maintain open rides and clearings which may contain larval feeding sites and flowers for the adults to feed on. Coppicing could be beneficial.

THREAT The clearance of heathland and woodland for agriculture or intensive forestry and the removal of dead stumps at least in the southern sites. The shading out of rides and clearings within woodland sites.

MANAGEMENT Retain any dead wood at southern sites, attempt to produce an open structured wood using coppicing and maintain open rides and clearings. Use rotational heathland management to produce a mosaic of vegetation types in this habitat and prevent scrub invasion, though noting that the control of tree invasion, especially Pinus, can produce the stumps required. In Caledonian pine forests maintain an open structured woodland with a range of ground conditions, noting those most favoured by wood ants.

**NOTABLE
SYRPHIDAE**

MICRODON MUTABILIS (Linnaeus)

DISTRIBUTION Records widely scattered in England, Wales and Scotland. It is perhaps most frequent in the wetter climates of the west country.

HABITAT There is a close association with damp situations including boggy ground, dune slacks and damp meadows. On the Isle of Mull, in a high rainfall climate, it is able to use better drained slopes.

ECOLOGY The armoured, slug-like larvae live as commensals in the nests of ants where they feed on the discarded food pellets of the adult ants. A number of ant species appear to be used including Formica lemani, F. fusca, Lasius niger, Myrmica ruginodis and, abroad, F. transkaucasica, and nest sites include Sphagnum moss and under stones. Adults recorded from May to July and may be found sitting on vegetation near their breeding sites.

STATUS This species appears to have undergone a decline in England. It used to be a fairly common insect in the south-west and New Forest, but recent records from the former area are rather few and it is hardly common in the New Forest. It is not infrequent on the Isle of Mull. There is evidence to suggest it could have been overlooked in parts of Wales and Scotland. About 25 post 1960 sites are known. Status revised from RDB3 (Shirt 1987).

THREAT The drainage of wetland sites such as bogs on heaths and dune slacks and improvement of grassland for agriculture or intensive forestry. Pollution such as agricultural run-off could be a problem and scrub invasion through the lowering of the water table.

MANAGEMENT Retain marshy areas and damp, unimproved meadows and prevent the invasion of scrub, bracken or coarse grasses which could affect ant populations.

**VULNERABLE
SYRPHIDAE**

MICRODON DEVIUS (Linnaeus)

DISTRIBUTION Scattered records in southern England as far north as Worcestershire and Norfolk, also North Wales. The majority of records are for the chalk grassland on the North Downs and the Chilterns.

HABITAT Calcareous grassland and scrub.

ECOLOGY The armoured, slug-like larvae live as commensals in the nests of ants where they feed on the discarded food pellets of the adult ants. There have been reports that the yellow hill ant Lasius flavus acts as host but this needs confirmation and it is possible that various other ant species are equally good candidates. Adults recorded from May to August and may be found sitting on vegetation near their breeding sites.

STATUS Very local and declining with about a dozen known post 1960 sites, mainly from Wealdon, Hampshire, the North Downs and the Chilterns with one (possibly two) sites in North Wales (Merionethshire). It was also recorded from Middle Harling Fen, Norfolk in 1988.

THREAT Habitat loss to agriculture and intensive forestry and changes in the grazing management of calcareous grassland with a subsequent change in vegetation structure such as scrub invasion and loss of the ants.

MANAGEMENT Maintain a mosaic of vegetation types including areas of short cropped grass to encourage the ants. Use rotational grazing policies if necessary and prevent scrub invasion.

**NOTABLE
SYRPHIDAE**

MICRODON EGGERI Mik

DISTRIBUTION A disjunct distribution is shown, with records centred on the heathland sites of the London Basin, Western Weald, New Forest and east Dorset in England and then in heathy woods in valleys of the Central Highlands of Scotland.

HABITAT Open heathy woodlands are preferred, occasionally woodland rides on clay soils being used. Dead stumps are a requirement at least in the southern part of its range.

ECOLOGY The armoured, slug-like larvae live as commensals in the nests of ants where they feed on the discarded food pellets of the adult ant. Lasius niger is used at least in the south, and builds its nests under bark or in stumps. In Scotland ants of the Formica rufa group appear to be used, which may lead to different habitat needs, especially with respect to the requirement for dead wood. Adults recorded from March to July and may be found sitting on vegetation near their breeding sites.

STATUS About 25 known post 1960 sites including a handful of Scottish sites, mainly from Speyside. However the area of suitable habitat must be diminishing fast. Status revised from RDB3 (Shirt 1987).

MYOLEPTA LUTEOLA (Gmelin)
NOTABLE
SYRPHIDAE

DISTRIBUTION South-east England, stretching to Wiltshire and Dorset in the west and Cambridgeshire and Suffolk in the north.

HABITAT Broadleaved woodland, occasionally fens such as Wicken in Cambridgeshire. There is a requirement for old and diseased trees and dead wood.

ECOLOGY The larvae have been found in a small rot hole on an old beech from which was dripping a black watery liquid at about three metres height. Adults recorded from June to August and visit flowers such as lime, bramble and umbels.

STATUS Recorded sporadically in the major old woodlands of southern England with about 20 known post 1960 sites. Status revised from RDB3 (Shirt 1987).

THREAT The clearance of woodlands for agriculture or intensive forestry and removal of old trees and dead wood.

MANAGEMENT Maximise the number of post mature trees, especially those with rot holes and ensure continuity of such trees in the future. Maintain open rides and clearings with flowers for adult feeding.

MYOLEPTA POTENS (Harris)
ENDANGERED
SYRPHIDAE

DISTRIBUTION All records are from a small area near Bristol (Coombe-Dingle/Blaise Castle) and in the Shapwick/Edington district of Somerset.

HABITAT Old broadleaved woodland, probably with a requirement for old or diseased trees with rot holes.

ECOLOGY Unknown, though presumably living in rot holes of trees like the related _M. luteola_. Adults recorded from mid May to early June.

STATUS All records are from the mid 1940s and it has not been found since, despite numerous visits to the area, suggesting it is either now very rare or extinct. Blaise Castle (Coombe-Dingle) has undergone some changes since these records, though whether this has affected the dead wood fauna is uncertain.

THREAT Clearance of the known sites for agriculture or intensive forestry and removal of the old or diseased trees and dead wood.

MANAGEMENT Retain any old or diseased trees especially those with obvious wounds and rot holes, also dead wood and ensure a continuity of these in the future.

NEOASCIA GENICULATA (Meigen)
NOTABLE
SYRPHIDAE

DISTRIBUTION Records scattered widely in England, Wales and Scotland including Orkney.

HABITAT Marshes and water margins where there is lush emergent vegetation such as Glyceria.

ECOLOGY Larvae probably living in wet mud or vegetation as detritus feeders. Adults recorded from April to October and visit flowers such as forget-me-not and fool's celery Apium nodiflorum.

STATUS Widespread but very local with about 35 known post 1960 sites, and not infrequent in the Scottish Highlands and parts of northern England (Yorkshire, Cheshire).

THREAT The destruction of wetland habitats through drainage for agriculture or intensive forestry and the removal of marginal vegetation from ditches and ponds; pollution such as agricultural run-off; mis-management of water levels with subsequent scrub invasion and a loss of breeding sites.

MANAGEMENT Maintain a high, stable water level and employ rotational ditch and pond management if necessary to ensure all successional stages are present every year.

NEOASCIA INTERRUPTA (Meigen)
NOTABLE
SYRPHIDAE

DISTRIBUTION Confirmed records restricted to the southeast of England as far west as Sussex, Buckinghamshire and Berkshire and north to Suffolk and Huntingdonshire. It is perhaps most frequent on coastal marshes, especially the Thames marshes, though it occurs at some sites well inland. A 1987 record from North Wales awaits confirmation.

HABITAT Ditches and ponds on brackish coastal marshes and inland fens and marshes. There appears to be some association with Typha, and lush ditches with fool's celery Apium nodiflorum are particularly favoured.

ECOLOGY Larvae probably living in wet mud or vegetation as detritus feeders. Adults recorded from May to September and visit flowers such as forget-me-not and fool's celery.

STATUS Only added to this British list in 1981 since when it has shown itself to be locally frequent on the coastal marshes of Sussex, Kent and Essex with about 20 known post 1960 sites (12 in Essex).

THREAT The destruction of marshes (especially coastal) through drainage for agriculture and urban or industrial development, and the removal of marginal vegetation from ponds and ditches. Also pollution from industry and agricultural run-off.

MANAGEMENT Maintain a high, stable water level and employ rotational ditch and pond management if necessary to ensure all successional stages are present every year.

NEOASCIA OBLIQUA Coe

DISTRIBUTION Records widely dispersed in England, South Wales and Scotland, becoming most frequent in northern England and Scotland.

HABITAT Marshes and water margins at the edges of woods.

ECOLOGY Larvae probably develop in wet mud or vegetation as detritus feeders. Adults recorded from May to July.

STATUS A very local though widespread species with 25 known post 1960 sites and locally frequent in some areas such as Derbyshire and Yorkshire fen localities. Status revised from RDB3 (Shirt 1987).

THREAT The destruction of marshes through drainage for agriculture or intensive forestry and the removal of marginal vegetation from ponds and ditches; mis-management of water levels with a subsequent loss of breeding sites and scrub invasion.

MANAGEMENT Maintain a high, stable water level and employ rotational ditch and pond management if necessary to ensure all successional stages are present every year.

NEOCNEMODON BREVIDENS (Egger)

DISTRIBUTION Only four sites to date: Mitcham Common, Surrey (1949); Scout Park, Middlesex (1948); Denford, Berkshire (1989) and Clowes Wood, Warwickshire (1976).

HABITAT Uncertain, probably damp woodland. At the Surrey site an adult was on the flowers of Caltha suggesting an association with alder carr or other wet habitat and the recent Berkshire record was from similar situations.

ECOLOGY Known larvae of Neocnemodon species are arborial predators of adelgid plant bugs on conifers, though it is unlikely that this species is associated with conifers and it may utilise woolly aphids on trees such as alders. Adults recorded from late April to early May.

STATUS Only the Warwickshire record is recent. Its occurrence in Britain has only been recognised in the past few years and it may yet prove to be more widespread. Females of this genus cannot yet be identified further reducing the potential number of records.

THREAT Clearance of woodland and carr for agriculture and intensive forestry.

MANAGEMENT Maintain the presence of open rides and clearings within woodland, with flowers for adult feeding.

NEOCNEMODON LATITARSIS (Egger)

DISTRIBUTION Records widely dispersed in England and as far north as Lancashire with an isolated one for Midlothian in Scotland. A southerly bias is shown.

HABITAT Uncertain;, it is known from woodland rides and edges, sallow scrub and commons.

ECOLOGY On the continent the larvae of this species have been found attacking the woolly aphid Dreyfusia piceae on fir Abies alba, so fir plantations may prove to be important in Britain. Adults recorded from May to August and have been observed feeding on the flowers of cow parsley Anthriscus sylvestris and tormentil Potentilla erecta.

STATUS Only a handful of widely dispersed post 1960 sites. The secretive and perhaps canopy dwelling nature of the adults combined with some taxonomic difficulty in the genus (females cannot yet be identified) may had led to under recording. N. latitarsis does not appear to be indigenous to the Scottish Highlands and may be a relatively recent addition to the British fauna, especially if a non-native conifer proves to be the normal larval situation.

THREAT Uncertain other than the clearance of woodland for agriculture and afforestation.

MANAGEMENT Maintain open rides and clearings in woods with flowers for adult feeding.

ORTHONEVRA BREVICORNIS Loew

DISTRIBUTION Recorded widely in England, Wales and Scotland as far north as Ross and Cromarty.

HABITAT Marshes and fens, especially where seepages and streamlets are present.

ECOLOGY Larvae said to occur in organically rich mud by ponds and streams. Adults recorded from May to August and have been observed visiting flowers such as umbels and shrub blossom.

STATUS A very local but widespread species with about 30 known post 1960 sites. Status revised from RDB3 (Shirt 1987).

THREAT The drainage of marshes for agriculture or intensive forestry and the removal of marginal vegetation from ponds and ditches; pollution such as agricultural run-off; mis-management of water levels with a subsequent loss of breeding sites and scrub invasion. The seepage sites are especially fragile and vulnerable.

MANAGEMENT Maintain a high stable water level and the presence of marshy areas around seepages and streamlets and employ rotational ditch and pond management where necessary to ensure all successional stages are present every year.

ORTHONEVRA GENICULATA Meigen

DISTRIBUTION Recorded widely in England and Scotland, with most records for the Scottish Highlands. It is probably present in Wales, though no records are known as yet.

HABITAT Bogs and occasionally fens as in Cambridgeshire and parts of East Anglia.

ECOLOGY Larvae probably occurring in organically rich mud by ponds and streams. Adults recorded from April to July and have been observed visiting flowers such as marsh marigold, bog bean, umbels and shrub blossom.

STATUS An extremely local though widespread species with about 35 known post 1960 sites. It is comparatively frequent and widespread in parts of the Scottish Highlands and English strongholds include the New Forest bogs and the fens of the East Midlands and East Anglia. Status revised from RDB3 (Shirt 1987).

THREAT The drainage of bogs for agriculture, intensive forestry and peat cutting in certain areas; pollution such as agricultural run-off; mis-management of water levels with a subsequent loss of breeding sites and scrub invasion.

MANAGEMENT Ensure a high, stable water level and employ rotational ditch and pond management if necessary to ensure all successional stages are present every year.

NEOCNEMODON PUBESCENS Delucchi & Pschorn-Walcher

DISTRIBUTION The few records are widely dispersed in England (Dorset, Sussex, Surrey, Cambridgeshire, Herefordshire, Yorkshire) with an isolated record from Grantown, Elgin (1937).

HABITAT Woodland, probably associated with conifers.

ECOLOGY Known larvae of Neocnemodon species are arborial predators of adelgid plant bugs on conifers, though British records seem associated with broadleaved situations. Adults recorded in May and they have been observed in numbers feeding on pollen on male flowers of Mercurialis perennis.

STATUS Only about half a dozen known post 1960 sites. The secretive and perhaps canopy dwelling nature of the adults combined with some taxonomic difficulty in the genus (females cannot yet be identified) may have led to under recording. The Grantown record indicates that the species may be indigenous to the Scottish Highlands, though should the biology prove to relate to a non-native conifer, its native British status will need to be questioned.

THREAT Clearance of woodland for agriculture and intensive forestry.

MANAGEMENT Maintain open rides and clearings in woods with flowers for adult feeding.

NEOCNEMODON VERRUCULA (Collin)

DISTRIBUTION Scattered records mainly the the south of England (Dorset, Hampshire, Sussex, Suffolk, Cambridgeshire, Herefordshire), but also from Lancashire and from Fife, Perthshire and Midlothian in Scotland.

HABITAT Probably woodland.

ECOLOGY Known larvae of Neocnemodon species are arborial predators of adelgid bugs on conifers, though it is unclear if this species is associated with coniferous or broadleaved woods. Adults recorded in May and June.

STATUS Five known post 1960 sites: Studland, Dorset (1986); Botley Wood, Hampshire (1986); Haugh Wood, Herefordshire (1981); Tentsmuir Forest, Fifeshire (1983) and Blackwood of Rannoch, Perthshire (early 1960's). The secretive and perhaps canopy dwelling nature of the adults combined with some taxonomic difficulty in the genus (females cannot yet be identified) may have led to some under recording. N. verrucula does not appear to be indigenous to the Scottish Highlands and may be a relatively recent addition to the British fauna, especially if a non-native conifer proves to be the normal larval situation.

THREAT Clearance of woodland for agriculture or intensive forestry.

MANAGEMENT Maintain open rides and clearings in woods with flowers for adult feeding.

PARAGUS ALBIFRONS (Fallen)   VULNERABLE
                                              SYRPHIDAE

DISTRIBUTION Scattered records in southern England (Devon, Wiltshire, Dorset, Sussex, Surrey, Kent, Essex, Oxfordshire, Suffolk). The vast majority of records are coastal, though it is recorded well inland at sites in Wiltshire and Oxfordshire.

HABITAT Preferences unclear. Known sites include a grassy flood embankment adjacent to coastal levels and a shell beach with sparse vegetation.

ECOLOGY Larvae aphidophagous and abroad have been found on the thistle Cirsium arvense feeding on aphids. Adults recorded from May to August.

STATUS Infrequent and declining. Only three known post 1960 sites: Blackgrounds Marsh, Essex (1983) and two sites in North Kent. Habitat loss probably places this species in a vulnerable position. Status revised from RDB3 (Shirt 1987).

THREAT Main ones likely to be management of flood embankments, including raising height with fresh soil/sediment; coastal development and recreational pressure on beaches and sand or shingle areas nearby.

MANAGEMENT Maintain a full succession of vegetation types on coastal sites, paying special attention to the continuity of dry sparsely vegetated ground.

PARAGUS TIBIALIS (Fallen)   NOTABLE
                                                SYRPHIDAE

DISTRIBUTION Scattered records in England and South Wales extending as far north as Durham but with a strong southerly bias.

HABITAT Heathland, though associated with sand dunes in Denmark and limestone pavement in Ireland.

ECOLOGY Larvae aphidophagous though details unknown. Adults recorded from June to October and visit flowers such as tormentil Potentilla erecta and bedstraws.

STATUS A poorly known species only separable from the very similar P. haemorrhous in the male, and only recognised as British in recent years. It is likely to be under recorded to some extent.

THREAT Clearance of heathland for agriculture or intensive forestry and mis-management of heath with resultant scrub or bracken invasion and a loss of vegetation diversity.

MANAGEMENT Maintain a mosaic of heathland vegetation types, including areas of sparse vegetation, using traditional heath management. The presence of bare or sparsely vegetated paths and tracks is likely to be crucial, also bare ground within heathland vegetation such as heathers.

PARASYRPHUS NIGRITARSIS (Zetterstedt)   ENDANGERED
                                              SYRPHIDAE

DISTRIBUTION A few individuals (females) are known from the Scottish Highlands: Grantown, Elgin (1937) and Morrone Birkwood, Aberdeenshire (needs confirmation). More recently, a series of males were taken in a garden at Rhyd y Gwin, Cardiganshire (1987, 1988) and a single male from Scotchwell Path, near Haverfordwest, Pembrokeshire (1988).

HABITAT Usually in the vicinity of damp broadleaved woodland.

ECOLOGY Abroad, young larvae have been recorded feeding on larvae of chrysomelid beetles (Galerucella and Lentinotarsa) and aphids (Rhopalosiphoninus). Larger larvae require the larvae of another chrysomelid, Melasoma and it is possible that a range of related beetles are also used. Adults recorded in May and June.

STATUS A very poorly known hoverfly which has recently been rediscovered at two sites in south-west Wales. The great resemblance to common species of the genus Syrphus should be noted, and it may prove to be under recorded. Abroad the species is a northern European and Alpine species.

THREAT Clearance of native woodland for intensive forestry and agriculture. At Morrone, excessive grazing by deer appears to be having a detrimental effect on the ground flora and tree regeneration, which could be affecting this species. The shading out of rides and clearings within woods is also likely to be deleterious.

MANAGEMENT Maintain native broadleaved woodland in a natural state, with at least some open structured areas. Use fenced compartments to exclude deer and encourage a herb rich ground flora and some tree regeneration at sites such as Morrone Birkwood.

PARHELOPHILUS CONSIMILIS (Malm)   **VULNERABLE SYRPHIDAE**

DISTRIBUTION Records are few though widely dispersed in southern England (notably the south west), the Norfolk Broads, the Lincolnshire coast, South Wales and the Galloway coastal belt of south west Scotland. Whilst most records are coastal, inland records are present such as those from the Watford area of Hertfordshire, and Radnorshire in Wales.

HABITAT It seems to favour pools which are transitional between bog and fen, often in association with Typha.

ECOLOGY Larvae aquatic and of the rat-tailed maggot type, possibly living between the leaf sheaths of Typha. Adults recorded from May to August.

STATUS Post 1960 records from nine sites: Crymlyn Bog, Glamorganshire (1980), with a very long history stretching back to 1906), a site on the Gwent levels (1980); Aberithan Bog, Radnorshire (1982); Llyn Hafodol, Anglesey (1987); Cassiobury Park (several records in 1986) and possibly nearby at Bricketts Wood (determination correct, date needs checking), both in Hertfordshire; Little Matlock Wood, Derbyshire (1987); Gordon Moss, Berwickshire (1988); Carrick Pools and Newnham Moss, Kirkcudbrightshire (1979). There is the possibility of further sites existing and the close resemblance to commoner species of the genus may have led to some under recording.

THREAT The drainage of suitable marshland for agricultural improvement, afforestation and industrial coastal developments (at Crymlyn). Also pollution from agricultural run-off and industry (Crymlyn). Over enthusiastic clearance of Typha.

MANAGEMENT Maintain a stable regime with Typha, any necessary management being on rotation to ensure continuity of a good population of Typha..

PELECOCERA TRICINCTA Meigen   **RARE SYRPHIDAE**

DISTRIBUTION Most records relate to the heaths of the New Forest and East Dorset, though it has also been recorded from Ash (1984) and Chobham (1987, 1988), Surrey; Parkhurst Forest, Isle of Wight (1970, 1974) and Stover Country Park, Devon (1986).

HABITAT Heathland and in particular the margins of bogs and wet heaths (e.g. Erica tetralix heath).

ECOLOGY Biology unknown, though possibly associated with damp mud or vegetation at the edges of bogs. Adults recorded from May to September and have been observed visiting the flowers of various dandelion type composites and heather Calluna.

STATUS About 15 known post 1960 sites and regularly found on the New Forest and Dorset heaths, sometimes in good numbers. The area of suitable habitat must be diminishing however. The recent record from Devon (Stover Country Park) is a most unexpected extension of its range.

THREAT Clearance of heathland and drainage of bog areas for agricultural improvement and afforestation. Mis-management of heath with a resultant loss of bogs and scrub/bracken invasion. Pollution such as agricultural run-off.

MANAGEMENT Maintain a mosaic of conditions within the heath particularly ensuring the presence of boggy pools. Employ traditional heathland management to prevent scrub invasion.

PIPIZA LUGUBRIS (Fabricius)   **NOTABLE SYRPHIDAE**

DISTRIBUTION Scattered records in England as far north as Durham and with an old record for North Wales.

HABITAT Uncertain though possibly heathland areas adjacent to old broadleaved woodland.

ECOLOGY Larvae probably aphidophagous though details unknown. Adults recorded from May to October.

STATUS About 10 known post 1960 sites, with many old records likely to be incorrect and applying to the common P. noctiluca.

THREAT Clearance of woodland and heathland for agricultural or intensive forestry.

MANAGEMENT Maintain open rides and clearings in woods; ensure a mosaic of vegetation types on heathland, using traditional management techniques to prevent scrub invasion.

DISTRIBUTION Records widely dispersed in England and Scotland (also the Isle of Man).

HABITAT Broadleaved woodland (where it will probably require open rides and clearings) and scrub areas of heaths etc.

ECOLOGY Larvae probably aphidophagous though details unknown. Adults recorded from April to June and frequent the blossom of sloe Prunus spinosa and other spring flowers.

STATUS A very local but widespread fly with about a 15 known post 1960 sites and occasionally not uncommon at ancient woodland sites such as the New Forest and certain parts of the Scottish Highlands, especially Speyside. The rather early flight period (peaks in April and May) and resemblance to the commoner P. albimanus and P. ambiguus may have led to some under recording.

THREAT Clearance of old woodland and heathland for agriculture and afforestation. Shading out of rides and clearings within woodland.

MANAGEMENT Maintain open rides and clearings in woods which may contain larval feeding sites and flowers for the adults and a mosaic of vegetation types on heathland, using traditional management and retaining limited areas of scrub, trees and bushes.

PLATYCHEIRUS IMMARGINATUS (Zetterstedt)
NOTABLE SYRPHIDAE

DISTRIBUTION Records widely dispersed in England, Wales and Scotland.

HABITAT Mainly brackish coastal marshes, including saline marsh along tidal rivers. There are some records for fens and river margins but these need verification.

ECOLOGY Larvae probably aphidophagous. Adults recorded from May to August and are known to visit a range of flowers.

STATUS A very local but widespread species with about 25 known post 1960 sites and occasionally recorded in abundance.

THREAT The drainage of coastal wetlands for agricultural improvement and coastal development. River improvement schemes and the loss of riverside vegetation. Pollution such as agricultural run-off. Overgrazing could be detrimental and mis-management of water levels could lead to scrub invasion and other changes in vegetation.

MANAGEMENT Maintain a natural hydrological regime and ensure a full succession or mosaic of vegetation types including pools, ditches and their marginal vegetation.

PIPIZELLA MACULIPENNIS (Meigen)
RARE SYRPHIDAE

DISTRIBUTION The few records present are mainly scattered around southern England, though records are present from Dumfriesshire and Argyllshire in Scotland.

HABITAT Uncertain, some records are from coastal marshes whilst others are from inland heaths and grassland.

ECOLOGY Larvae aphidophagous and abroad are said to have been reared from populations of the aphids Anoecia cornia, A. major, A. nemoralis and Tetraneura ulmi. It is presumed that the summer generations of these aphids are used ie those inhabiting the roots of various grasses. Adults recorded in June and July.

STATUS About half a dozen widely scattered post 1960 records. Its separation from the more frequent P. virens is not particularly easy and it may be under recorded to some extent.

THREAT Habitat loss through drainage for agriculture, afforestation and coastal developments. Pollution such as agricultural run-off.

MANAGEMENT Uncertain. A mosaic of vegetation types at sites, including pools and ditches, would be desirable.

PIPIZELLA VIRENS (Fabricius)
NOTABLE SYRPHIDAE

DISTRIBUTION Records widely dispersed in southern England with isolated ones extending as far north as Yorkshire.

HABITAT Uncertain, known sites include woods, fens, coastal marshes and commons, perhaps with a preference for dry grassland and woodland rides and margins.

ECOLOGY Larvae reported abroad as feeding on aphids on the roots of umbelliferous plants. Adults recorded from May to July.

STATUS Very local, though not infrequent in some parts of the south (Essex, Kent, Dorset), with about 20 known post 1960 sites. Records of P. virens in old literature may refer to the commoner P. varipes.

THREAT Habitat loss to agriculture, intensive forestry. Mis-management of grassland with subsequent loss of certain vegetation elements and invasion by scrub and bracken.

MANAGEMENT Maintain a mosaic of vegetation types including rides and clearings in woods, retain a mosaic of vegetation types on heathland using traditional management techniques to prevent scrub invasion, and employ rotational grazing policies on grasslands.

PLATYCHEIRUS MELANOPSIS Loew

DISTRIBUTION The few records known for this species are from the Central Highlands of Scotland (Perthshire, Aberdeenshire, Easterness, Westerness, West Ross, Argyllshire) and the Lake District (in Westmorland).

HABITAT Montane habitats, exceeding 1000 m in Perthshire and the Cairngorms though it may also extend into valleys at altitudes below the tree line. At Creag Meagaidh NNR, Westerness where the species was recorded in abundance on south facing slopes in 1983, a preference was shown for altitudes between 510m and 790m in Calluna or Vaccinium heath. At Braeriach in the Cairngorms recent captures were also for a south-facing slope, in Deschampsia caespitosa grassland at 1050m.

ECOLOGY Larvae probably aphidophagous though details unknown. Adults recorded in June and July, males characteristically hovering close to the ground over roads and bare tracks.

STATUS A highly restricted species with four known post 1960 sites: Coille Choire Chuilc (1979, 1985) and Ben Lawers NNR (1977), Perthshire; Creag Meagaidh, Westerness (1983); Braeriach, Cairngorms (1986) and Ben Lui, Argyllshire (1979).

THREAT Afforestation of upland areas and drainage of boggy areas and flushes which may support the required vegetation. Skiing and excessive trampling could have a local impact through soil erosion and a loss of vegetation.

MANAGEMENT Prevent excessive disturbance on mountainous areas retaining any boggy areas. Resist ski developments that may have an extensive influence on montane habitats and limit the damage caused by trampling in areas receiving high public pressure, such as by the re-routing of paths.

PLATYCHEIRUS PERPALLIDUS Verrall

DISTRIBUTION Records widely dispersed in in the NW half of England, Wales and Scotland with most records from the Scottish Highlands.

HABITAT Marshes, especially where sedges (e.g. Carex rostrata) grow in wet poor fen or boggy areas at the margins of ponds, lakes and rivers.

ECOLOGY Larvae probably aphidophagous though details unknown. Adults recorded from May to August and are known to feed on the pollen of sedges.

STATUS Extremely local in Britain as a whole with about 35 known post 1960 sites though locally frequent in parts of the Scottish Highlands. Status revised from RDB3 (Shirt 1987).

THREAT The drainage of wetlands for agricultural improvement or afforestation. River improvement schemes and the loss of marginal vegetation through clearance, excessive trampling or overgrazing. Pollution such as agricultural run-off.

MANAGEMENT Maintain a high stable water level and ensure a full succession or mosaic of vegetation types including pools and ditches and their marginal vegetation.

PLATYCHEIRUS PODAGRATUS (Zetterstedt)

DISTRIBUTION Widely distributed in Scotland (especially the Highlands), northern England, with isolated records in the north west half of England.

HABITAT Bogs, poor fen and river margins both in lowland and submontane areas exceeding 450m. Occasionally on coastal dunes (Monadh Mor, East Ross) probably utilizing dune slacks or other marshy areas and acidic conditions may be a requirement in all such cases.

ECOLOGY Larvae probably aphidophagous though details unknown. Adults recorded from May to August.

STATUS Very local over most of Britain with about 35 known post 1960 sites, and locally frequent in some parts of Scotland and northern England.

THREAT Drainage of marshy areas for agricultural improvement or afforestation. River improvement schemes and the loss of marginal vegetation through clearance, excessive trampling or overgrazing. Pollution such as agricultural run-off.

MANAGEMENT Maintain a high stable water level and ensure a full succession or mosaic of vegetation types including pools and ditches.

DISTRIBUTION Records widely dispersed in England, Wales and Scotland as far north as West Ross.

HABITAT Broadleaved woodland and adjacent grassland, often near to rivers, and possibly favouring a lush ground flora and damp, unimproved meadows.

ECOLOGY Larvae probably aphidophagous though details unknown. Adults recorded from April to September and have been observed feeding on buttercups and amongst dense stands of sweet cicely Myrrhis odorata along the River Dee in Scotland.

STATUS An extremely local though widespread species with some eight known post 1960 sites though probably overlooked to some extent due to its small size and rather secretive habits in vegetation.

THREAT Clearance of woodlands and improvement of grassland for agriculture or afforestation. The loss of lush vegetation along wood margins and river banks through overgrazing, river improvement schemes and excessive trampling.

MANAGEMENT Ensure the presence of open and clearings in woods and maintain a lush vegetation in these, along wood edges and river margins.

POCOTA PERSONATA (Harris)
VULNERABLE
SYRPHIDAE

DISTRIBUTION Southern England, extending as far north as Yorkshire and west to Devon, with most records for Windsor Forest, Berkshire and the New Forest.

HABITAT Broadleaved woodland and parkland, almost exclusively in ancient sites with a requirement for old trees with rot-holes.

ECOLOGY Larvae develop in rot holes of old trees at some height above the ground. Beech is especially favoured, though poplar may also be used. Adults are recorded from April to June and may be found hovering around tree trunks or on umbels and hawthorn blossom. Certain trees seem to provide regular sightings at least in Windsor suggesting the breeding sites are rather specialised and few.

STATUS Infrequent except for Windsor and a handful of New Forest sites where it is regularly seen. Additional post 1960 records exist for Colehays Park, Devon (1979); a site in Dorset (1986); Blackheath (1964, 1966) and Malling Down SSSI (1985), Kent and a sighting at Duncombe Park, Yorkshire (1983) It is possible that adults are partly overlooked due to the height of the breeding sites and a largely canopy-dwelling habit. Larvae have been found in profusion in suitable rot holes, but such breeding sites are rarely numerous within an area of woodland and such a specialised choice of site places this species in a particularly vulnerable position as a large number of old trees would be required to provide a continuity of such sites from one year to the next.

THREAT The clearance of ancient broadleaved woodland and parkland, especially for intensive forestry and the removal of large post mature trees with rot holes, within these sites. Shading out of rides and clearings within woodland.

MANAGEMENT Retain all large post mature and diseased trees within a site and ensure a continuity of these in the future. Maintain rides and clearings in an open condition with blossoms for adult feeding.

PSILOTA ANTHRACINA Meigen
VULNERABLE
SYRPHIDAE

DISTRIBUTION A small number of sites in southern England (Dorset, Wiltshire, Hampshire, Surrey, Essex, Berkshire, Warwickshire). The New Forest and Windsor are its stronghold.

HABITAT Broadleaved woodland and parkland, almost exclusively in ancient sites.

ECOLOGY Biology entirely unknown though the distribution suggests a possible link with dead wood. Adults recorded from April to June and characteristically visit the blossoms of hawthorn and sloe. A female was also swept from a lush ditch at Windsor.

STATUS Frequent at Windsor and the New Forest, with known additional post 1960 sites at: Bentley Woods (late 1960's) and possibly Barnridge Copse, Wiltshire; Chobham Common (1979) and Wisley RHS Gardens (1988), Surrey; Dagnam Park (1980's) and Weald Park (1985), Essex; Ryton Wood, Warwickshire (1989). A record from Richmond Park, Surrey is undated. The strongholds both suffer pressures from unsympathetic management, with large areas of the New Forest now being coniferised and continual removal of dead wood and old trees being a major problem at Windsor.

THREAT The clearance of ancient broadleaved woodland mainly for intensive forestry and agriculture and removal of dead wood. Shading out of rides and clearings within woodland.

MANAGEMENT Retain any dead wood and old trees within a site; maintain the presence of open rides and clearings with blossom for adult feeding and ditches or streams with a rich and varied vegetation.

RHINGIA ROSTRATA (Linnaeus)
NOTABLE
SYRPHIDAE

DISTRIBUTION Records widely dispersed in southern England extending as far north as Worcestershire and also in Wales (Carmarthenshire, Pembrokeshire, Cardiganshire, Denbighshire).

HABITAT An association with ancient broadleaved woodlands is apparent (shaded conditions could be required).

ECOLOGY Larval biology unknown and circumstantial evidence suggests it is unlikely to be cow dung like the common R. campestris though some other form of decaying organic matter such as carrion is a possibility. Adults recorded from May to September probably as two broods. They feed on a range of tubular flowers including bluebell, alkanet Pentaglottis sempervirens and ragged robin Lychnis flos-cuculi and seem to prefer red and purple flowers, though they are occasionally reported visiting spring flowering shrubs.

STATUS Infrequent and very erratic, it may suddenly appear in abundance and then will not be seen for many years. About 25 post 1960 sites are known and are scattered widely. It was particularly frequent in Kent in the 1960s with some eight sites but has since declined. A number of the more recent records are from Wales, where it may be under-recorded. Status revised from RDB2 (Shirt 1987).

THREAT Clearance of woodland for agriculture and intensive forestry. Mis-management of heath and woodland rides and clearings, with resultant scrub and bracken invasion.

MANAGEMENT Maintain open rides and clearings in woods, with flowers for adult feeding.

SPHAEROPHORIA LOEWI Zetterstedt
VULNERABLE
SYRPHIDAE

DISTRIBUTION Relatively few records scattered widely in England and Scotland (Dorset, Hampshire, Sussex, Kent, Essex, Lincolnshire, Lancashire, Easterness).

HABITAT Wetlands, especially brackish coastal marshes with stands of Scirpus maritimus or Phragmites, although it is known from an inland site on Phragmites. Abroad it is associated with coastal dune lakes and brackish lagoons.

ECOLOGY Larvae probably aphidophagous. Adults recorded from July to September.

STATUS Infrequent with only four recent records: Pett Levels, Sussex (1987); Fairfield Pit, Lincolnshire (1987); Leighton Moss, Lancashire (1960) and Kinrara, Easterness (1982).

THREAT The drainage of brackish coastal marshes for coastal development, agricultural improvement, etc. Removal of marginal vegetation from water bodies. Pollution such as agricultural run-off.

MANAGEMENT Maintain a high stable water level and a succession or mosaic of vegetation types using rotational pond or ditch management if necessary to ensure a continuous range of marginal conditions.

SPHAEROPHORIA VIRGATA (Goeldlin)
NOTABLE
SYRPHIDAE

DISTRIBUTION The relatively few records are centred on the south of England (Hampshire, Surrey), the Scottish Highlands (Perthshire, Elgin, Easterness, Argyllshire) with additional sites from Northumberland and the Wyre Forest (Shropshire).

HABITAT Heathland in association with woodland, though abroad it is recorded from a wider range of habitats including broadleaved woods and coniferous plantations.

ECOLOGY Larvae probably aphidophagous. Adults recorded in May and June.

STATUS Only described in 1974 and belonging to a genus that is only just becoming fully understood. It appears to be locally frequent in parts of the Scottish Highlands with about a dozen known post 1960 sites. Recent records also exist for sites in Northumberland, the New Forest and the Wyre Forest.

THREAT Clearance of heathland sites and associated woodland for agriculture or intensive forestry. Mis-management such as undergrazing and resultant scrub or bracken invasion, also overgrazing with a loss of ground cover and flowers for adult feeding.

MANAGEMENT Maintain a pattern of traditional heath management to ensure a mosaic of vegetation types including short turf with flowers such as tormentil Potentilla and bedstraws Galium for adult feeding.

SPHEGINA VERECUNDA Collin
NOTABLE
SYRPHIDAE

DISTRIBUTION Records widely dispersed in England, Wales and Scotland.

HABITAT Broadleaved woodland, especially wet shaded areas near streams.

ECOLOGY Biology unknown, though larvae probably living in dead wood. Adults recorded from June to August.

STATUS A widespread but highly localised species with about 20 known post 1960 sites. Possibly under recorded to some extent through the secretive nature of the adults and confusion with other Sphegina.

THREAT The clearance of broadleaved woodland sites especially the damper areas near streams and conversion to agriculture or intensive forestry. Ditching of streams, drainage of moist areas in woods, removal of dead wood.

MANAGEMENT Maintain damp areas of woodland, especially those near to streams, in an undisturbed state with a lush vegetation and retain any dead wood.

TRIGLYPHUS PRIMUS Loew

DISTRIBUTION Records widely scattered over southern England as far north as Yorkshire.

HABITAT A wide range of habitats have been recorded including woodlands ruderal sites and gardens, though no particular preferences are apparent.

ECOLOGY Larvae aphidophagous and have reared from aphids on mugwort Artemisia vulgaris. Adults recorded from April to early October and may be found visiting the flowers of umbels or resting on foliage, though by all accounts this appears to be a fly with a particularly secretive nature.

STATUS Very local, occasionally abundant at a site and possibly overlooked to some extent through the small size and secretive habits. About 30 known post 1960 sites.

THREAT Clearance of woodland and drainage of marshy areas for agriculture, intensive forestry and urban development.

MANAGEMENT Attempt to maintain a mosaic of vegetation types including open rides and clearings in woods, copses in more open areas, and encourage a rich vegetation at such interfaces. Retain any marshy areas.

VOLUCELLA INANIS (Linnaeus)

DISTRIBUTION Southern England from Kent to Cornwall and north to Oxfordshire. Records most frequent in south east England, in particular Kent, Sussex, Surrey, Middlesex and Essex.

HABITAT Preferences unclear, though records include scrub, heaths, chalk grassland and ruderal sites well into urban areas including London, where it can be particularly numerous.

ECOLOGY The larvae develop as commensals in nests of wasps including Vespula germanica, V. vulgaris and Vespa crabro. The larvae probably feed on organic debris accumulating in the nest cavity below the nest itself. Adults recorded from July to September and visit a range of flowers especially favouring thistles Carduus and Cirsium.

STATUS Regular and locally frequent in the Greater London area, less so elsewhere in the south east. About 30 known post 1960 sites.

THREAT This species does not seem to be unduly threatened by man's activities and actually seems to thrive in suburbs perhaps due to enhanced populations of certain wasps. The restricted range seems to be purely a response to climatic factors.

MANAGEMENT Maintain a range of conditions at sites including open rides and clearings within woodland, some limited scrub or bushes on grassland and heathland, but prevent excessive scrub invasion through rotational cutting or grazing where necessary.

VOLUCELLA INFLATA (Fabricius)

DISTRIBUTION Scattered localities in southern England as far north as Derbyshire, Cheshire and also into Wales.

HABITAT Old broadleaved woodland with a probable requirement for old and diseased trees with sap runs, especially those attacked by the goat moth Cossus cossus.

ECOLOGY The exact life history is unknown, though one recent observation suggests that it is possible that the larvae can feed on debris within the tunnels produced by caterpillars of the goat moth. However, it is probable that the larvae also exploit other situations because this species has been recorded from sites where goat moth is absent and it may prove to be more associated with sap runs. An association with wasps nests like its relatives does not seem likely and its distribution does not completely match that of the hornet Vespa crabro which would be its most likely host. Adults recorded from May to July, often visiting blossoms and flowers such as umbels.

STATUS An extremely local species but not infrequent in some areas, especially in Hampshire, Sussex and the south west where it is locally common. About 65 known post 1960 sites.

THREAT The clearance of old broadleaved woodlands for agriculture and intensive forestry and removal of old diseased trees, especially those with sap runs and infested with the goat moth. The shading out of rides and clearings within woodland.

MANAGEMENT Retain all old and diseased trees and ensure a continuity of these in the future. Maintain the presence of open rides, clearings and wood edges rich in flowers for adult feeding.

VOLUCELLA ZONARIA (Poda)

DISTRIBUTION Essentially south-eastern though records extending as far west as Devon. It is particularly frequent in the London suburbs, even penetrating into the city centre itself on occasions.

HABITAT Preferences unclear though records include scrub, heath, woodland and ruderal sites well into towns and cities, in fact this species seems particularly numerous in urban areas.

ECOLOGY The larvae develop as commensals in nests of wasps including Vespula germanica and V. vulgaris. The larvae probably feed on organic debris accumulating in the nest cavity below the nest itself and are increasingly being reported from within houses where they are presumably derived from wasp nests in roofs or beneath floor boards. The striking adults which resemble worker hornets Vespa crabro are recorded from June to October and feed on a wide range of flowers including thistles Cirsium and Carduus, brambles and in gardens, privet and Buddleia. The adults are somewhat migratory.

STATUS Increasing dramatically since its first record in 1901. However its numbers fluctuate markedly from one year to the next. It is possible that it only becomes resident in England in years following substantial continental influxes and that cold, wet summers reduce its resident population severely. Recent work in the Netherlands has suggested that it is the females that are migratory and in some years large numbers of them accumulate in coastal areas. In Britain we also experience years dominated by females and these probably represent mass immigrations. Subsequent years tend to have equal numbers of males and females, probably representing resident populations. In good years it is a reasonably common insect in the south east.

THREAT This species does not seem to be unduly threatened by man's activities and actually seems to thrive in suburbs, perhaps due to enhanced populations of certain wasps. The restricted range seems to be purely a response to climatic factors.

MANAGEMENT Maintain a range of conditions at sites including open rides and clearings within woodland, some limited scrub or bushes on grassland and heathland, but prevent excessive scrub invasion through rotational cutting or grazing where necessary.

XANTHANDRUS COMTUS (Harris)

DISTRIBUTION Predominantly a species of southern England though with records extending to North Wales and the Scottish Highlands (Elgin, Banffshire).

HABITAT Exact requirement unclear, records include woodland rides and edges and scrubland.

ECOLOGY On the continent the larvae have been found feeding on a range of micro moth caterpillars including semi-gregarious torticoid and yponomeutid moths on both shrubs and herbs; at Shoreham, Kent recently, a larva was found on a hogweed leaf. Adults recorded from May to October.

STATUS An uncommon and somewhat elusive species, though not perhaps as rare as previously thought. Though always regarded as scarce, there was a marked sparsity of records in the 1950's-1970's, but it seems to have become more frequent, with a total of almost 30 known post 1960 sites, including some on the fringes of London. Many records are autumnal, a time when recording is reduced, so it may be overlooked to some extent. Status revised from RDB2 (Shirt 1987).

THREAT Clearance of wood and scrub areas for agriculture or intensive forestry. The shading out of rides and clearings within woodland.

MANAGEMENT Maintain open rides and clearings, and copses on more open areas, ensuring the presence of a variety of vegetation types including shrubs.

XYLOTA ABIENS Meigen

DISTRIBUTION Widely recorded in southern England with records as far north as Norfolk, Cheshire and possibly Durham (needs confirmation).

HABITAT Broadleaved woodland, especially close to streams and sometimes in carr and fens where there has been a continuity of the breeding resource. There is a requirement for old diseased trees and dead wood.

ECOLOGY Larvae have been reared from the rotten cavity at the base of an oak trunk and it is possible that other trees may be used such as alder. Adults recorded from May to September and may be found on sunlit foliage and tree trunks.

STATUS Very local, though widely distributed in the south, and not quite as rare as formerly believed, with about 50 known post 1960 sites. Quite frequent at some ancient woodland sites (Windsor, New Forest) and fens such as Chippenham.

THREAT The clearance of old woodland for agriculture and intensive forestry and removal of dead wood and old or diseased trees.

MANAGEMENT Retain any old or diseased trees and dead wood within a site ensuring a continuity of these resources in the future. Maintain open rides and clearings.

XYLOTA COERULEIVENTRIS Zetterstedt

DISTRIBUTION A northern and western species with records scattered widely in Scotland, northern England as far south as the West Midlands, much of Wales and isolated records in south west England (Devon, Somerset and Dorset).

HABITAT Coniferous woodland, including both ancient Caledonian pine forest in Scotland and modern plantations elsewhere, with a requirement for dead wood and old or diseased trees.

ECOLOGY Larvae develop in dead wood, probably only of conifers, and the choice of sites suggests that it can exploit dead wood situations such as log piles or windblown trees. Adults, recorded from June to August and may be found on sunlit foliage and are known to visit the flowers of buttercups, globeflower, bramble and various umbellifers.

STATUS Possibly declining in Scotland where it seems to have been particularly widespread and common at the turn of the century yet with few recent records. However its range in the south appears to be expanding rapidly probably through modern forestry practices and it is now not infrequent in many parts of Wales. About 35 known post 1960 sites, mostly representing plantations away from native pine woods.

THREAT The apparent ability to utilize areas of modern forestry means that its future is probably assured.

MANAGEMENT Maintain good levels of dead wood at sites (logs, stumps and branches); also open rides and clearings with flowers for adult feeding.

XYLOTA FLORUM (Fabricius)

DISTRIBUTION An essentially southern species with records extending as far north as Durham and to Caernarvonshire in Wales.

HABITAT Old broadleaved woodland especially by water or in damp valleys. Dead wood or old and diseased trees are a requirement.

ECOLOGY Larvae develop in dead wood, possibly of ash, beech or oak. Adults recorded from June to August and may be found on sunlit foliage or trunks, including logs resting in water or on marsh, possibly giving a clue as to the breeding site.

STATUS Regular but very local in old woodlands in the south, especially the New Forest, and also well established at some sites as far north as Yorkshire. About 50 known post 1960 sites.

THREAT The clearance of old woodland for intensive forestry and agriculture and removal of the dead wood within.

MANAGEMENT Retain any dead wood and post mature or diseased trees ensuring a continuity of these in the future. Maintain open rides and clearings.

XYLOTA TARDA Meigen

DISTRIBUTION A disjunct distribution with most records for southern England up to the Midlands and also in the Scottish Highlands from Perthshire to Sutherland.

HABITAT Broadleaved woodland usually at the edges of wet woods or near streams, and also adjacent to heathlands and it is recorded regularly in both lowland and upland sites. The presence of dead wood such as stumps or logs or old and diseased trees is a requirement.

ECOLOGY Larvae developing in dead wood, with the wood of birch and aspen likely to provide the preferred breeding sites, though other broadleaved trees are probably also utilised. Adults recorded from June to August and have been observed feeding on umbels.

STATUS A very local but widely distributed species with about 25 known post 1960 sites. It used to be locally frequent along Speyside, but recent records are relatively few. It may be under recorded to some extent through a close resemblance to small individuals of the common X. segnis.

THREAT The clearance of old woodland sites or the removal of old trees in heathy areas for agriculture or afforestation, and the removal of the old or diseased trees and dead wood.

MANAGEMENT Retain all old or diseased trees and any dead wood in a site and ensure a continuity of these in the future. Maintain the presence of open open rides and clearings with flowers for adult feeding.

XYLOTA XANTHOCNEMA Collin

DISTRIBUTION Widely recorded in the south, extending as far north as Shropshire and Leicestershire.

HABITAT Broadleaved woodland with a requirement for old or diseased trees and possibly dead wood.

ECOLOGY Larvae have been reared from the exudate and rot-holes of yews, though a recent observation from Windsor Forest, Berkshire refers to several males around water filled holes between visible roots of an old beech. They would hover about a foot above the holes, or guard the entrance, frequently going down to walk around the waters edge (D. Moore, pers comm). Such situations in broadleaved trees may prove to be a more typical breeding location than yew rot holes, as it is frequently taken at sites where yews are absent. Adults recorded from June to August and are most easily observed running about sunlit foliage.

STATUS Extremely local though not as rare as formerly believed, with in excess of 35 post 1960 sites. The resemblance to the commoner X. sylvarum may have led to under recording in the past, and recent records are thus comparatively frequent.

THREAT The clearance of woodlands for agriculture or intensive forestry and the removal of old trees and dead wood.

MANAGEMENT Retain any old trees with rot holes, water filled trunks or roots. Maintain the presence of open rides and clearings.

ATYLOTUS FULVUS (Meigen)
NOTABLE
TABANIDAE

DISTRIBUTION Recorded widely in southern England as far north as Norfolk, Wales and a few old records are present from Scotland (Perthshire, Argyllshire). It is comparatively frequent in New Forest, south-west England and south Wales.

HABITAT Wet acid heaths and bogs, and nearby woodland, especially in areas with some open water.

ECOLOGY Larvae are predatory upon other invertebrates in damp bog soil. Adults recorded from June to August and females suck the blood of horses, cattle and man.

STATUS Locally common and regularly recorded in the New Forest, more infrequent elsewhere with a distinct western bias, probably reflecting a requirement for damper areas with a higher frequency of bogs. About 20 known post 1960 sites, at least half in the New Forest.

THREAT The drainage of bogs for agricultural improvement or intensive forestry.

MANAGEMENT Maintain a high stable water level in bogs, encouraging a mosaic of vegetation types including some open water if possible. Maintain some animal grazing in the vicinity of potential breeding sites (this is usually already present).

ATYLOTUS LATISTRIATUS (Brauer)
RARE
TABANIDAE

DISTRIBUTION Sparsely recorded from coastal areas of southern England (Dorset, Hampshire, Kent, Essex, Suffolk, Norfolk) with records predominating in East Anglia and the Poole Harbour, Solent area.

HABITAT Saltmarsh and some shores with spits or bars of sand forming sheltered lagoons.

ECOLOGY Recently reared from a larva obtained in a core sample from Limonium saltmarsh in Essex (D. Gibbs - pers. comm.). In Brittany, France the larvae have also been obtained from sand and seaweed at the drift line of shores. Larvae are probably predatory on other invertebrates. Adults recorded from May to August. Females have been observed sucking the blood of sheep and attacking humans, and both sexes feed on the flowers of sea lavender.

STATUS A very restricted species with about 15 known post 1960 sites within Hampshire, Kent, Essex and Norfolk. Many of its old haunts are now either destroyed or unsuitable and its Essex populations are under particular threat from rising sea levels.

THREAT The loss of saltmarsh and sandy shores through coastal developments (such as sea walls, harbours etc), recreational pressures and pollution. Agricultural reclamation of areas adjacent to saltmarsh.

MANAGEMENT Maintain a full transition of vegetation types in saltmarshes and on shores, allowing natural tidal patterns and an undisturbed drift line.

ATYLOTUS PLEBEIUS (Fallen)
ENDANGERED
TABANIDAE

DISTRIBUTION Records confined to the Cheshire Plain and nearby areas, with Cheshire records for Abbots Moss and possibly other sites in Delamere Forest (last known record 1943) and Wybunbury Moss (1956); also 2 nearby Flintshire sites: Whixall Moss (1955) and Bettisfield (1955).

HABITAT Probably boggy wetlands. At Abbots Moss, Whixall Moss and possibly some of the other sites it was recorded from the distinctive kettle hole terrain characteristic of wetlands in the area.

ECOLOGY Larvae apparently occur in marshy areas near peat bogs and are probably predatory on other invertebrates. Adults recorded in June and July; females have yet to be recorded biting, though are likely to require mammalian blood. They do not appear to show interest in humans.

STATUS Last recorded with certainty in 1956, possibly now extinct through habitat destruction. Little bog habitat remains in the Cheshire Plain today.

THREAT Destruction of bogs on the Cheshire Plain and nearby areas, through drainage for agriculture, intensive forestry and recreational pressure.

MANAGEMENT Maintain a full range of conditions at sites, ensuring a high, stable water level in bogs and a natural transition of surrounding vegetation. Prevent scrub invasion.

94

ATYLOTUS RUSTICUS (Linnaeus)
ENDANGERED
TABANIDAE

DISTRIBUTION The few records are mainly concentrated into two separate areas, the Lewes/Pevensey levels area of East Sussex and the Huntingdonshire/Cambridgeshire area of the East Midlands where it is probably now extinct. An isolated record is also present for Bradwell, Essex in 1986.

HABITAT Recent records suggest a preference for grazing levels with ditches, and old fenland areas in Cambridgeshire may have provided similar conditions.

ECOLOGY Larvae probably inhabit pools or damp mud in fens and grazing levels. Adults recorded from June to September and females are recorded as sucking the blood of a range of grazing animals and of man.

STATUS The Cambridgeshire records appear to be old and though this species was claimed to be numerous in Cambridgeshire in 1938, it appears to be extinct in the East Midlands, probably as the result of agricultural changes. Recent records include the Essex site, a site near Lewes in the early 1960s and the Pevensey Levels in 1981.

THREAT Agricultural improvement of coastal grazing levels in East Sussex and fenland areas in the East Midlands; coastal development of the Sussex coast; pollution such as agricultural run-off.

MANAGEMENT Maintain a high stable water level in marshes and employ rotational pond or ditch management on coastal levels if necessary. Maintain any transition of salinity across the marsh (though this species is probably not associated with strongly brackish conditions) and retain any animal grazing in the vicinity of potential breeding sites.

CHRYSOPS SEPULCRALIS (Fabricius)
ENDANGERED
TABANIDAE

DISTRIBUTION Numerous old records exist from the Dorset heaths, but otherwise only single records from the New Forest and the Galloway area of SW Scotland. Purported records from other parts of Britain probably refer to dark forms of the commoner C. caecutiens.

HABITAT Usually near ponds and boggy areas on heaths. The Scottish site is probably acid mire.

ECOLOGY Larvae probably developing in the wet peat of bogs. Adults recorded from May to September and females are known to suck the blood of man.

STATUS Very few modern records exist, though this species was occasionally quite numerous at several Dorset sites earlier this century with the last Dorset record for Stoborough Heath in 1953. Single specimens were found at Holmhill in the New Forest on 11 July 1983, and a site in SW Scotland (post 1970, collected by A.E. Stubbs) and these appear to be the only post 1960 records. Its present status therefore appears to be rather precarious. Status revised from RDB2 (Shirt 1987).

THREAT Loss of bogs and mires through drainage and afforestation; also in Dorset, ball clay extraction, oil-related developments and building developments.

MANAGEMENT Maintain damp areas and pools for larval development. Retain animal grazing in the vicinity of potential breeding sites.

HAEMATOPOTA BIGOTI Gobert
RARE
TABANIDAE

DISTRIBUTION Coastal, with a southern bias (Somerset, Dorset, Hampshire, Kent, Essex, Suffolk, Norfolk, Lincolnshire, Yorkshire) with isolated records from Lancashire (Ribble Estuary, 1952) and Dumfriesshire (Caerlaverock 1979).

HABITAT Saltmarshes, though adults occasionally occur a short distance inland.

ECOLOGY Larvae probably predators of other invertebrates in damp saline soil. Adults recorded from June to August.

STATUS Infrequent though occasionally locally common. Post 1960 records include the Poole Harbour area of Dorset; Middle Hope, Somerset (1983) Colne Estuary NNR, Essex (1987) and the above Scottish site.

THREAT Loss of salt marshes through coastal developments (sea walls, harbours etc), recreational pressures and pollution.

MANAGEMENT Maintain a full transition of vegetation types in saltmarshes, allowing unimpeded tidal patterns.

HAEMATOPOTA GRANDIS Meigen
RARE
TABANIDAE

DISTRIBUTION Coastal with a southern bias (Cardiganshire, Glamorganshire, Cornwall, Hampshire, Sussex, Kent, Essex, Suffolk). Some records are a short distance inland.

HABITAT Coastal marshes and sometimes a short distance inland along tidal rivers.

ECOLOGY Larvae probably predators of other invertebrates in damp soil. Adults recorded from July to September.

STATUS A poorly known coastal species. Post 1960 records include Sudbourne (1985) and Walberswick NNR (1986), Suffolk; Ryers Down, Glamorganshire (1963); Hackets Marsh, Hampshire (1987) and possibly some sites on the south coast of Wales. It seems to have declined considerably in some areas such as the Essex coast where it used to be locally frequent.

THREAT Drainage of coastal levels and riverside meadows for agriculture, coastal developments etc. Pollution such as agricultural run-off.

MANAGEMENT Maintain a high stable water level at sites and employ rotational ditch or pond management if necessary to provide a constant supply of potential breeding sites. Maintain the presence and salinity levels of any brackish pools or ditches on the seaward size of coastal marsh, which may possibly support the larvae, and maintain any transition of salinity across the marsh.

HYBOMITRA CIUREAI (Seguy)
RARE
TABANIDAE

DISTRIBUTION Only six known localities as follows: Dagnam Park (1980's), Fingringhoe Marsh (1983) and Brentwood (1846), all in Essex; Orlestone Forest (1980) in Kent; Walberswick NNR (1977, 1986) in Suffolk and Offham, Sussex (1986).

HABITAT Probably brackish coastal marshes or grazing levels in Britain, though a wider range of habitats are used abroad.

ECOLOGY Larvae possibly develop in damp soil and the marginal zones of ponds and ditches. Eggs are laid on vegetation at such sites. Adults recorded in July and August, and abroad females are known to suck the blood of a range of grazing animals and man.

STATUS Six of the seven records are recent, despite reasonably intense levels of recording along the Essex coast in the past. Whilst this may suggest increasing status, the species is not easy to identify, and there is no doubt that considerable suitable habitat has been destroyed. Most of its modern sites experience some degree of threat.

THREAT Drainage of coastal levels and marshes on the Essex/Suffolk coast for agricultural reclamation, coastal developments etc.; pollution such as agricultural run-off.

MANAGEMENT Maintain a high, stable water level and employ rotational ditch management on coastal levels if necessary, to ensure a constant supply of potential breeding sites. Maintain the presence and salinity levels of any brackish pools or ditches on the seaward side of the marsh, which may possibly support the larvae, and maintain any transition of salinity across the marsh. Retain animal grazing in the vicinity of potential breeding sites.

HYBOMITRA EXPOLLICATA (Pandelle)
VULNERABLE
TABANIDAE

DISTRIBUTION Seven known sites on southern coasts: Studland, Dorset (1909); Thorney Island, Sussex (post 1960) and five sites in Essex: Hadleigh (1969), Langenhoe Marsh (1983), Tollesbury Wick Marshes (1983), Copthall Saltings (1988) and Old Hall Marshes (1983).

HABITAT Brackish coastal levels with ditches; possibly saltmarsh at Studland and some Essex sites.

ECOLOGY Larvae probably developing in damp soil and the marginal zones of saline ponds and ditches. Adults recorded in July and August and abroad females are known to suck the blood of a range of grazing animals and man.

STATUS Most of the records are recent and there is no doubt that this species is very local within high grade sites. Its Essex populations are under particular threat from rising sea levels. Status revised from RDB1 (Shirt 1987).

THREAT Drainage of coastal levels for agricultural reclamation, coastal developments such as sea walls and flood barriers and pollution such as agricultural run-off.

MANAGEMENT Maintain a high, stable water level and employ rotational ditch management on coastal levels if necessary, to ensure a continuous supply of potential breeding sites. Maintain the presence and salinity levels of any brackish pools or ditches on the seaward side of the marsh, which may possibly support the larvae, and maintain any transition of salinity across the marsh. Retain animal grazing in the vicinity of potential breeding sites.

MANAGEMENT Maintain pools and damp areas and retain any dead wood and old or diseased trees, any of which may provide breeding sites. Retain animal grazing in the vicinity of potential breeding sites.

HYBOMITRA MUEHLFELDI (Brauer)

RARE
TABANIDAE

DISTRIBUTION Records are few and highly scattered. It has had a long history at Crymlyn Bog, Glamorganshire (up to 1975), and was found to be widespread and frequent throughout the Norfolk Broads during 1988. Additional records include Foulden Common (1985) and East Walton Common (1989), Norfolk; Leech Pool, Herefordshire (1867), Lochinver, Sutherland (1911); Worcestershire (1867); Ffrwd Mire (1986) and Pembrey Forest (1986), Carmarthenshire.

HABITAT Rather unclear as it occurs at both fen and bog sites in Britain. This suggests a need for a subtle type of transition, such as poor fen.

ECOLOGY Larvae are probably predators of other invertebrates in wet mud or at the edges of pools. Adults recorded from June to August and females suck the blood of a range of grazing animals and man.

STATUS A species which has declined considerably with only six known post 1960 sites. Its stronghold is now clearly in the Norfolk Broads and on the south coast of Wales. Not listed in Shirt (1987).

THREAT Habitat loss to coastal development, agriculture, intensive forestry and the effects of recreational pressure at coastal sites; pollution such as agricultural run-off or industrial effluent and resultant eutrophication of sites.

MANAGEMENT Maintain a high, stable water level, ensuring the presence of some pools and ditches using rotational management if necessary. Prevent scrub invasion.

HYBOMITRA LURIDA (Fallen)

RARE
TABANIDAE

DISTRIBUTION Mostly recorded from the Scottish Highlands (Elgin, Easterness, East Ross, Isle of Bute) with a few records from the Whixall Moss area of Shropshire (1934 and 1936) and a very recent record for Brown Moss, Cheshire (1987/8), though it may have been taken in this county as early as 1956 by H.L. Burrows (NCC Files).

HABITAT Probably boggy areas, including those besides streams, lochs and in boggy glades of forests.

ECOLOGY Larvae probably predators of other small invertebrates in damp soil or pools in bogs. Adults present from May to July and females suck the blood of a range of grazing animals and man.

STATUS A local species in Scotland with about a dozen known post 1960 sites, with the Spey Valley representing its apparent stronghold. Its status in England is uncertain and habitat destruction is likely to have had a major impact on its West Midland populations. Not listed in Shirt (1987).

THREAT Loss of boggy areas through drainage for intensive forestry, pastureland and peat cutting in some areas.

MANAGEMENT Maintain a high, stable water level in boggy areas, retaining any pools and ditches. Retain animal grazing in the vicinity of potential breeding sites.

HYBOMITRA MICANS (Meigen)

VULNERABLE
TABANIDAE

DISTRIBUTION Old records widely dispersed in England and Wales with a few records for Scotland.

HABITAT Heathy woodland glades and boggy areas in woods.

ECOLOGY The breeding site is unknown and could be either damp soil or the edges of pools or conceivably beneath the bark of rotten stumps and other such damp situations. Adults recorded in June and July. Females suck the blood of a range of grazing animals and man, and both sexes are known to visit umbels, feed on honeydew (from aphids) on foliage and to drink at streamsides and damp soil.

STATUS Whilst apparently locally common in the past at some sites in East Dorset, Berkshire and Oxfordshire, recent information is very sparse with post 1960 records confined to Hafren Forest (1971-1979) and Coed Sarnau Forest (1975), Radnorshire and Windsor Great Park, Berkshire (1984). It may prove to be under recorded in some parts of Wales, though it is clear that the species has undergone a substantial decline. Not listed in Shirt (1987).

THREAT The destruction of heathy and boggy woodland areas for agriculture or intensive forestry.

TABANUS BOVINUS Linnaeus   **INSUFFICIENTLY KNOWN**
TABANIDAE

DISTRIBUTION The only acceptable record is a male from Lyndhurst in the New Forest taken at the turn of the century. Much purported female material exists and a thorough review of such specimens is required once reliable characters have been defined.

HABITAT Wetlands, often within a wooded setting.

ECOLOGY Larvae predatory upon other invertebrates, presumably in wet soils or bogs. Adults liable to be present between June and August, and females suck the blood of a range of grazing animals.

STATUS Much confusion surrounds this species. Only one genuine record is present and it is claimed the females cannot be reliably separated from the commoner T. sudeticus. In the past small rufous females of T. sudeticus have automatically been assigned to T. bovinus, but these should now be dismissed. Not listed in Shirt (1987).

THREAT Loss of wetlands where the larvae develop through drainage. Clearance of broadleaved woodland for conifer plantations.

MANAGEMENT Retain any marshy areas around ponds and any animal grazing in the vicinity of potential breeding sites.

TABANUS CORDIGER Meigen   **NOTABLE**
TABANIDAE

DISTRIBUTION A disjunct distribution is shown with scattered localities in southern England from Surrey to Devon, but especially Hampshire, several localities in Wales and then in the Scottish Highlands, mainly from the Spey Valley but extending to Sutherland, Perthshire, Fifeshire. Single records are also present from Cumberland and Durham.

HABITAT Typically recorded in old broadleaved woodland and forest in the south, possibly inhabiting areas of both broadleaved and Caledonian pine woodland in Scotland. There is probably a requirement for gravelly streams in these old woodland areas for breeding.

ECOLOGY In Britain this species has been reared on at least two occasions from the gravel of streams in or near to woods. One record refers to a typical moorland stream at forest edge, whilst the other refers to a chalk rubble stream near to a spring head. In France the larva was found in a soft but not rotten stump of a recently felled poplar, but this report may be the result of a misidentification. Adults recorded in June and July and females suck the blood of a range of grazing animals and man.

STATUS Locally frequent and widespread in the New Forest with numerous recent records, though the only other English post 1960 localities known are Bramshill Plantation and Ashford Hangers in Wealden Hampshire. A few post 1960 sites occur in Wales (within Carmarthenshire, Cardiganshire, Radnorshire and Denbighshire) and it may prove to be under recorded here. It used to be widespread though rather scarce in Scotland, though no post 1960 records are known.

THREAT The clearance of old woodland and forest areas, especially in the New Forest, the Welsh Valleys and the Scottish Highlands for intensive forestry or agriculture. Pollution of formerly clean streams and disturbance to any shingle banks through ditching, gravel extraction etc.

MANAGEMENT Retain any undisturbed gravelly streams, and especially any shingle banks. Retain animal grazing in the vicinity of potential breeding sites.

TABANUS GLAUCOPIS Meigen   **RARE**
TABANIDAE

DISTRIBUTION A characteristic species of Chalk downs in southern England. Records extend from Kent to Herefordshire and north to Oxfordshire.

HABITAT Chalk grassland, occasionally off the Chalk as around Oxford and Herefordshire. Goffe (1931) noted the species at an altitude of 60-90 metres, rather than lower ground, but it is unclear if this is related to available habitat types or to micro-climate.

ECOLOGY A female has been observed ovipositing onto leaves of Plantago lanceolata in a dry hay field. The larvae probably develop as predators of other invertebrates in damp soil and beneath logs or stones on chalk grassland. Adults recorded from July to September and females are known to suck the blood of a range of grazing animals and man.

STATUS A very local southern species with only a handful of known post 1960 localities (within Hampshire, Oxfordshire and Buckinghamshire). Not listed in Shirt (1987).

THREAT Habitat loss to agriculture and intensive forestry. Changes in the grazing management of chalk grassland, either overgrazing, or the cessation of grazing with subsequent invasion by scrub and coarse vegetation.

MANAGEMENT Maintain a mosaic of vegetation types using rotational grazing policies and maintain any logs, stones, boulders, etc. as potential breeding sites.

TABANUS MIKI Brauer

DISTRIBUTION The only acceptable records are from various sites within the New Forest, though questionable records are present for East Dorset (Oakes Wood, pre 1931), Wiltshire (Langley Wood, 1987), Warwickshire (Bubbenhall, pre 1931) and several other sites in southern England.

HABITAT Unclear, possibly damp woodland, or wetlands in a wooded setting.

ECOLOGY Life history unknown, larval development sites could include marshy areas besides pools or streams, or in damp rotting wood or leaf litter. Adults recorded in July and August and females suck the blood of various grazing animals.

STATUS Only two confirmed post 1960 sites: Matley Bog (1971) and Mark Ash (1988). Not listed in Shirt (1987).

THREAT Drainage of marshy areas and ditching of streams. Clearance of broadleaved woodland in the New Forest especially for intensive forestry. Overgrazing by ponies and recreational pressures in some areas could be detrimental.

MANAGEMENT Retain any marshy areas, pools and streams which may provide breeding sites. Retain animal grazing in the vicinity of potential breeding sites.

ACANTHIOPHILUS HELIANTHI (Rossi)

NOTABLE
TEPHRITIDAE

DISTRIBUTION Scattered localities in southern England (Cornwall, Dorset, Hampshire, Sussex, Surrey, Kent, Berkshire, Buckinghamshire, Norfolk); also Wales (Pembrokeshire).

HABITAT Dry grassland, meadows and occasionally gardens.

ECOLOGY The larvae have been reared from the flowerheads of common knapweed Centaurea nigra in this country though abroad they are known from some 50 species of Cardueae (tribe of the Compositae). Adults recorded from July to September.

STATUS Very local with about 10 post 1960 sites scattered widely over the known range.

THREAT Habitat loss to agriculture, afforestation and urban development. Mis-management of sites, through either overgrazing, or cessation of grazing with subsequent scrub invasion and a loss of the host plant(s).

MANAGEMENT Maintain a rich and varied flora with plenty of composites including knapweed. Use rotational grazing in larger sites to produce a mosaic of different vegetation types. Prevent cutting or mowing of vegetation until knapweed has produced seeds.

ACINIA CORNICULATA (Zetterstedt)

ENDANGERED
TEPHRITIDAE

DISTRIBUTION Scattered localities in southern England (Cambridgeshire, Norfolk, Sussex, Hampshire, Surrey, Herefordshire and Somerset).

HABITAT Meadows, fens and drier grassland.

ECOLOGY The larvae have been reared in Germany from flowerheads of the brown knapweed Centaurea jacea, a rare plant of south-east England which hybridises with the common knapweed C. nigra. It is unknown to which extent, if any, the fly can utilise C. nigra. Adults recorded from July to September.

STATUS Only three known post 1960 sites: Wicken Fen (exact date unknown) and Chippenham Fen NNR (1983, 1986), Cambridgeshire and Foulden Common, Norfolk (1980s). All the sites are protected.

THREAT Habitat loss through drainage and improvement for agriculture and afforestation. Mis-management of sites, through either overgrazing, or the cessation of grazing with subsequent scrub invasion and a loss of the host plant(s).

MANAGEMENT Maintain a rich and varied flora including strong populations of knapweed. Use rotational grazing regimes on larger sites to produce a mosaic of vegetation types. Do not mow or cut vegetation until the knapweed has produced seeds.

CAMPIGLOSSA ARGYROCEPHALA (Loew)

RARE
TEPHRITIDAE

DISTRIBUTION Confined to the Scottish Highlands: Pass of Drumochter, Perthshire (1982); Aviemore (1934), Nethy Bridge (1907), Kinrara (1982, 1984), Boat of Garten (1984), Elgin; Strath Rory, East Ross (1984).

HABITAT Damp heaths and meadows in upland areas.

ECOLOGY The larvae develop in the flower heads of common sneezewort Achillea ptarmica and induce a distinctive rosette-shaped gall. Adults recorded in May and June.

STATUS Very local within its known range with only three post 1960 sites. Searching for galls may be a more efficient way of recording this species. Status revised from RDB2 (Shirt 1987).

THREAT Habitat loss to agriculture and afforestation, including the effects of over grazing and scrub invasion through a cessation of grazing.

MANAGEMENT Maintain strong populations of the host plant and prevent any cutting or mowing until it has produced seeds.

CAMPIGLOSSA GRANDINATA (Rondani)

ENDANGERED
TEPHRITIDAE

DISTRIBUTION Apparently only three old localities in Sussex: Tilgate and Copthorne? (both 1872) and Rye (1949).

HABITAT Unclear. The known host grows in a range of conditions.

ECOLOGY Abroad, the larvae are known to induce stem galls on golden-rod Solidago virgaurea. Adults recorded from March to June.

STATUS Very poorly known with no recent records. Extremely rare if not extinct in Britain and also rare in continental Europe. Status revised from RDB2 (Shirt 1987).

THREAT Unclear, this may simply be a species at the extreme edge of its European range. The foodplant is widespread and under no real threat.

MANAGEMENT Unclear other than maintaining strong populations of the host plant.

DISTRIBUTION The available information suggest a rather disjunct distribution with records for Cornwall, Hampshire, Berkshire, Herefordshire and Gloucestershire in southern England and Dumfriesshire, Elgin, Midlothian and Renfrewshire in Scotland.

HABITAT Probably lush vegetation rich in umbellifers at margins of water or in damp woods.

ECOLOGY The larvae have been reared from Heracleum in Great Britain and are known to mine the leaves of a range of umbelliferous plants on the continent. Adults recorded from June to August.

STATUS Possibly declining with only three known post 1960 sites: Leckford, Hampshire (1974 and 1983); The Flits, Herefordshire (1986) and Aldermaston Old Mill, Berkshire (1974).

THREAT River improvement schemes and ditching of streams. Overgrazing and excessive trampling of water and woodland margins, also scrub invasion.

MANAGEMENT Maintain a lush vegetation rich in umbellifers at water and woodland margins. Prevent cutting of any such vegetation until the late summer or early autumn to allow unimpeded development of the fly.

DISTRIBUTION Records widely dispersed in England as far north as Yorkshire and with an old record from Kinrara, Speyside, Scotland (1936).

HABITAT Preferences unclear, records include marshes and wet areas on commons and dunes.

ECOLOGY The larvae usually develop in the flowerheads of the local tripartite bur-marigold Bidens tripartita. Adults recorded from June to October.

STATUS Widespread but local with nine known post 1960 sites, including a succession of records from Runneymede, Surrey between 1970 and 1983. This is the Paroxyna bidentis of past literature.

THREAT Habitat loss to agriculture, afforestation and coastal development. Canalisation or rivers, ditching of streams and excessive trampling of banks. Loss of the host plant through either overgrazing, or cessation of grazing with subsequent scrub invasion.

MANAGEMENT Maintain healthy levels of the host plant. Bidens species appear to require ground which is flooded in the winter, but not in the summer, so it is essential that water levels are not interfered with.

DISTRIBUTION Confirmed pre 1960 records exist for the Isle of Wight and Surrey and a confirmed post 1960 one for Easton Royal, Wiltshire.

HABITAT Probably chalk grassland and scrub with the great knapweed Centaurea scabiosa.

ECOLOGY Abroad, larvae reared from the flowerheads of C. scabiosa.

STATUS A poorly known species only recently recognised as British and not formally published at the time of writing. It appears to be a rare and vulnerable species of southern chalk grassland and scrub. Not listed in Shirt (1987).

THREAT Habitat loss to intensive agriculture and afforestation. Mis-management of sites, either overgrazing, or the cessation of grazing with subsequent scrub invasion and a loss of the host plant.

MANAGEMENT Maintain a rich and varied flora with good levels of the host plant. Use rotational grazing at larger sites to produce a mosaic of vegetation types. Prevent any mowing or cutting of vegetation until the host plant has produced seeds.

DISTRIBUTION Records restricted to the southernmost counties of England (Cornwall, Devon, Dorset, Hampshire, Surrey and Sussex).

HABITAT Coastal areas are preferred, with records referring to gardens in at least three cases (Mens and the Cut, Bournemouth and Havant). The Kennack Cove specimen was swept along a track bordered by coarse herbaceous vegetation at the lower edge of a wood.

ECOLOGY Life history unknown though a related Russian species develops in the berries of honeysuckle Lonicera and the association with gardens suggests a berry bearing garden shrub may be possible in Britain. Adults recorded from April to October.

STATUS Six known post 1960 sites: Kennack Cove, Cornwall (1983); Havant, Hampshire (1973); Bournemouth, Dorset (1978) Mens and The Cut, Sussex (1977) Guildford (1986) and White Beech (1988),Surrey. Status revised from RDB1 (Shirt 1987).

THREAT Unclear as the foodplant is not known.

MANAGEMENT Uncertain.

================================
EUPHRANTA TOXONEURA (Loew)   NOTABLE
                                                TEPHRITIDAE
================================

DISTRIBUTION Scattered localities in England (Somerset, Hampshire, Berkshire, Buckinghamshire, Suffolk, Cambridgeshire, Worcestershire, Warwickshire, Yorkshire).

HABITAT Preferences unclear, records include commons, woods and carr.

ECOLOGY The larvae live in galls produced by the sawfly Pontania on Salix. Adults present in May and June.

STATUS Highly localised with about nine known post 1960 sites and comparatively frequent in Yorkshire. The specialised life history may have led to this species being under recorded through a foliage inhabiting nature of the adults. This is the Rhacochlaena toxoneura of past literature. Status revised from RDB3 (Shirt, 1987).

THREAT Habitat loss to agriculture or intensive forestry. Drainage of carrland.

MANAGEMENT Maintain populations of sallows at known sites, though prevent their spread into high quality grassland or wetland habitats.

================================
GONIGLOSSUM WIEDEMANNI (Aleigen)   NOTABLE
                                                TEPHRITIDAE
================================

DISTRIBUTION Southern Britain as far north as Coventry.

HABITAT Open scrubby areas and woodland edge.

ECOLOGY The larvae feed within the fruits of Bryonia dioica in Britain. Adults are usually seen on and around Bryonia plants.

STATUS A scarce species which is far less common than its host plant. It is a species that recorders are aware of and look for, and is therefore unlikely to be substantially under-recorded.

THREAT The loss of downland, hedgerows and scrubby grassland localities through changing agricultural practices and development. The maturing of scrubby localities leading to dense secondary woodland and the loss of the host plant, over-enthusiastic scrub control and insensitive ride management.

================================
ICTERICA VESTERMANNI (Meigen)   NOTABLE
                                                TEPHRITIDAE
================================

DISTRIBUTION Records widely dispersed in south-east England from Kent to Hampshire and as far north as Cambridgeshire and Norfolk.

HABITAT Preferences unclear, records include grassland, coastal marshes, fen, woodland and heathland.

ECOLOGY Larvae have been reared from the flowerheads of ragworts Senecio erucifolius and S. jacobaea. Adults recorded from April to September, especially August.

STATUS Very local within its range with about 20 known post 1960 sites.

THREAT Habitat loss to agriculture, afforestation and urban development. The known host plants are under no threat but this species may prove to have low powers of dispersal and require sites with a long continuity of the host plants.

MANAGEMENT Maintain strong populations of ragworts and do not cut or mow vegetation until the seeds are produced. Use rotational grazing policies at large sites and retain open rides and clearings in woods.

================================
MYOPITES EXIMIA Seguy   RARE
                                                TEPHRITIDAE
================================

DISTRIBUTION Scattered records on the coast of southern England (Isle of Wight, Dorset, ?Surrey, Essex and Kent).

HABITAT Saltmarsh and coastal shingle banks.

ECOLOGY The larvae induce galls in the flowerheads of golden samphire Inula crithmoides. Adults recorded from June to September.

STATUS Highly restricted with seven known post 1960 sites: Portland Bill, Dorset (1965); Shalfleet, Isle of Wight (1965); Murston (1982), Grain (1988) and Isle of Sheppey (1982), Kent; Tollesbury (1983) and Mersea (1983), Essex. A Surrey record of M. inulaedyssentericae reared from Inula conyza at Mickleham (1955) may refer to this species. Its modern stronghold seems quite clearly to be in the Thames estuary and this area is presently under a good deal of pressure from the threats below. This is the Myopites frauenfeldi of past literature.

THREAT Habitat loss to coastal developments such as harbours, sea walls and flood barriers, also agricultural reclamation. The Essex saltmarshes are under particular threat from rising sea levels.

MANAGEMENT Maintain a full transition of vegetation types on saltmarsh with an emphasis on retaining any stands of the host plant. Ensure unimpeded tidal patterns at sites.

MYOPITES INULAEDYSSENTERICAE Blot

RARE
TEPHRITIDAE

DISTRIBUTION Southern England (Dorset, Isle of Wight, Sussex, ?Surrey, Kent).

HABITAT There appears to be a fairly strong association with chalk grassland.

ECOLOGY Larvae have been reared from the flowerheads of common fleabane Pulicaria dysenterica. Adults recorded in July and August.

STATUS Highly localised with post 1960 records from at least four sites in Kent (Whitstable, Murston, Chattenden, Stodmarsh); also Bere Stream and Turners Puddle in Dorset (both 1984) and Uckfield, Sussex (1984, 1985). The Surrey record (Mickleham, 1955 'ex Inula conyza') may prove to be M. eximia. This is the M. blotii of past literature.

THREAT The loss of chalk grassland to agriculture or afforestation and scrub invasion through inappropriate management.

MANAGEMENT Maintain strong populations of the foodplant and prevent any cutting or mowing of sites until the seeds are produced. Use rotational grazing regimes on large sites to produce a mosaic of vegetation types.

ORELLIA FALCATA (Scopoli)

NOTABLE
TEPHRITIDAE

DISTRIBUTION Southern England (Somerset, Wiltshire, Hampshire, Surrey, Kent, Gloucestershire) and an isolated record from Yorkshire.

HABITAT Preferences unclear, records include chalk downland, commons and marshes.

ECOLOGY Larvae develop in the root stock and stem bases of goats-beard Tragopon pratensis. Adults recorded from April to July, generally peaking in late spring.

STATUS Infrequent, post 1960 records include Shoreham (1969) and Woolwich Common (1980), Kent; Leckford (1970) and a site near Oakshott, Hampshire (1979); a site in Wiltshire, and Riddlesdown, Surrey ((1985). Adults are felt to have a short flight period which may partly account for the apparent rarity.

THREAT Habitat loss to agriculture, afforestation and urban development. Mis-management of sites, through either overgrazing or cessation of grazing with subsequent scrub invasion and a loss of the host plant.

MANAGEMENT Maintain strong populations of the host plant. Use rotational grazing on larger sites and prevent scrub invasion.

OXYNA FLAVIPENNIS (Loew)

NOTABLE
TEPHRITIDAE

DISTRIBUTION Confirmed pre 1960 records exist for Cornwall, Suffolk, Surrey and Sussex, post 1960 ones for Cornwall and Norfolk.

HABITAT Unclear, the host plant is common in a wide range of open situations and grasslands. The fly may require the host plant in particularly warm and sheltered situations.

ECOLOGY Larvae induce root galls in yarrow Achillea millefolium.

STATUS A scarce southern species that has been confused with the more frequent O. parietina. Old records should be treated with some caution.

THREAT Uncertain other than habitat loss.

MANAGEMENT Uncertain other than retaining good levels of the host plant in warm and sheltered situations. The host plant favours areas experiencing grazing or cutting.

OXYNA NEBULOSA (Wiedemann)

RARE
TEPHRITIDAE

DISTRIBUTION Scattered localities in southern England (Somerset, Hampshire, Isle of Wight, Sussex, Berkshire, Oxfordshire) and an isolated record for Yorkshire.

HABITAT Grassland and meadows.

ECOLOGY Abroad the larvae are known to induce root galls in the ox-eye daisy Leucanthemum vulgare. Adults recorded in June and July.

STATUS Only two known post 1960 sites: Wychwood Forest NNR, Oxfordshire (1962) and Dinton Pastures Country Park, Berkshire (1983). A decline seems to have occurred. The host plant is not a threatened resource, though the fly may have low powers of dispersal and require old, unimproved sites. This is the O. proboscidea of past literature. Not listed in Shirt (1987).

THREAT Habitat loss to agriculture and afforestation. Mis-management of sites, through either overgrazing, or cessation of grazing with subsequent scrub invasion and loss of the host plant.

MANAGEMENT Maintain strong populations of the host plant. Use rotational grazing or cutting policies on larger sites to produce a mosaic of vegetation types and discourage scrub invasion. Do not mow or cut vegetation until the host plant has set seed (larval development should then be complete).

PAROXYNA PRODUCTA (Loew)

DISTRIBUTION Scattered records in England (Cornwall, Hampshire, ?Surrey, Kent, Suffolk, Norfolk, Yorkshire).

HABITAT Preferences uncertain, records include a wide range of grasslands.

ECOLOGY No British rearing data but elsewhere the larvae develop in the flower heads of a range of dandelion type composites including Sonchus arvensis, Hypochaeris radicata, Taraxacum, Crepis and Leontodon. Adults recorded from June to August.

STATUS Highly localised with about six known post 1960 sites, these being from the Kent coast, several sites in Yorkshire (these need checking) and possibly a site in London. This is the P. tessellata of past literature. Abroad it is a common insect in most areas of the Palaeartic.

THREAT Uncertain as its hosts are numerous. Excessive grazing, scrub invasion and the use of agricultural chemicals would have a serious effect on potential hosts.

MANAGEMENT Maintain a rich and varied flora at sites, using rotational grazing policies or mowing at larger sites and prevent invasion by scrub or coarse vegetation.

PAROXYNA SOLIDAGINIS (White)

DISTRIBUTION Records widely dispersed over England: Lynton, Devon (1941); Firestone Copse, Isle of Wight (1980); Copthorne, Sussex (1946); Haugh Wood, Herefordshire (1906, 1907); Grange-over-Sands, Lancashire (1939, 1945, 1946); Witherslack, Westmorland (1939).

HABITAT Preferences unclear; the host plant is common in a wide range of situations.

ECOLOGY Larvae develop in goldenrod Solidago virgaurea (location in plant unclear). Adults recorded from April to August.

STATUS Only recently described as new to science from British material (White, 1986) and clearly widespread though very local, with only the single post 1960 locality. Surprisingly, no continental specimens can be found in the extensive collections of E.M. Hering in the NHML.

THREATS Unclear.

MANAGEMENT Unclear other than maintaining strong populations of the host plant at known sites.

PAROXYNA ABSINTHII (Fabricius)

DISTRIBUTION Recorded widely in England as far north as Durham and also South Wales (Pembrokeshire). Records from the Outer Hebrides require confirmation.

HABITAT Preferences unclear, records include coastal locations, grassland, marshes and ruderal areas.

ECOLOGY The larvae are known to attack the flowerheads of the sea wormwood Artemisia maritima and mugwort A. vulgaris. Adults recorded from June to September.

STATUS Very local with about 10 known post 1960 sites. The host plants are not a threatened resource though the fly may have low powers of dispersal and require sites where there has been a long continuity of host plants.

THREAT Habitat loss to agriculture, afforestation and coastal development; loss of the host plant through overgrazing or the cessation of grazing and subsequent scrub invasion.

MANAGEMENT Maintain strong populations of the host plant.

PAROXYNA LHOMMEI Hering

DISTRIBUTION Only known from two sites in Kent: Castle Hill (1970s) and Dungeness (1980s).

HABITAT The former site is chalk grassland, the latter is an area of coastal shingle.

ECOLOGY Adults have been seen in numbers on ragworts Senecio, though this is not yet a confirmed host. Adults recorded in May and June.

STATUS A relatively recent addition to the British list which appears to be exceedingly restricted. Both sites are SSSIs but could be affected by the proposed Channel Tunnel project, Castle Hill due to its close proximity to the tunnel entrance and Dungeness through possible gravel extraction. Also very rare abroad with only a few sites in coastal France and Holland.

THREAT Habitat loss to agriculture, coastal development etc. Loss of the host plant through either overgrazing, or cessation of grazing, with subsequent scrub invasion.

MANAGEMENT Maintain a full transition of vegetation types limiting the amount of disturbance and retain strong populations of ragworts.

PLATYPAREA DISCOIDEA (Fabricius)
VULNERABLE
TEPHRITIDAE

DISTRIBUTION Recorded from about 10 sites in Yorkshire and apparently from a site in Dumfriesshire in Scotland.

HABITAT Damp limestone grassland and woodland in hilly areas, including gorges.

ECOLOGY Larvae develop in the stems of the giant bellflower Campanula latifolia. Adults have a short flight period from late May to early June.

STATUS Very restricted with four certain post 1960 sites: Hawks Wood (1977), Wensleydale (1977), Colt Park (1987), Pot Riding Wood (post 1965) and possibly Housedene Wood, all in Yorkshire. This is the Platyparella discoidea of past literature. It is also a very rare species abroad.

THREAT The loss of the host plant and its habitat through afforestation, excessive grazing, or the cessation of grazing with subsequent invasion by scrub and coarse vegetation.

MANAGEMENT Ensure healthy levels of the host plant and avoid excessive grazing, perhaps using rotational policies and prevent scrub invasion.

RHAGOLETIS MEIGENII (Loew)
APPENDIX
TEPHRITIDAE

DISTRIBUTION Only known with certainty from Lyndhurst, Hampshire (June 1897); also as unconfirmed record from Moseley, Worcestershire (August 1908).

HABITAT Preferencers uncetain, the host plant is largely a hedgerow species.

ECOLOGY In Europe it develops in the fruits of barberry Berberis vulgaris. Adults recorded from June to August.

STATUS No recent information. Believed to be extinct. It is a common species in most of Europe. Not listed in shirt (1987).

THREAT The loss of its host plant which has been actively removed in the past due to its harbouring a fungal rust of economic importance.

MANAGEMENT Maintain existing sites for the host plant.

TEPHRITIS PRAECOX (Loew)
ENDANGERED
TEPHRITIDAE

DISTRIBUTION Old records exist for Mudeford, Dorset and Aldeburgh, Suffolk.

HABITAT Preferences unclear.

ECOLOGY In Israel this species has been reared from field marigold Calendula arvensis.

STATUS Both records are old and this species may now be extinct in Britain. The host plant is widespread and an agricultural weed and abroad it is a common insect in most of its range which extends to Afghanistan. This is the Paroxyna praecox of past literature.

THREAT Unclear other than destruction of sites rich in the host plant. Removal of hedgerows and a loss of fallow conditions and 'weedy' field margins through intensive agriculture could be particularly damaging as could agricultural chemicals. This species is stated to require the host plant at abundant levels.

MANAGEMENT Maintain strong populations of the host plant and ensure vegetation is not cut until the host plant has set seed (larval development should then be complete).

TEPHRITIS sp. NEAR SEPERATA Rondani
INSUFFICIENTLY KNOWN
TEPHRITIDAE

DISTRIBUTION Only recorded from Barton Mills, Suffolk (pre 1943).

HABITAT Preferences unclear, the site would have consisted of breck heathland and grassland and the riverside vegetation of the River Lark.

ECOLOGY Larvae phytophagous though precise host(s) unknown.

STATUS A poorly known species originally published as T. seperata (Collin 1943), though White (1986) states a number of differences from T. seperata and its taxonomic status remains uncertain. The site has been highly degraded since the species was recorded and may now be unsuitable. Not listed in Shirt (1987).

THREAT The site is already degraded through a combination of river improvement schemes along the River Lark, afforestation and construction of a major road roundabout in the vicinity.

MANAGEMENT Retain any surviving semi-natural or ruderal vegetation remaining at the site.

TERELLIA VECTENSIS (Collin)   RARE
TEPHRITIDAE

DISTRIBUTION Southern England (Dorset, Hampshire, Isle of Wight) and an unknown location in south Wales. An old specimen labelled 'Rundirch' cannot be assigned to any county.

HABITAT Records include chalk grassland and open heathy woods.

ECOLOGY The larvae develop in the flowerheads of the local saw-wort *Serratula tinctoria*. Adults recorded from April to August.

STATUS Highly restricted with only three known post 1960 sites: Leckford Reserve (1974 to 1983) and Roydon Woods (1984), Hampshire and Hod Hill, Dorset (1967). A series of records is also present for Cranmore, Isle of Wight between 1935 and 1951 and it may still persist there. This is the *Orellis vectensis* of past literature.

THREAT Habitat loss to agriculture and intensive forestry. Mis-management of sites, through either overgrazing or cessation of grazing with subsequent scrub invasion and a loss of the host plant.

MANAGEMENT Maintain strong populations of the host plant. Use rotational grazing or cutting regimes on larger sites and prevent scrub invasion. Do not mow or cut vegetation until the host plant has set seed (larval development should then be complete).

TERELLIA VINTHEMI (Meigen)   RARE
TEPHRITIDAE

DISTRIBUTION Mainly recorded in southern England (Devon, Dorset, Wiltshire, Surrey, Kent, Hertfordshire). However there is a record for Brown Hill Burn, East Ross (1984) though this needs checking.

HABITAT Grassland and ruderal habitats where the host plants are present. Usually, though not exclusively, on calcareous soils.

ECOLOGY The larvae develop in the flowerheads of the thistle *Carduus acanthoides*. Adults recorded from May to July.

STATUS Possibly declining with only three known post 1960 sites: Downe, Kent (1985), Riddlesdown, Surrey (1960s, 1980s) and the unconfirmed Scottish record. It tends to be highly localised within a site. This is the *Orellia winthemi* of past literature. Not noted in shirt (1987).

THREAT Habitat loss to agriculture, afforestation and urban development. Mis-management of sites, through either overgrazing, or the cessation of grazing with subsequent scrub invasion and a loss of the host plant.

MANAGEMENT Maintain strong populations of the host plant, using rotational grazing policies or cutting on larger sites to produce a mosaic of vegetation types but do not cut vegetation until the host plants have set seed (larval development should then be complete).

TRUPANEA AMOENA Frauenfeld   VULNERABLE
TEPHRITIDAE

DISTRIBUTION Only two known localities: Alborough, Suffolk (July 1894) and Dawlish, Devon (June 1958).

HABITAT Probably coastal grassland.

ECOLOGY Abroad this species is stated as attacking the flowerheads of a wide range of composites, of no particular group. Adults recorded in June and July.

STATUS No recent information. Probably on the edge of its European range and thus more sensitive to habitat change or loss. Abroad it is common over most of its range which extends to India and Ethiopia. Not listed in shirt (1987).

THREAT Habitat loss to coastal development, agricultural reclamation and afforestation. Overgrazing, or the cessation of grazing with subsequent scrub invasion and a loss of floristic richness and diversity.

MANAGEMENT Maintain a rich and varied flora using rotational grazing regimes where necessary and preventing scrub invasion.

VIDALIA CORNUTA (Scopoli)   RARE
TEPHRITIDAE

DISTRIBUTION Southern England: Devon (old record, site unknown); Luccombe Chine, Isle of Wight (1980); Leckford, Hampshire (1970); Barton Broad area (1937) and Beeston Common (1975), Norfolk.

HABITAT Marshes, seepages and riverside situations.

ECOLOGY In Britain the larvae mine the leaves of hemp agrimony *Eupatorium* and elsewhere it has been reared from a *Senecio* species. Adults recorded in June and July.

STATUS Highly localised with three known post 1960 sites. Possibly under recorded to some extent. This is the *Trypeta cornuta* of past literature.

THREAT Drainage of wetlands for agriculture. Complete or extensive clearance or modification of marginal vegetation beside water such as though ditching of streams, river improvement schemes and excessive trampling of banks. Scrub invasion and a loss of certain vegetation elements through mis-management of water levels.

MANAGEMENT Maintain a high stable water level in wetlands, and riverbanks in a natural condition with good stands of the host plant.

VIDALIA SPINIFRONS (Schroeder)

DISTRIBUTION Only three known sites: Grange-over-Sands, Lancashire (1944); a site in Kent (recent) and a site in Herefordshire (old).

HABITAT Preferences unclear, the food plants occur in a range of habitats.

ECOLOGY The larvae mine the leaves of goldenrod Solidago virgaurea and a cultivated Aster species. Adults recorded in July.

STATUS A poorly known species, possibly under recorded to some extent. This is the Trypeta spinifrons of past literature.

THREAT Uncertain as its habitat requirements are unclear and its known hosts widespread.

MANAGEMENT Retain strong populations of host plants at known sites.

UROPHORA CUSPIDATA (Meigen)

DISTRIBUTION Purported records widely dispersed in the chalk areas of southern England (Dorset, Hampshire, Kent, Oxfordshire, Bedfordshire, Norfolk, Cambridgeshire) though many of these will require confirmation due to recent taxonomic changes in the genus.

HABITAT Chalk grassland.

ECOLOGY The larvae develop in the flowerheads of great knapweed Centaurea scabiosa. Adults recorded from May to July.

STATUS Very local with some eight post 1960 sites known, though only some localities in Dorset and Cambridgeshire have been confirmed.

THREAT Loss of habitat to intensive agriculture and afforestation. Overgrazing of sites, or cessation of grazing, with subsequent scrub invasion and loss of floristic richness and diversity.

MANAGEMENT Maintain strong populations of the host plant and use rotational grazing policies on larger sites to produce a range of vegetation types and discourage scrub invasion. Do not cut vegetation until the host plant has set seed (larval development should then be complete).

UROPHORA SOLSTITIALIS (Linnaeus)

DISTRIBUTION Confirmed post 1960 records exist for Hampshire, Suffolk and Surrey, pre 1960 ones for Glamorganshire, Somerset and Sussex.

HABITAT Probably calcareous grassland and scrub.

ECOLOGY Larvae form galls in the flowerheads of the thistles Carduus nutans and C. acanthoides.

STATUS A scarce species which has been much confused with the common U. jaceana in the past. Not listed in Shirt (1987).

THREAT Habitat loss to agriculture and afforestation. Mis-management of sites with a loss of the host plants, either through overgrazing, or a cessation of grazing with subsequent scrub invasion.

MANAGEMENT Maintain a rich and varied flora ensuring good levels of the host plants. Use rotational grazing on larger sites to produce a mosaic of different vegetation types. Prevent cutting or mowing until thistles have produced seeds.

UROPHORA SPOLIATA (Haliday)

DISTRIBUTION Southern England: Bray's Cot Pool (1983), Clahar (1981), Goonhilly (1980) and Boscastle (1980s) all in Cornwall; Cranmore (1935, 1951) and Compton Down (1984), Isle of Wight; Leckford Reserve, Hampshire. (1970, 1983).

HABITAT Recorded from coastal grassland and heathland (including tall heath and short heath types on the Lizard, cornwall, and inland on chalk grassland.

ECOLOGY Larvae develop in the seedheads of saw-wort Serratula tinctoria. Adults recorded from June to August.

STATUS Exceedingly rare but with most known records recent. The Lizard area of Cornwall may represent an important stronghold. Not known outside Great Britain.

THREAT Habitat loss to intensive agriculture, afforestation and coastal development. Loss of the host plant through either overgrazing, or cessation of grazing, with subsequent scrub invasion.

MANAGEMENT Maintain strong populations of the host plant and use rotational grazing on larger sites to produce a range of vegetation types and discourage scrub invasion. Do not cut vegetation until the host plant has set seed (larval development should then be complete).

DIALINEURA ANILIS (Linnaeus)   RARE
                                                          THEREVIDAE

DISTRIBUTION Mainly recorded from sand dunes of the Welsh coast (Glamorganshire, Carmarthenshire, Merionethshire, Anglesey) and on the east coast of Scotland (Sutherland and Easter Ross) with additional old sites in Somerset and Lancashire.

HABITAT Sand dunes, in particular areas with open structured vegetation on the mid dunes.

ECOLOGY Life history unknown, though larvae probably developing in sand at the base of vegetation. Adults recorded from May to July and characteristically sit on bare sand.

STATUS Post 1960 records are known for five dune systems in Wales: Merthyr Mawr and Whiteford, Glamorganshire; Pembrey Burrows and Pendine MOD, Carmarthenshire and Aberffraw Dunes, Anglesey. It may also persist at some of its older localities such as Oxwich NNR, Morfa Harlech NNR and Morfa Dyffryn NNR, undetected through low levels of recording. Not listed in Shirt (1987).

THREAT Coastal development and recreational pressure, the latter leading to erosion and 'blow outs'.

MANAGEMENT Maintain a full range of vegetation types and use fences or boardwalks if necessary to allow normal dune fixation.

PSILOCEPHALA MELALEUCA (Loew)   ENDANGERED
                                                          THEREVIDAE

DISTRIBUTION Records restricted to ancient forests in the Windsor Forest/Ascot area of Berkshire. A female was also found inside Royal Holloway College in nearby Egham (1973) probably representing a stray and a possible record exists for Woolwich Park, Kent, based on a larva found in rotting wood in 1980 which died before pupation.

HABITAT Ancient broadleaved woodland, with a requirement for dead stumps.

ECOLOGY The larvae have been recorded most frequently in red rotten oak stumps, also in mould and frass beneath the bark of a dead oak (together with numerous larvae of the chafer Gnorimus variabilis) and from a hollow beech stump. The larvae can be found in very dry wood, though it is not known if this is typical, or whether pupation can occur in these conditions. Larvae are said to be reasonably easy to find at Windsor but difficult to rear. Adults recorded from May to July. They occur near dead stumps and have also been observed at the banks of a stream, where they apparently settled to drink, and visiting sappy wounds of living trees.

STATUS Found on numerous occasions at Windsor since 1930 and up to the present. This site is owned by the Crown Estates and has experienced removal of dead wood and old or diseased trees, and also afforestation of some areas.

THREAT Removal of old stumps and dead trees for fire wood and habitat loss through afforestation.

MANAGEMENT Retain any old stumps and old or diseased trees ensuring continuity of these in the future.

PSILOCEPHALA RUSTICA (Panzer)   RARE
                                                          THEREVIDAE

DISTRIBUTION A rather scattered distribution with records concentrated in West Sussex, and the Welsh borders from Cheshire to Herefordshire. Records are also present from Yorkshire (1962), Derbyshire (1962), Cumberland (1986) and Berkshire (undated).

HABITAT Sand or shingle river banks, usually in the shade of trees such as alders.

ECOLOGY Larvae have been recorded from a shingle river bank. Adults recorded from May to July and are usually to be found sitting on foliage near rivers, or resting on the ground.

STATUS A very local species, even at its strongholds. About 10 post 1960 sites are known and scattered widely over the known range.

THREAT The disturbance of sand and shingle banks through river improvements, gravel extraction, excessive trampling of banks; also pollution such as agricultural run-off.

MANAGEMENT Maintain sand and shingle banks in a natural and undisturbed state with some trees and shrubs for shade.

THEREVA FULVA (Meigen)

RARE
THEREVIDAE

DISTRIBUTION Most records are for North Kent (Darenth, Foots Cray, Dartford, Farningham Road Station) and the south coast of Wales (Glamorganshire, Carmarthenshire) with isolated records in West Sussex, West Kent and possibly Gloucestershire, (old) and Lincolnshire (1896).

HABITAT Coastal dunes in Wales and probably sandy open areas adjacent to the Thames estuary in the case of Kent. It seems to prefer areas of fixed sand, with well established vegetation and small patches of bare sand.

ECOLOGY Life history unknown, though larvae probably developing in sand or soil at the base of vegetation. Adults recorded from June to August.

STATUS Most records are from the early part of this century and it has had a well documented history in North Kent between 1868 and 1939, though it is likely most of the sites involved are now destroyed. Recent records include Pembrey Burrows, Carmarthenshire (1985); Whitford Burrows, Pennard Burrows and Llangenith Burrows, all Glamorganshire (1986) and Sandwich, Kent (1975). Not listed in Shirt (1987).

THREAT Loss of sand dunes and sandy areas through coastal development, agricultural reclamation and intensive forestry; recreational pressure, the latter leading to erosion and 'blow-outs'; scrub invasion on hind dune through lack of grazing.

MANAGEMENT Maintain a full range of vegetation types, using fences and boardwalks if necessary to allow normal dune fixation; prevent scrub invasion upon open fixed dune.

THEREVA HANDLIRSCHI Krober

RARE
THEREVIDAE

DISTRIBUTION The Scottish Highlands, mainly within Elgin (Aviemore, Nethy Bridge, Forres, Logie), also Golspie, Sutherland.

HABITAT Many of the records suggest that it is a river bank species, and a few records are up to about 500m altitude.

ECOLOGY The females have been observed laying eggs in dry soil. Adults recorded from June to early September.

STATUS No known records after 1946. There has been some taxonomic confusion in the past, together with two other Scottish species T. inornata and T. valida.

THREAT Disturbance to river banks through river improvement schemes, excessive trampling, gravel or sand extraction, pollution and the effects of adjacent afforestation.

MANAGEMENT Maintain river banks in a natural state, free from excessive trampling, gravel or sand extraction, pollution and the effects disturbance retaining any banks of sand, shingle or mud.

THEREVA INORNATA Verrall

RARE
THEREVIDAE

DISTRIBUTION Scattered localities in Scotland (Perthshire, Elgin, Easterness, Banffshire, ? Wigtownshire, Argyllshire, Sutherland), and especially along the Spey Valley.

HABITAT Possibly a river bank species, most records applying to upland sites, though the Wigtownshire record (Torrs Warren) is coastal and may require checking.

ECOLOGY Life history unknown, though larvae probably developing in soil at the base of vegetation. Adults recorded from mid June to mid August.

STATUS Recent records rather few and requiring confirmation, though with many records from Speyside sites especially in the first half of this century. This species has been the victim of some taxonomic confusion in the past together with two other Scottish species T. handlirschi and T. valida.

THREAT Disturbance to river banks through river improvement schemes, gravel or sand extraction, adjacent afforestation, excessive trampling and pollution such as agricultural run-off.

MANAGEMENT Maintain river banks in a natural state, free from excessive disturbance and with some trees and shrubs for shade.

THEREVA LUNULATA Zetterstedt

RARE
THEREVIDAE

DISTRIBUTION Most records are for the Central Highlands of Scotland (Perthshire, Elgin, Easterness and especially along the Spey Valley). Additional records exist for Northumberland, Yorkshire, Radnorshire, Carmarthenshire and Herefordshire.

HABITAT Dry, sand or shingle areas beside rivers and streams, especially banks with sandy alluvium deposits and sparse vegetation.

ECOLOGY Life history unknown. The larvae probably develop in sandy soil at the base of vegetation. Adults recorded from late May to late July and characteristically rest on bare sandy areas on river banks.

STATUS Fairly regular in the Central Highlands with about half a dozen post 1960 sites with sporadic records elsewhere: Llanwrda, Carmarthenshire (1989) and East Keswick, Yorkshire (1980) representing the only other known recent records.

THREAT Disturbance of river banks through river improvement schemes, gravel or sand extraction, the effects of adjacent afforestation, excessive trampling and pollution such as agricultural run-off.

MANAGEMENT Maintain river banks in a natural and undisturbed state, especially sand and shingle banks and retain some trees or bushes for shade.

THEREVA PLEBEIA (Linnaeus) NOTABLE
THEREVIDAE

DISTRIBUTION Old records are widely distributed in southern England as far north as Warwickshire, Cambridgeshire and Norfolk (records from further north require confirmation), though a strong south-eastern bias is present with records comparatively numerous for Greater London and surrounding areas.

HABITAT The limited habitat and site information suggests that a range of dry habitats, such as heathland, commons, ruderal and suburban situations can be exploited, though some disturbance may be necessary to produce areas of loose soil and sparse vegetation (general requirements of the genus).

ECOLOGY Larval development seems to occur in dry soil, and it was recently reared from a larva found in an allotment in Epsom, Surrey (J. Owen - unpublished). There is also an old published account of the larvae attacking plants in disturbed soil at Wisley, Surrey (the material has not been checked). Adults apparently recorded from late April to mid August, though mainly late May to July.

STATUS Formerly widespread and relatively frequent, especially in the London area, though it is clear that a decline has taken place during the course of this century. This has only come to light during 1987/8 due to previous taxonomic difficulties with the genus. Despite attempts to check most modern records, only a handful of modern sites have so far been confirmed. The decline closely resembles that undergone by many ground nesting aculeates and suggests that changing land use, and in particular reduced areas of disturbed, open habitat, may be largely responsible.

THREATS The loss of disturbed, open habitats, such as those outlined above, to development, intensive agriculture and commercial forestry. At remaining sites, the reduced levels of disturbance are likely to have widely led to the encroachment of coarse vegetation and scrub, with a loss of bare soil.

MANAGEMENT Maintain some areas of bare or sparsely vegetated sand and soil using mild forms of disturbance as necessary. Prevent the invasion of scrub and coarse vegetation. At some sites, grazing may be important in producing correct situations, especially where limited poaching of the soil is occurring.

THEREVA STRIGATA Fabricius RARE
THEREVIDAE

DISTRIBUTION Only four known records: Niton (1909) and Freshwater (1948) both on the Isle of Wight; Torquay, Devon (1901) and Dover, Kent (1974).

HABITAT The records suggest that hot, south-facing coastal cliffs are its normal habitat.

ECOLOGY Life history unknown. The larvae possibly develop in soil at the base of vegetation on cliffs. Adults recorded from late May to July.

STATUS Four records, only one recent. It has been suggested that it may be an occasional migrant from the continent, though there is no evidence that Therevidae migrate any distance, and it seems more likely that its specialised choice of sites has led to it being somewhat overlooked.

THREAT The destruction of south facing cliffs through coastal developments and cliff stabilisation. Its Kent locality is on the site of the Channel Tunnel works.

MANAGEMENT Oppose the above threats maintaining sites in a natural and undisturbed state.

THEREVA VALIDA Loew RARE
THEREVIDAE

DISTRIBUTION The few mainly old records are largely from the Spey Valley (Aviemore, Nethy Bridge and Grantown) together with a record from Kindrogan (Perthshire) in 1978.

HABITAT River margins, including those with adjacent wooded and grassy habitats.

ECOLOGY Life history unknown. The larvae possibly develop in soil at the base of vegetation. Adults recorded in June and July.

STATUS Only the single recent record and very few old ones. This species has been the victim of some taxonomic confusion in the past together with T. inornata and T. handlirschi.

THREAT The disturbance of river banks through river improvement schemes, gravel or sand extraction, effects of adjacent afforestation, excessive trampling and possibly pollution such as agricultural run-off.

MANAGEMENT Maintain river banks in a natural, undisturbed state, especially areas of sand or shingle, and retain some trees or shrubs for shade.

DISTRIBUTION Dorset, Herefordshire, Cheshire and Lancashire in England and Elgin in Scotland, with records predominating along the River Spey (at Aviemore and Nethy Bridge).

HABITAT Sandy river banks, usually in the shade of trees and with patches of vegetation such as sedges, and it has been taken amongst stands of butterbur Petasites hybridus. The recent Dorset record was from a cliff seepage.

ECOLOGY Life history unknown, larvae possibly developing in wet sand or rotting vegetation beside rivers. Adults recorded from May to August.

STATUS Only four known post 1960 sites: Lyme Regis, Dorset (1988); Monmouth Cap, Herefordshire (1985); Nethy Bridge (1985) and Broomhill (1982) both in Elgin. Status revised from RDB1 (Shirt 1987).

THREAT Excessive disturbance of riverbanks through river improvement schemes such as canalisation, trampling and pollution such as agricultural run-off.

MANAGEMENT Maintain the semi-natural vegetation along banks together with banks of bare sand or gravel and some trees or bushes for shade.

DISTRIBUTION Very local with records widely scattered in England, Wales and Scotland.

HABITAT Usually associated with Phalaris or Phragmites stands beside rivers and streams in sheltered situations.

ECOLOGY Life history unknown. Adults recorded from May to August.

STATUS About 25 known post 1960 sites scattered widely throughout the range.

THREAT The degrading of marginal vegetation along streams and rivers through canalisation and ditching to produce steep sided banks; excessive trampling of banks; pollution such as agricultural run-off and resultant eutrophication.

MANAGEMENT Maintain a rich marginal vegetation alongside rivers and ditches, including stands of Phalaris or Phragmites, and trees for shade and shelter. When ditches require management, undertake this on a small-scale, rotational basis, and retain a shallow marginal profile.

DISTRIBUTION Records scattered widely in England, Wales and Scotland. It is curiously absent from the New Forest (according to NCC data) which would appear to be ideal for this dead wood insect, though it does occur in woods nearby.

HABITAT Old broadleaved woodland and heathland with a possible preference for birch and alder. There is a requirement for dead wood.

ECOLOGY The larvae develop in decaying logs and fallen trunks of a range of trees including birch, alder, oak, beech, poplar and lime. C. atrata apparently favours harder dead wood for larval development than other Ctenophora species. Adults recorded from May to August.

STATUS A rather marked decline seems apparent with about 20 known post 1960 sites. Old records are numerous and it was often recorded as locally abundant at certain sites. Evidence suggests it may be under recorded in Wales. Status revised from RDB2 (Shirt 1987).

THREAT The destruction of old woodland through clearance for agriculture or intensive forestry, and the removal of large dead wood from within such sites.

MANAGEMENT Retain any dead wood in situ, maximising the amount and range of dead wood and ensuring continuity of this resource in the future.

DISTRIBUTION Records widely dispersed in southern England but there are a few isolated ones in Yorkshire and mid Wales.

HABITAT Ancient broadleaved woodland, especially beech, though probably oak in north and west parts of its range. There is a requirement for dead wood and old or diseased trees.

ECOLOGY The larvae develop in dead wood though no British rearing records are available. Old trees and stumps of particularly large girth are probably essential for this species. Adults recorded from April to June and visit blossoms such as hawthorn which may be important to their survival.

STATUS Declining with only about a dozen known post 1960 sites (from a historic total in excess of 25): Wychwood NNR (1983) and Goring Heath (1964 and another year between 1965 and 1972) both in Oxfordshire; Denny Wood (1970), Woodcrates (1986), Eyeworth (1987) and Minstead (1969) in the New Forest; a single site in the East Hampshire Hangers (1988); Savernake Forest, Wiltshire (1964 and 1980); Green Hill, Dorset (1970-79); Windsor Forest, Berkshire (1975, 1982); Rockford, Devon (1988) and Cwm Coel, Radnorshire (1986). Status revised from RDB1 (Shirt 1987).

THREAT The destruction of ancient woodland through clearance for agriculture or intensive forestry and the removal of very old trees and dead wood within such sites.

MANAGEMENT Maximise the amount of dead wood and number of very old trees ensuring continuity of these in the future. Ensure the presence of blossom such as hawthorn and retain open rides and clearings.

DISTRIBUTION A local species with records scattered in England, Wales and Scotland with a strong bias towards the south.

HABITAT Old broadleaved woodland with a requirement for dead wood and old or diseased trees.

ECOLOGY Larvae develop in decaying wood, especially of beech, though other species such as oak and field maple are apparently also used. The larvae seem to use a range of sites including shattered ends of trunks and branches, and beneath bark, from ground level to some height. Adults recorded from April to July.

STATUS A widespread but local species with about 30 known post 1960 sites.

THREAT The destruction of old woodland through clearance for agriculture or afforestation, and the removal of old or diseased trees and dead wood from such sites.

MANAGEMENT Maximise the number of old trees and the amount of dead wood, ensuring continuity of these in the future.

CTENOPHORA NIGRICORNIS Meigen   RARE
TIPULIDAE

DISTRIBUTION Records scattered widely in England, Wales and Scotland.

HABITAT Old broadleaved woodland, parkland and heaths. There is a requirement for dead wood and old or diseased trees.

ECOLOGY The larvae develop in dead wood from a range of trees including oak, birch and ash, though the exact conditions of dead wood required are unclear. Adults recorded from April to July. A female was recently found at a large standing dead hollow oak in a woodland clearing.

STATUS A rather marked decline seems apparent with only 10 known, widely scattered post 1960 sites, and very little recent information from the New Forest where it was formerly quite frequent. It still appears to be relatively frequent in broadleaved areas of the Spey Valley in Scotland and may be under recorded in the Scottish part of its range, where it is clearly widely distributed.

THREAT The destruction of old woodland through clearance for agriculture or intensive forestry, and the removal of old or diseased trees and dead wood from such sites.

MANAGEMENT Maximise the number of old or diseased trees and the amount of dead wood, ensuring continuity of these in the future.

DACTYLOLABIS SEXMACULATA (Macquart)   NOTABLE
TIPULIDAE

DISTRIBUTION Hilly limestone areas of Britain, in particular the Scottish Highlands, the Pennines, Peak District and Lake District, North Wales and single records from Monmouthshire (1968), Somerset (1930) and Devon (1968).

HABITAT Limestone upland areas, especially with bare rock faces or limestone pavement. It has been taken at heights exceeding 900m in Perthshire.

ECOLOGY The larvae develop amongst damp mosses and ferns on wet limestone rocks. Adults recorded mainly in May and early June.

STATUS About 15 known, widely scattered post 1960 sites, though its choice of habitats probably means it is under recorded. It probably has localised stable populations throughout the hilly areas mentioned above. Status revised from RDB3 (Shirt 1987).

THREAT Uncertain, though the removal of limestone pavement and quarrying of limestone are the more obvious threats, and afforestation could degrade sites significantly.

MANAGEMENT Maintain areas of upland and mountainous terrain in a natural, undisturbed state, retaining any bare rocks and wet rock faces for breeding sites.

CTENOPHORA ORNATA Meigen   ENDANGERED
TIPULIDAE

DISTRIBUTION Most records are from the New Forest or nearby sites in Hampshire, with additional localities including Windsor Forest, Berkshire (1938, 1988); Aldbury, Hertfordshire (1967); Portmadoc, Caernarvonshire (1955); Ashtead (1949) and Addington (1942) both in Surrey.

HABITAT Ancient broadleaved woodland with a requirement for dead wood and old or diseased trees.

ECOLOGY This species has recently been reared from wet 'porridge' woodmould in a beech at Windsor Forest by Professor J Owen. Old trees and stumps of particularly large girth are probably essential for this species. Adults recorded from June to August and have been taken at moth traps at night and in the vicinity of old, living oaks.

STATUS An unmistakable hornet mimic yet with only five known post 1960 sites, Aldbury, Hertfordshire (1967); Windsor Forest, Berkshire (1988); Minstead (1971) and Matley Wood (1972) both in the New Forest and another unspecified New Forest site (1976). This suggests a serious contraction of its former range. The Hertfordshire record is for February and the circumstances of this observation must have an unusual explanation.

THREAT The destruction of old woodland through clearance for agriculture or intensive forestry, and the removal of old diseased trees and dead wood from such sites.

MANAGEMENT Maximise the number of old trees and the amount of dead wood and ensure continuity of these in the future.

DACTYLOLABIS TRANSVERSA (Meigen)

DISTRIBUTION A northern and western species with records for Wales (Glamorganshire, Montgomeryshire, Breconshire); England (Herefordshire, Worcestershire, Lancashire, Westmorland, Yorkshire, Northumberland) and Scotland (Ayrshire, Lanarkshire).

HABITAT A range of habitats containing non-limestone rocks are used, especially in moist, sheltered valley woods.

ECOLOGY The larvae develop amongst damp moss and ferns on damp rocks. Adults recorded from May to July.

STATUS About 10 widely scattered post 1960 sites known, though possibly under recorded to some extent.

THREAT Possibly the clearance and drainage of damp valley woodland for pastures or intensive forestry.

MANAGEMENT Retain bare rocks and wet rock faces with mosses and ferns for breeding sites.

DICRANOPTYCHA FUSCESCENS (Schummel)

DISTRIBUTION Only three known sites: Darenth Wood (1973), Cuxton (1976), Kent and Grays Chalk Pit, Essex (1970s).

HABITAT Abroad, this species favours dry woodland and scrub, conditions which are found in its known British sites.

ECOLOGY Biology unknown, presumably larvae develop in dry soil. Adults recorded in June.

STATUS A very poorly known species, only added to the British list as recently as 1974 and not listed in Shirt (1987).

THREAT Changes in the character and management of woodland, including afforestation. Grays Chalk pit has been subject to building development and the remainder is liable to recreational pressure and perhaps further development projects.

MANAGEMENT Oppose the above threats and maintain areas of scrub and woodland with a rich ground flora, using coppicing if possible.

113

DICRANOTA GRACILIPES Wahlgren

DISTRIBUTION Upland areas of Britain, in particular the Scottish Highlands, the Peak District and North Wales, with additional sites in Gloucestershire, Herefordshire and Westmorland.

HABITAT High altitude moorland streams and rivers or lower level sites with rocky beds where the grass Phalaris is present or where braided channels occur.

ECOLOGY Larvae aquatic in upland streams where they are probably predatory on smaller invertebrates. Adults recorded from August to November.

STATUS About 25 known post 1960 sites though its choice of habitats probably means it has been under recorded. It probably has localised stable populations throughout the hilly areas mentioned above. Status revised from RDB3 (Shirt 1987).

THREAT Afforestation of upland sites; canalisation and other modification of rivers; excessive trampling of banks.

MANAGEMENT Maintain streams in upland districts in a natural, undisturbed condition.

DICRANOTA GUERINI Zetterstedt

DISTRIBUTION A northern and western distribution with records in upland areas of Scotland, including the Isle of Bute, and northern England as far south as Cheshire.

HABITAT Springs, small streams and boggy flushes in upland and montane terrain, including trickle streams from snow caps at heights exceeding 900m. Some sites are at low altitudes. A preference for well vegetated streamsides (as opposed to rocky ones) has been noted at Moor House, Westmorland.

ECOLOGY In Ireland larvae are reported to be aquatic in sand and gravel in the middle of streams below 300m, though the circumstances under which they were found are not entirely typical of the British sites. They are probably predatory on smaller invertebrates. Adults recorded from May to October.

STATUS About 20 known post 1960 sites, and this species probably has localised stable populations throughout the upland areas outlined above. Edwards found it commonly at a good number of sites in the Killin district of Perthshire in the early 1930s.

THREAT Disturbance to upland springs, flushes and ditching of streams; afforestation of upland areas. Skiing activities could pose a local problem in some areas (with resultant soil erosion and a loss of vegetation).

MANAGEMENT Maintain unspoilt areas of upland and mountainous terrain with plenty of small streams, springs and flushes.

DICRANOTA ROBUSTA Lundstroem — NOTABLE / TIPULIDAE

DISTRIBUTION A very local and clumped distribution in north and west England, (Devon, Herefordshire, Cheshire, Lancashire, Westmorland, Yorkshire) and Scotland (sites in Dumfriesshire and Loch Avon in the Cairngorms).

HABITAT Fast-flowing streams with banks of sand or gravel and occuring as high as 750m in the Cairngorms.

ECOLOGY Larvae aquatic and develop in sand and gravel in streams where they are probably predatory on smaller invertebrates. Adults are almost flightless but can aquaplane across water and may be found beside streams and under stones between April and July.

STATUS A widespread but very local species with post 1960 sites including the River Monnow, Herefordshire (1988); Dartmeet, Devon (1970s); several sites in the Bolton area of Lancashire (1982); Sinking Wood, Yorkshire (1985) and the Sanquhar area of Dumfriesshire. It has been found in abundance beneath stones in Lancashire recently and its rather secretive habits means it is unlikely to be found unless specifically searched for. Status revised from RDB3 (Shirt 1987).

THREAT Disturbance of sand or shingle riverbanks through ditching of streams, gravel extraction, pollution such as agricultural run off, excessive trampling and adjacent afforestation.

MANAGEMENT Maintain upland streams in a natural, undisturbed state retaining any sand or shingle banks.

DICRANOTA SIMULANS Lackschewitz — RARE / TIPULIDAE

DISTRIBUTION Records scattered in upland areas of Scotland (mainly in the Cairngorms, also Perthshire), northern England, the Peak District and North Wales.

HABITAT Upland streamsides, especially those with shingle. It has been recorded from sites above 900m in the Cairngorms.

ECOLOGY Larvae aquatic and developing in stream beds and gravel of upland streams where they are probably predators of smaller invertebrates. Adults recorded in June and July.

STATUS Eight known post 1960 sites, though its choice of habitat means it has probably been under-recorded to some extent.

THREAT Afforestation of upland sites; ditching of upland streams and excessive trampling of banks; gravel extraction; the localised effects of skiing activities in some areas (with resultant soil erosion and a loss of vegetation).

MANAGEMENT Maintain upland streams in a natural, undisturbed condition retaining any shingle banks.

DIOGMA GLABRATA (Meigen) — NOTABLE / TIPULIDAE

DISTRIBUTION Records dispersed widely in England, Wales and Scotland.

HABITAT Damp woodland, generally in calcareous lowland areas.

ECOLOGY The greenish larva usually develops in terrestrial mosses growing on stones, less often in wet mosses growing on soil. It is also possible that mosses on large trees and bodies of dead wood are used. Adults recorded from June to August.

STATUS Sixteen known post 1960 sites from widely throughout its range.

THREAT Clearance and drainage of damp woodland for agriculture or intensive forestry. Removal of large trees and any dead wood and boulders which support a rich and varied moss flora.

MANAGEMENT Maintain a rich moss flora and a good age class structure of trees, retaining larger trees which have a well developed moss flora on their trunks; also retain any dead wood (stumps, fallen trunks) and boulders for the same reason.

ELLIPTERA OMISSA Schiner — INSUFFICIENTLY KNOWN / TIPULIDAE

DISTRIBUTION Known solely from two pupal skins sticking out of rotten logs in a waterfall at Patley Bridge, Yorkshire in June 1924.

HABITAT Rivers and streams with partly submerged dead wood on the basis of the above record.

ECOLOGY The larvae have been said to develop in partly submerged wood but a recent review in Switzerland regarded water-side moss on boulders as the required habitat.

STATUS Only the single record, though possibly overlooked through its rather scarce and hard to survey larval development site. The conflicting habitat association for the early stages and the absence of voucher material make this a rather unsatisfactory species on the British list. Status revised from RDB1 (Shirt 1987).

THREAT The clearance of moss covered boulders, dead trees and logs from streams and rivers through river improvement.

MANAGEMENT Maintain streams and rivers in a natural state, in particular retaining any moss covered, waterlogged fallen trees and logs.

ERIOPTERA BIVITTATA (Loew)   VULNERABLE
                                               TIPULIDAE

DISTRIBUTION Originally discovered on the North Kent marshes in 1966, where it is now known to be widespread, and subsequently found at Romney Marsh, Kent; Walberswick NNR, Suffolk; Stiffkey/Holkam NNR, Cley Marshes and Catfield Fen in Norfolk; Langenhoe Hall Marshes and Pitsea Hall Fleet in Essex.

HABITAT Coastal levels with mildly brackish ditches and ponds, favouring muddy areas with sparse vegetation. Occasionally occurring on inland fens where a saline influence is present.

ECOLOGY The larvae are thought to breed in wet, slightly brackish mud. Adults recorded from June to August.

STATUS All the known sites are post 1960 and the populations seem quite stable. However the total area of potential habitat is becoming very reduced because of agricultural reclamation and on the safer sites it remains to be seen whether the right brackish conditions and appropriate management regime can be maintained. The improvement of the sea walls associated with construction of the Thames flood barrier may well reduce the saline influence at some of its major sites.

THREAT The drainage of coastal levels for agriculture and the loss of salinity following sea wall construction or improvements, these being serious threats to the populations on the North Kent marshes. Also the more general threats of the loss of salinity at sites and of pollution and eutrophication from fertiliser run-off.

MANAGEMENT Maintain a high relatively stable water level at sites and use rotational ditch management if necessary to provide some open water and muddy conditions as described above. Attempt to maintain some brackish situations on coastal levels.

ERIOPTERA EDWARDSII (Lackschewitz)   INSUFFICIENTLY KNOWN
                                               TIPULIDAE

DISTRIBUTION Only one record: Strath Rory, Ross and Cromarty (1976).

HABITAT Barren upland streamsides.

ECOLOGY Larvae possibly developing in damp riverside shingle, or moss. Adults recorded in June.

STATUS The record is recent. It appears to be very restricted, though more thorough search of the Scottish Highlands may eventually yield more sites. This species is not listed in Shirt (1987).

THREAT Ditching of streams, gravel extraction, excessive trampling of banks and afforestation of sites.

MANAGEMENT Maintain upland streams in a natural and undisturbed state, retaining marshy areas or shingle banks which may provide breeding sites.

ERIOPTERA LIMBATA Loew   VULNERABLE
                                               TIPULIDAE

DISTRIBUTION Only known from five sites in southern Britain: Seabrook Valley (including Asholt Wood), Kent (1974 and 1986); Newbridge-on-Usk, Monmouthshire (1972); Glanvilles Wootton (1864), Aunt Mary's (1987) and Lower Kingscombe (1987), Dorset.

HABITAT At Asholt Wood it was taken beside a shaded calcareous stream in a wood and at Newbridge from beneath willows besides the River Usk, which has sandy river banks.

ECOLOGY Larvae possibly develop in damp riverside and streamside sediment. Adults recorded from June to August.

STATUS A very restricted species with only four known post 1960 sites.

THREAT River improvement schemes and ditching of streams; pollution such as agricultural run-off and resultant eutrophication; clearance of shading trees for agriculture or intensive foresty; excessive trampling of banks. Asholt Wood may be adversely affected by developments associated with the construction of the Channel Tunnel.

MANAGEMENT Maintain streams and rivers in a natural, undisturbed state retaining sandy banks and trees for shade on river margins.

ERIOPTERA MEIGENI (Zetterstedt)   RARE
                                               TIPULIDAE

DISTRIBUTION Only known from Aviemore (1903 and 1904) and the River Dulnain (1982) both in Elgin; the Struy Oxbows, Strathglass, Easterness (1981 and 1984) and Hatfield Moor, Yorkshire (pre 1952). A record from St Mary's, Scillies (1904?) requires confirmation.

HABITAT Upland rivers with sand banks, often under the shade of alders. Deltas and oxbows are particularly preferred, probably because of the sheltered sand and shingle banks associated with them.

ECOLOGY Larvae possibly develop in damp sand, shingle or soil at the water edge. Adults recorded in June and appear to have a rather short flight period.

STATUS The River Dulnain and Struy Oxbows of Strathglass appear to be its modern strongholds.

THREAT The disturbance of sandy river banks through excessive trampling, adjacent forestry, gravel extraction, river improvement and pollution such as agricultural run-off.

MANAGEMENT Maintain sandy river banks in a natural, undisturbed condition, with some trees or bushes for shade.

ERIOPTERA MEIJEREI Edwards

VULNERABLE
TIPULIDAE

DISTRIBUTION Nine widely scattered English sites: Welsh's Common (1979 or 1980) and Three Bridges (1855) both in Sussex; Orford (pre 1938) and Walberswick NNR (1975), Suffolk; Catfield Great Fen, Norfolk (1975); Catlow (1946) and Sabden (1946) both in Lancashire and Rushy Moor, Yorkshire (1982).

HABITAT Fens and carr, possibly in association with large sedges.

ECOLOGY Larvae possibly develop in wet sedge litter. Adults recorded from June to August.

STATUS Only four post 1960 sites as outlined above and many of its old haunts may now be destroyed or unsuitable.

THREAT Drainage and clearance of suitable habitat for agriculture or intensive forestry; pollution such as agricultural run-off and resultant eutrophication; mis-management of water levels with subsequent drying out of the soil surface.

MANAGEMENT Maintain a high and relatively stable water level ensuring a mosaic or succession of vegetation types including ponds, ditches and their marginal vegetation using rotational management if necessary. Maintain carr where the species is present, but do not allow its invasion into good open fen.

ERIOPTERA NIELSENI de Meijere

NOTABLE
TIPULIDAE

DISTRIBUTION A widespread but clumped distribution in England, Wales and Scotland. Its strongholds appear to be in Wales and the New Forest.

HABITAT Usually associated with mildly acid bogs, sometimes poor fens and it may in fact require bog areas with some base rich flushing.

ECOLOGY Larvae probably develop in damp soil or moss. Adults recorded from June to August.

STATUS About 25 known post 1960 sites, but mostly restricted to the two strongholds mentioned above. In 1981 it was taken in at least 10 different localities in the New Forest and at least five sites in North Wales. Status revised from RDB3 (Shirt 1987).

THREAT The modification of bog hydrology including drainage and the alteration of pattern of flushing.

MANAGEMENT Maintain a high and relatively stable water level, ensuring natural patterns of flushing and retaining any vegetation transitions between bog and more base enriched areas.

ERIOPTERA NIGRIPALPIS Goetghebuer

RARE
TIPULIDAE

DISTRIBUTION Records widely dispersed in England (Sussex, Berkshire, Gloucestershire, Cheshire, Derbyshire, Yorkshire, Durham).

HABITAT Densely shaded streams with incised banks, almost exclusively on clay.

ECOLOGY Larvae probably develop in damp clay soil beside streams. Adults recorded in May and June.

STATUS Eight known post 1960 sites from within Berkshire, Sussex, Gloucestershire, Yorkshire and Durham.

THREAT Canalisation of streams, pollution such as agricultural run off or from industry and resultant eutrophication; clearance of trees for agriculture or intensive forestry; excessive trampling of banks.

MANAGEMENT Maintain suitable streams in a natural, undisturbed state, retaining trees for shading. Retain naturally incised clay banks which appear to be the specific requirement of this species.

ERIOPTERA PUSILLA (Schiner)

ENGANGERED
TIPULIDAE

DISTRIBUTION Only known from the River Monnow, where it was taken on 17 July 1907, 31 July 1908 and 30 May 1911 by J H Wood.

HABITAT Possibly associated with sand or shingle river banks.

ECOLOGY Larvae possibly develop in damp soil, sand or shingle beside rivers. Adults recorded from May to July.

STATUS No records for over 75 years. However recent recording along the Monnow Valley has demonstrated that a surprising number of Wood's rarities are still present at surviving sites and the modern existence of E. pusilla cannot be ruled out.

THREAT The destruction of sand and shingle river banks along the River Monnow through river improvement schemes and possibly pollution such as agricultural run-off.

MANAGEMENT Maintain sand or shingle river banks in a natural, undisturbed state with some trees or shrubs for shade.

<table>
<tr><td>

ERIOPTERA SCOTICA Edwards

</td><td>

ENDANGERED
TIPULIDAE

</td></tr>
</table>

DISTRIBUTION A very poorly known species with a single old record from Dingwall, East Ross on 30 August 1902.

HABITAT Unknown.

ECOLOGY Larvae possibly develop in damp sand or soil.

STATUS Only the single old record. It may be extinct, although the northernmost parts of Scotland are comparatively under recorded. This species is not listed in Shirt (1987).

THREAT Unclear.

MANAGEMENT Unclear.

<table>
<tr><td>

ERIOPTERA SORDIDA Zetterstedt

</td><td>

RARE
TIPULIDAE

</td></tr>
</table>

DISTRIBUTION Restricted to the Scottish Highlands with most records for sites along Speyside including Aviemore (1981), Kingussie (1981), Insh Marshes (1981), Corrour Marsh (1984), Nethy Bridge (1931); also a record from Pitmaduthy Moss, East Ross (1976).

HABITAT Associated with more eutrophic areas of marsh and fen.

ECOLOGY Larvae possibly develop in wet peat. Adults recorded in June.

STATUS Five known post 1960 sites as outlined above, but with limited areas of available habitat.

THREAT Wetland drainage for intensive forestry or agriculture.

MANAGEMENT Maintain a high and relatively stable water level, retaining areas exhibiting natural high fertility through the presence of nearby flushes or seepages.

<table>
<tr><td>

GNOPHOMYIA ELSNERI Stary

</td><td>

ENDANGERED
TIPULIDAE

</td></tr>
</table>

DISTRIBUTION Known only from the Badgers Brook area of High Standing Hill, Windsor Forest, Berkshire.

HABITAT Ancient broadleaved woodland, possibly favouring beech. There is a requirement for old or diseased trees and dead wood.

ECOLOGY At Windsor larvae were found in porridge-like wood mould at the base of a hollow beech tree. Adults were recorded in July.

STATUS All records date from the late 1970s. It was originally discovered in England as an adult and subsequently as larvae. The species was later described as new to science from European material. It is apparent from its late recognition both within Europe as a whole and at a well worked site such as Windsor, that it is a very rare insect indeed. This species is not listed in Shirt (1987).

THREAT The removal of dead wood and old or diseased trees coupled with a potential decline in the number of ancient beeches at the known site due to the current age class structure of this forest.

MANAGEMENT Retain any old or diseased trees and maximise the amount and range of dead wood, ensuring continuity of these in future.

<table>
<tr><td>

GNOPHOMYIA VIRIDIPENNIS (Gimmerthal)

</td><td>

NOTABLE
TIPULIDAE

</td></tr>
</table>

DISTRIBUTION Records scattered widely in England as far north as Durham, with a strong southerly bias.

HABITAT Fens and carr.

ECOLOGY The larvae develop in the fibrous layer beneath the bark of recently fallen trees (with bark still intact) with a preference for poplars, especially Populus nigra s.l. and including non-native balsams though it probably also used the larger, long-leaved willows. There is a record of it being reared from moss on a felled beech trunk, though an association with beech is unusual. Adults recorded from May to August.

STATUS About 15 known post 1960 sites scattered widely over the known range and not infrequent around the outskirts of London. Status revised from RDB3 (Shirt 1987).

THREAT The general loss of wetlands and carr through drainage and the removal of old trees and dead wood. The continuity of recently fallen trees in a site could be a problem especially with poplar.

MANAGEMENT Retain any old trees and freshly fallen limbs and trunks, ensuring continuity of these in the future.

GONOMYIA ABBREVIATA Loew   RARE TIPULIDAE

DISTRIBUTION About 20 sites widely dispersed in England and Wales, as far north as Yorkshire.

HABITAT Usually restricted to small shaded streams in woods on calcareous soils.

ECOLOGY Larvae probably develop in damp soil besides streams. Adults recorded from June to September.

STATUS About 10 known post 1960 sites within Cornwall, Hampshire, Yorkshire, Glamorganshire, Monmouthshire, Radnorshire, Pembrokeshire, Flintshire, and Derbyshire. It may be under recorded within Wales. Status revised from RDB2 (Shirt 1987).

THREAT The loss and degradation of small wooded streams in calcareous districts through clearance of woodland for agriculture or intensive forestry, canalisation, pollution such as agricultural run-off and excessive trampling of banks.

MANAGEMENT Maintain wooded streams in a natural, undisturbed state with adequate shading.

GONOMYIA ALBOSCUTELLATA (von Roeser)   ENDANGERED TIPULIDAE

DISTRIBUTION Only three certain sites: Haugh Wood, Herefordshire (found in 1898 and 1986); Wyre Forest, Worcestershire (1987); Whitewell, Yorkshire (1958) and possibly another site in northern England.

HABITAT Associated with mossy calcareous flushes in a glade at Haugh Wood.

ECOLOGY Larvae possibly develop in the wet soil or moss of flushes. Adults recorded in July and the records point towards a short flight period.

STATUS Only two known post 1960 sites, including Haugh Wood where it was observed in abundance in 1986. It has a long history from the site and should remain secure if flushes do not dry out or become shaded through growth of nearby trees. This species is not listed in Shirt (1987).

THREAT Drainage of flushes and clearance of associated woodland for agriculture or intensive forestry. Shading out of the glade at Haugh Wood could render the site unsuitable. Local water abstraction could also affect flushes.

MANAGEMENT Maintain a natural pattern of flushing at sites and associated marsh. Do not allow the shading out of glades. The Haugh Wood site is a County Trust reserve within Forestry Commission woodland; the Forestry Commission have recently removed some of the encroaching trees.

GONOMYIA BIFIDA Tonnoir   NOTABLE TIPULIDAE

DISTRIBUTION About 15 known sites scattered widely over southern England (Devon, Hampshire, Wiltshire, Surrey, Berkshire, Herefordshire, Suffolk, Northamptonshire, Lincolnshire) and Monmouthshire in Wales.

HABITAT Small streams and seepages in wet usually calcareous woods.

ECOLOGY Larvae possibly develop in damp soil beside streams and flushes. Adults recorded between June and August.

STATUS A long gap in the records of this species is present between the original Devon record in 1885 and the 1960s when it was found at a number of sites in southern England. It is now known from about a dozen post 1960 sites. Status revised from RDB3 (Shirt 1987).

THREAT Ditching of streams, drainage of seepages and clearance of damp calcareous woodland for agriculture or intensive forestry.

MANAGEMENT Maintain wooded streams and seepages in a natural, undisturbed state and with a high, relatively stable water level in seepage marsh.

GONOMYIA BRADLEYI Edwards   VULNERABLE TIPULIDAE

DISTRIBUTION An old specimen exists for the Wyre Forest, Worcestershire taken by Bradley in July 1889 and the species was rediscovered at Gwbert, near Cardigan in Wales (July 1987) and at three sites on the Yorkshire coast (in the Scarborough and Bridlington districts) during 1988.

HABITAT The Welsh site is a coastal cliff landslip in boulder clay, where it was associated with seepages on sparsely vegetated clay. The Yorkshire localities also refer to seepages of soft rock cliffs. Information concerning the older record is not available.

ECOLOGY Larvae probably develop in the damp soil of the above situations.

STATUS Formerly regarded as a species likely to be extinct in Britain, so the recent records are encouraging and involve a different habitat type. Its position still seems precarious. Status revised from RDB1 (Shirt 1987).

THREAT Coastal development and associated cliff drainage and stabilisation. Much of the habitat type associated with the recent records has already been destroyed and what remains is vulnerable to further cliff stabilisation measures.

MANAGEMENT Maintain cliffs and landslips in a natural and undisturbed state, with a natural pattern of cliff drainage and seepages.

GONOMYIA CONNEXA Loew
VULNERABLE
TIPULIDAE

DISTRIBUTION Only known from four sites: Porthcawl, Glamorganshire (1903 and 1906); Murroch Glen, Dunbartonshire (pre 1938, possibly much older); Aboyne Bridge and Ballater, Aberdeenshire (both 1984).

HABITAT Probably streamsides and springs.

ECOLOGY Larvae probably develop in damp soil besides streams and springs. Adults recorded in June and July.

STATUS A poorly known species with little recent information, despite the recent intensive level of recording in this group. Status revised from RDB1 (Shirt 1987).

THREAT Alteration in the drainage patterns of springs and ditching of streams; excessive trampling of banks; the removal of adjacent trees; pollution such as agricultural run-off and resultant eutrophication.

MANAGEMENT Maintain stream banks in a natural undisturbed state with some trees for shading and maintain natural drainage patterns in springs, retaining any associated marshy areas.

GONOMYIA CONOVIENSIS Barnes
NOTABLE
TIPULIDAE

DISTRIBUTION Records widely dispersed in England, Wales and Scotland. Many records are coastal though it can occur well inland, usually in upland areas.

HABITAT Seepages, especially on vertical rock faces such as on coastal cliffs, and more rarely beside streams and seepages in upland districts.

ECOLOGY Larvae probably develop in seepages and in streamside sediment. Adults recorded from March to September and have been taken in profusion at a light trap in Bolton, Lancashire.

STATUS About 20 known post 1960 sites, many of which are from the rocky coasts of Wales and West Scotland. Status revised from RDB3 (Shirt 1987).

THREAT Probably fairly secure at most of its coastal sites due to the inaccessible nature of the habitat, though coastal development and associated cliff drainage and stabilisation could be a problem in some areas, especially on soft rock cliffs. Inland sites are perhaps more vulnerable though drainage or ditching of seepages and through adjacent afforestation.

MANAGEMENT Safeguard seepages on cliffs and rock faces, maintain natural drainage patterns and any associated vegetation or marshy areas.

GONOMYIA LIMBATA (von Roeser)
ENDANGERED
TIPULIDAE

DISTRIBUTION Only a single Welsh record: Nant Sere Wood, Breconshire on 27 June 1976.

HABITAT The known locality is a series of flushes in a valley woodland on rich Devonian soils.

ECOLOGY Larvae probably develop in the soil or mosses of flushes.

STATUS Published as British in 1977 with only the single recent record. A more intensive search of damp valley woodlands in the area may eventually reveal more sites. The known site is just outside a Trust reserve, so the boundary could be usefully extended.

THREAT Destruction of the known and similar nearby sites for agriculture or intensive forestry; also the drainage of flushes and local water abstraction.

MANAGEMENT Maintain habitat diversity at the known woodland site, ensuring no undue disturbance to the flushes and associated vegetation. Extend the limits of the Trust reserve, if possible.

GONOMYIA PUNCTATA Edwards
VULNERABLE
TIPULIDAE

DISTRIBUTION Only four known sites: Melkinthorpe, Westmorland (1922); Monnow Valley, Herefordshire (1906); Mulgrave Woods, Yorkshire (1937) and Wyre Forest, Worcestershire (1938).

HABITAT Probably the sandy banks of rivers in shaded situations.

ECOLOGY Larvae probably develop in damp soil or vegetation beside rivers. Adults recorded from June to September.

STATUS No recent records, suggesting that it is now in a most vulnerable position. It has not been re-found in the Monnow Valley despite recent visits.

THREAT Canalisation, excessive trampling of river banks and removal of riverside trees; pollution such as agricultural run-off and resultant eutrophication.

MANAGEMENT Maintain sandy river banks in a natural undisturbed state with trees for shading.

GONOMYIA SEXGUTTATA (Dale)
ENDANGERED TIPULIDAE

DISTRIBUTION Only two known sites: St Merryn, Cornwall (June 1912) and Glanvilles Wootton, Dorset (about 1860).

HABITAT Thought to be associated with streamsides.

ECOLOGY Larvae of this genus generally develop in damp soil beside rivers and springs.

STATUS No recent records. If not extinct it must be very rare. The St Merryn site is highly degraded today due to conversion to a golf course and recreational pressures on the adjacent beach.

THREAT Ditching of streams, excessive trampling of banks, pollution such as agricultural run-off and recreational pressures at the Cornwall site.

MANAGEMENT Maintain streams in a natural state, free from excessive disturbance.

HELIUS PALLIROSTRIS Edwards
NOTABLE TIPULIDAE

DISTRIBUTION Records widely dispersed in England, Wales and Scotland. Both inland and coastal sites are known and it is especially frequent on the North Kent marshes.

HABITAT A wide range of wetlands are used including marshes, ditches on coastal levels, dune slacks and beside sluggish calcareous rivers. There seems to be an association with tall emergent vegetation besides ditches and ponds (often, though not exclusively, Typha).

ECOLOGY Larvae have been found between leaf sheaths of Typha. Basden reared it from the nest of a coot. Adults recorded from May to September.

STATUS About 35 known post 1960 sites and especially frequent on the North Kent marshes, though this stronghold is vulnerable to development and agricultural reclamation.

THREAT Wetland drainage and in particular the removal of tall emergent vegetation at the margins of water bodies. Also pollution such as agricultural run-off leading to eutrophication and river improvement schemes. Loss and modification of ponds.

MANAGEMENT Maintain a high, relatively stable water level ensuring areas of tall emergent vegetation. Perform any necessary ditch, pond or river bank vegetation management in rotation.

LIMNOPHILA ABDOMINALIS Staeger
NOTABLE TIPULIDAE

DISTRIBUTION Records widely dispersed in England (except the south-east), Wales and Scotland.

HABITAT Usually bogs, occasionally fens, especially around exposed peat amongst herbage.

ECOLOGY Larvae semi-aquatic, probably developing in wet peat. Adults recorded from May to August.

STATUS About 20 known post 1960 sites scattered widely. Very few old records. Status revised from RDB2 (Shirt 1987).

THREAT Drainage of sites for agriculture or afforestation; mis-management of water levels with a resultant drying out of peat and invasion by scrub and coarse vegetation.

MANAGEMENT Ensure a high, relatively stable water table with patches of bare peat as probable breeding sites.

LIMNOPHILA APICATA (Loew)
NOTABLE TIPULIDAE

DISTRIBUTION A north and western species with records mainly for northern England, Wales and Scotland.

HABITAT Streamsides.

ECOLOGY Larvae probably develop in stream sediment. Adults recorded from June to August.

STATUS About 15 known post 1960 sites from widely throughout its range.

THREAT Canalisation of streams and removal of trees from the banks which probably afford shade and shelter; also excessive trampling of banks and pollution such as agricultural run-off.

MANAGEMENT Maintain stream banks in a natural and undisturbed condition retaining any trees or bushes for shade.

LIMNOPHILA FASCIATA (Linnaeus)   ENDANGERED   TIPULIDAE

DISTRIBUTION Only known from eight (possibly nine) sites in northern England within Cheshire, Westmorland and Yorkshire.

HABITAT The recent Hatchmere record was from a boggy area besides a mere and boggy conditions seem to be the main feature in common for the known sites.

ECOLOGY Life history unknown. The larvae possibly develop in damp boggy soil. Adults recorded from June to August.

STATUS Only two known post 1960 records: Hatchmere, Cheshire in 1975 and another unknown Cheshire site in 1964.

THREAT Drainage of bogs for agriculture or intensive forestry; also trampling through recreational use at some sites and mis-management of water levels leading to invasion by scrub or coarse vegetation.

MANAGEMENT Maintain a high and relatively stable water level in the bogs and prevent scrub invasion.

LIMNOPHILA GLABRICULA (Meigen)   NOTABLE   TIPULIDAE

DISTRIBUTION Mainly recorded in Wales and Scotland with a few English records in Hampshire, Lancashire and Westmorland.

HABITAT Carr and shaded streams or seepages in woods, sometimes in more open wetland habitat.

ECOLOGY Biology unknown. The larvae possibly develop in wet soil beside springs and streams. Adults recorded from June to August.

STATUS Some 15 known post 1960 sites, nine in Scotland, two in Wales, two in Devon and two in Hampshire. Status revised from RDB2 (Shirt 1987).

THREAT The destruction of carr, damp woods and open mire through drainage for agriculture or intensive forestry; also ditching of streams, excessive trampling of banks and pollution such as agricultural run-off.

MANAGEMENT Maintain seepages and streams in a natural and undisturbed state with a high and relatively stable water level in adjacent marshes. Retain any carr, bushes or trees for shade and shelter. There is preliminary evidence from one open site that limited grazing may be beneficial, presumably through creating tiny open patches of bare peat.

LIMNOPHILA HETEROGYNA Bergroth   ENDANGERED   TIPULIDAE

DISTRIBUTION Only a single record: Whixall Moss, Shropshire on 22 August 1936.

HABITAT The record is probably from an area of open wet heath and bog, though the site includes other habitat types such as woodland.

ECOLOGY Biology unknown. The larvae possibly develop in damp peat or moss.

STATUS Only a single old record. Whixall Moss is a relatively well known site and the lack of recent information suggests it may now be very rare if not extinct.

THREAT Drainage for peat extraction, agriculture or afforestation; mis-management of water levels with a resultant drying out of peat and subsequent invasion by coarse vegetation and scrub.

MANAGEMENT Maintain a high and relatively stable water level to prevent the drying out of peat or moss.

LIMNOPHILA MUNDATA (Loew)   NOTABLE   TIPULIDAE

DISTRIBUTION Recorded widely in Scotland, northern England, Wales and the Welsh borders as far south as the Forest of Dean.

HABITAT Streams in upland or hilly areas, usually partly shaded by alders, though occasionally beside exposed moorland streams (eg Moor House, Westmorland).

ECOLOGY Biology unknown. The larvae probably develop in stream sediments. Adults recorded in June and July and at Moor House they have been observed swarming over stream banks at sunset.

STATUS About 15 known post 1960 sites from widely throughout the known range.

THREAT Ditching of streams; removal of streamside trees; excessive trampling of banks; pollution such as agricultural run-off or acidification through adjacent intensive forestry.

MANAGEMENT Maintain streams in a natural and undisturbed state retaining any trees for shade.

LIMNOPHILA PICTIPENNIS (Meigen)
VULNERABLE
TIPULIDAE

DISTRIBUTION Some 10 known sites scattered widely over England in Devon, Somerset, Sussex, Kent, Essex, Cambridgeshire, Huntingdonshire, Nottinghamshire and Yorkshire.

HABITAT Records include coastal marshes and inland gravel pit ponds and fens, and the presence of a rich marginal vegetation beside ditches and ponds may prove an important requirement.

ECOLOGY Biology unknown. The larvae are probably aquatic, in sediment among vegetation beside ponds, ditches and streams. Adults recorded from May and September.

STATUS Only three known post 1960 sites: Cliffe Marshes, Kent where it has been taken over a wide area on dates between 1968 and 1980; Epping Forest, Essex (late 1970s) and Godmanchester, Huntingdonshire (1969). The North Kent marshes are especially vulnerable to development and agricultural reclamation. Status revised from RDB1 (Shirt 1987).

THREAT Habitat loss to agriculture and development; drainage and infilling of ponds or excessive vegetation clearance or disturbance to water margins such as through ditching; pollution such as agricultural run-off and eutrophication.

MANAGEMENT Maintain a high and relatively stable water level and a rich marginal vegetation around standing water. Use rotational ditch or pond management where necessary to ensure a range of marginal conditions.

LIMNOPHILA PULCHELLA (Meigen)
NOTABLE
TIPULIDAE

DISTRIBUTION Very local though widely distributed in England, Wales and Scotland.

HABITAT Usually boggy ground in woodland, on wet heath and moorland, with patches of Sphagnum or exposed peat. It can occur at high altitudes in addition to lowland sites.

ECOLOGY The larvae probably develop in damp peat or moss. Adults recorded from April to September. The females are short winged and flightless which must greatly limit the dispersal powers of this species.

STATUS About 30 known post 1960 sites, mainly in Scotland and northern England with isolated records extending as far south as Dorset, Wiltshire, Hampshire and Berkshire.

THREAT The destruction of boggy areas through drainage or clearance for agriculture or intensive forestry. Mis-management of water levels with resultant invasion of scrub or coarse vegetation.

MANAGEMENT Maintain a high, relatively stable water level in boggy areas to prevent patches of moss or peat drying out and prevent scrub invasion.

LIMNOPHILA TRIMACULATA (Zetterstedt)
NOTABLE
TIPULIDAE

DISTRIBUTION Recorded widely in England, Wales and Scotland including Arran, with a northern and western bias.

HABITAT Small streams, usually in damp woodland and in association with acid ground near heaths or moors. At Meall Garbh (Ben Lawers NNR), Perthshire it was recorded on a flush at about 800m.

ECOLOGY The larvae are aquatic, developing in sandy stream sediment. Adults recorded from May to July.

STATUS About 10 known post 1960 sites from throughout its range.

THREAT Canalisation of streams, pollution such as agricultural run-off, excessive trampling of banks and removal of sheltering trees.

MANAGEMENT Maintain sandy streamside banks in a natural and undisturbed condition retaining any trees or shrubs for shade.

LIMNOPHILA VERRALLI (Bergroth)
NOTABLE
TIPULIDAE

DISTRIBUTION Records widely dispersed in England, Wales and Scotland with a northern and western bias.

HABITAT Small streams usually under the shade of alders.

ECOLOGY The larvae are aquatic in sandy stream sediment. Adults recorded in May and June.

STATUS Some 17 known post 1960 sites scattered widely throughout its range.

THREAT Canalisation of streams, excessive trampling of banks, pollution such as agricultural run-off and removal of sheltering trees.

MANAGEMENT Maintain sandy streamside banks in a natural and undisturbed condition with some trees or shrubs for shade.

LIMONIA ANNULATA (Linnaeus)

DISTRIBUTION A very disjunct distribution, with about six Scottish sites in Perthshire, Elgin, Banffshire and Easterness, additionally a number of old records for the New Forest, Hampshire (up to 1909).

HABITAT Broadleaved woodland but precise needs uncertain.

ECOLOGY The larvae have been reared from a fungus on beech in the New Forest (more detailed information is not available). Adults recorded in August.

STATUS Only four known post 1960 sites, all Scottish: Black Wood of Rannoch (1960) and Kinrogan Field Station (1975), Perthshire; Balranaich, Banffshire (1981) and Monadh Mor, East Ross (1979). Its status in the New Forest must be critical if it is not already extinct.

THREAT The destruction of woodland through clearance for agriculture or intensive forestry. Removal of any old or diseased trees and dead wood which may support suitable fungi.

MANAGEMENT Retain old trees and dead wood within sites and ensure continuity of these in future.

LIMONIA APERTA (Wahlgren)

DISTRIBUTION A northern species known from only five widely dispersed sites: Doire Donn, Westerness (1982); Kinloch, Rhum (1961) and Forres, Elgin (1904); Austwick (numerous specimens 1927 to 1930) and Ingleton (pre 1938) both in Yorkshire.

HABITAT Probably boggy ground.

ECOLOGY Biology unknown. The larvae possibly develop in wet peat or moss. Adults ... recorded from June to October and have been found sitting in the flowers of grass of parnassus.

STATUS Only two post 1960 sites, both in Scotland. The recent survey of Austwick Moss has not relocated this species.

THREAT The destruction of bogs through drainage for agriculture or afforestation. Mis-management of water levels with a loss of wet areas and invasion by scrub or coarse vegetation.

MANAGEMENT Ensure a high and relatively stable water level and minimise disturbance such as trampling by animals.

LIMONIA AQUOSA (Verrall)

DISTRIBUTION A mainly northern and western species with widely scattered records for Scotland, northern England, Wales, Somerset, and also well established on Lundy.

HABITAT Waterfalls, wet rocks and seepages on cliffs, in gulleys and gorges.

ECOLOGY Biology unknown. The larvae possibly develop in wet moss. Adults recorded from April to July.

STATUS About 30 known post 1960 sites from throughout the known range.

THREAT Tourism is perhaps the greatest threat in some areas, resulting in local damage to breeding sites, whilst at other sites quarrying, coastal development and nearby afforestation could be harmful.

MANAGEMENT Maintain sites in a natural state, retaining streams and seepages.

LIMONIA BEZZII (Alexander & Leonard)

DISTRIBUTION Known from only six southern coastal sites: Dawlish Warren, Devon (1981 and 1982); Arne (1971) and Chesil Bank, Portland (1891 and 1939) both in Dorset; Stiffkey, Norfolk (1976); Pagham Harbour, Sussex (1960s) and Shingle Street, Suffolk (1970s).

HABITAT Usually on intertidal gravel with Enteromorpha alga in coastal lagoons.

ECOLOGY Larvae probably develop within the alga on gravel in the above habitat. Adults recorded in July and August.

STATUS Five post 1960 sites. This is one of the few marine craneflies and its specialised habitat is of limited occurrence. Lagoonal shores with gravel unfortunately do not attract the same concern as muddy shores of high ornithological value.

THREAT Recreational pressures and coastal developments such as the construction of marinas, also pollution from industry and agricultural run-off.

MANAGEMENT Maintain sites in a natural state, retaining undisturbed gravel with Enteromorpha.

LIMONIA CALEDONICA (Edwards)   NOTABLE TIPULIDAE

DISTRIBUTION Confined to Scotland where it is local but fairly widespread in the Highlands, including Mull and Rhum.

HABITAT Boggy ground with rushes (Juncus), from sea level to altitudes exceeding 900m in Perthshire.

ECOLOGY Biology unknown. The larvae probably develop in wet boggy soil or moss. Adults recorded from June to August.

STATUS About 20 known post 1960 sites. It was recorded as locally abundant in the Killin District of Perthshire during the 1930s though this area has been rather under recorded in recent decades. The comparative lack of records from the Cairngorms could reflect a dislike for highly acid conditions or a need for damper climatic conditions.

THREAT The drainage of bogs and hillside flushes, conversion to intensive forestry, also peat cutting or recreational pressure (such as excessive trampling by walkers) in some areas.

MANAGEMENT Maintain natural drainage patterns in bogs and flushes with a high, relatively stable water level in the immediate vicinity.

LIMONIA COMPLICATA (de Meijere)   NOTABLE TIPULIDAE

DISTRIBUTION A coastal species with records in England (Hampshire, Kent, Suffolk, Norfolk), Scotland (Elgin, Easterness, Dumfriesshire, East Ross, Argyllshire) and Wales (Glamorganshire, Pembrokeshire, Cardiganshire, Merionethshire).

HABITAT Brackish coastal marshes or upper-saltmarsh, usually in areas where freshwater seepages are present at high tide level with Juncus maritimus and J. gerardii.

ECOLOGY Biology unknown. The larvae possibly develop in wet brackish mud. Adults recorded from May to October.

STATUS About a dozen known post 1960 sites scattered throughout the known range. The widespread truncation of saltmarsh, through reclamation of the upper margin for agriculture etc., will have left many former localities unsuitable for this species.

THREAT The destruction of coastal marshes through drainage and agricultural reclamation; coastal development schemes (construction of harbours, sea walls etc.) and pollution from agriculture or industry. The ditching or drainage of freshwater seepages along the upper margin of saltmarsh and brackish coastal marsh.

MANAGEMENT Maintain a high, relatively stable water level in coastal marshes. Retain the upper margin of saltmarshes and brackish coastal marshes at the point where they grade into terrestrial conditions. Take great care to retain undisturbed freshwater seepages onto salt marsh, resisting any ditching. Overgrazing should be avoided.

LIMONIA CONSIMILIS (Zetterstedt)   RARE TIPULIDAE

DISTRIBUTION Records scattered over the central Highlands of Scotland (Easterness, Elgin, Westerness and Aberdeenshire).

HABITAT Seepages, boggy ground and streamsides in shaded situations.

ECOLOGY Biology unknown. The larvae possibly develop in boggy mud or moss. Adults recorded in July and August.

STATUS Six known post 1960 sites: Archedive (1981), Glenroy (1973) and Roy Bridge (1973) all in Westerness; Loch Bran (1981) and Glen Tromie (1981) in Easterness and Glen Tanar, Aberdeenshire (1971).

THREAT The drainage and overgrazing of boggy ground and clearance of damp woodlands for conversion to intensive forestry; ditching of streams or seepages.

MANAGEMENT Maintain boggy ground and muddy streamsides in an undisturbed condition with a high, relatively stable water level and unimpeded patterns of seepage. Retain a shading influence.

LIMONIA CTENOPHORA (Loew)   VULNERABLE TIPULIDAE

DISTRIBUTION Eight known sites scattered in south-east England: two in the Cambridge area (1906 and 1921), Lode (post 1976) and Snailwell (1907), Cambridgeshire; Hitchin, Hertfordshire (1918); Matley Bog, Hampshire (1937); Beddington, Surrey (1964) and Wye, Kent (1963).

HABITAT Broadleaved woodland, requiring the presence of old trees and dead wood.

ECOLOGY The larvae have been reared from a range of dead wood including a rot hole in a presumably living horse chestnut, a hollow stump or fallen trunk of elm and also poplar and chestnut. A female has been observed ovipositing in elm sap. Adults are recorded from May to July.

STATUS Only three known post 1960 sites, suggesting it is now in a very vulnerable position.

THREAT The destruction of old woodlands in southern England; the removal of old diseased trees and dead wood from within such sites.

MANAGEMENT Retain any old or diseased trees and dead wood, ensuring continuity of these in the future.

LIMONIA DANICA (Kuntze)
RARE
TIPULIDAE

DISTRIBUTION Some 13 sites scattered over southern England (Somerset, Suffolk, Norfolk, Kent, Huntingdonshire, Gloucestershire, Essex and Northamptonshire). Its stronghold seems to lie in the marshes of the Thames estuary.

HABITAT Brackish marshland with bare mud and sparse vegetation, usually in coastal areas, though when occurring inland a brackish influence is usually present.

ECOLOGY Larvae develop in sparsely vegetated wet mud. Adults recorded from July to October.

STATUS All the known sites carry post 1960 records and about half of the sites belong to the Thames marshes in North Kent and Essex, and it has been noted as fairly abundant at Brightlingsea Manor Marsh, Essex (1983) and the Isle of Grain, Kent (1966). The Thames estuary sites are under particular threat. Status revised from RDB2 (Shirt 1987).

THREAT Drainage of wetlands for agricultural reclamation; pollution from industry or agricultural run-off; the loss of brackish conditions in coastal marshes following sea wall construction or improvements; complete or extensive clearance of marginal vegetation from beside water such as through ditching.

MANAGEMENT Maintain a high, relatively stable water level which should ensure patches of bare wet mud which may provide the breeding site. Employ rotational ditch or pond management if necessary. Attempt to maintain a continuity of brackish conditions in coastal marsh.

LIMONIA DISTENDENS (Lundstroem)
NOTABLE
TIPULIDAE

DISTRIBUTION A marked disjunct distribution, with most records from upland areas of Scotland and Wales especially north-west Wales, and with additional sites from the New Forest, Hampshire (not since 1937) and Devils Punch Bowl, Surrey (1974).

HABITAT Boggy ground, especially that with seepages.

ECOLOGY Biology unknown. The larvae possibly develop in boggy soil or moss. Adults recorded from May to July.

STATUS About 15 known post 1960 sites mainly from Scotland and North Wales with one site in Surrey.

THREAT The destruction of boggy ground through drainage and conversion to agriculture or intensive forestry; mis-management of water levels with a subsequent loss of breeding sites and scrub invasion; possibly excessive trampling with a consequent loss of vegetation.

MANAGEMENT Maintain a high, relatively stable water level in boggy areas and a natural pattern of seepage.

LIMONIA FRONTALIS (Staeger)
ENDANGERED
TIPULIDAE

DISTRIBUTION Only two known sites: Stroat, Gloucestershire (13 October 1979) and Hill House Wood, Bodenham, Herefordshire (11 October 1987).

HABITAT The Stroat site is alder carr in woodland with a stream. Hill House wood is an artificial terrace in woodland with bramble and bracken, but there is the possibility of a nearby river bank being the true breeding site.

ECOLOGY Biology unknown. The larvae possibly develop in damp soil. The adult flight period seems confined to the autumn.

STATUS A recent addition to the British list, possibly confined to the southern Welsh Borders.

THREAT The destruction of alder carr and damp woodland through drainage for agriculture or intensive forestry; ditching of streams and river improvement; excessive trampling of banks and pollution such as agricultural run-off.

MANAGEMENT Uncertain other than retaining sites in a natural state, free from undue disturbance.

LIMONIA CORITIENSIS (Mik)
RARE
TIPULIDAE

DISTRIBUTION Widely scattered records for rocky shores in England, Wales and Scotland, predominating in south-west England (including Lundy) and Wales.

HABITAT Seepages and less frequently streamlets, on coastal cliffs and rock faces.

ECOLOGY Biology unknown. The larvae probably develop in the damp soil of seepages. Adults recorded from April to October.

STATUS About 15 widely scattered post 1960 sites.

THREAT Probably fairly secure at most of its sites due to the innaccessible nature of the habitat, but in some areas coastal development and associated cliff drainage and stabilisation could be a problem.

MANAGEMENT Safeguard the presence of seepages on cliffs and elsewhere, maintaining natural drainage patterns and any associated vegetation or marshy areas.

LIMONIA HALTERELLA (Edwards)

DISTRIBUTION Confined to Scotland with four sites in Easterness, four sites in Westerness and old records from Arran, Elgin and Perthshire. This species is surprisingly unknown from the many well recorded sites along Speyside and Deeside.

HABITAT Boggy ground, usually beside streams in shaded situations.

ECOLOGY Biology unknown. The larvae possibly develop in streamside soil, gravel or moss. Adults appear to have a very limited flight period in August.

STATUS All the eight post 1960 records are from 13 to 18 August 1981 taken by A.E. Stubbs, with all records prior to this being pre 1938. This suggests that a short flight period is shown by this species during a month which is not favoured by recorders visiting Scotland (June seems most popular) and it may be that this species has been overlooked.

THREAT The destruction of boggy areas through drainage for intensive forestry; also ditching of streams and the localised effects of peat cutting.

MANAGEMENT Maintain streamsides and boggy areas in an undisturbed condition with a high, relatively stable water level and retaining any element of shade.

LIMONIA GRACILIS (Doane)

DISTRIBUTION Confined to Scotland with four sites in Easterness, four sites in Westerness and old records from Arran, Elgin and Perthshire. This species is surprisingly unknown from the many well recorded sites along Speyside and Deeside.

HABITAT Boggy ground, usually besides streams in shaded situations.

ECOLOGY Biology unknown. The larvae possibly develop in streamside soil, gravel or moss. Adults appear to have a very limited flight period in August.

STATUS All the eight post 1960 records are from 13 to 18 August 1981 taken by A. E. Stubbs, with all records prior to this being pre 1938. This suggests that a short flight period is shown by this species during a month which is not favoured by recorders visiting Scotland (June seems most popular) and it may be that this species has been overlooked.

THREAT The destruction of boggy areas through drainage for intensive forestry; also ditching of streams and the localised effects of peat cutting.

MANAGEMENT Maintain streamsides and boggy areas in an undisturbed condition with a high, relatively stable water level and retaining any element of shade.

LIMONIA HALTERATA (Osten Sacken)

DISTRIBUTION Only known from two coastal localities in Scotland: Inverscaddle Bay, Argyllshire (1983) and Muir of Ord, Ross and Cromarty (1984).

HABITAT The upper tidal fringe of saltmarsh.

ECOLOGY Biology unknown. The larvae possibly develop in wet brackish mud.

STATUS Only the two post 1960 sites. This species has not yet been published as British.

THREAT Habitat loss to coastal development and agriculture, including overgrazing of upper-saltmarsh which leads to an altered vegetation; pollution such as agricultural run-off and industrial run-off. This species is not listed in Shirt (1987).

MANAGEMENT Prevent overgrazing and maintain upper saltmarsh fringe in a natural state, retaining any pools or ditches.

126

LIMONIA INUSTA (Meigen)

DISTRIBUTION A local species in England as far north as Yorkshire and Wales, records predominating in southern counties.

HABITAT Damp woodland and carr in lowland areas.

ECOLOGY The larvae breed within fungi including decaying Merulius tremellosus. Adults recorded from June to September.

STATUS About 40 known post 1960 sites from throughout the known range, but old records are very few. It is a rather nondescript species that seems to occur at very low population levels, making it difficult to detect in the field.

THREAT The destruction and degrading of damp woodland and carr through clearance and drainage for intensive agriculture or forestry.

MANAGEMENT Maintain habitat diversity in woods with a high, relatively stable water level in marshy areas and retain any dead wood and old or diseased trees which could support suitable fungi.

LIMONIA LUCIDA (de Meijere)

DISTRIBUTION Records scattered widely in England as far north as Lancashire, also North Wales.

HABITAT Normally associated with stands of hemlock water-dropwort Oenanthe crocata in carr and wet woodland

ECOLOGY Biology unknown. The larvae probably develop in saturated mud or leaf litter. Adults recorded from June to August.

STATUS About 30 known post 1960 sites from throughout the known range.

THREAT The destruction of carr and damp woodland through drainage and clearance for agriculture or intensive forestry; the loss of O. crocata stands through river improvement schemes, ditching of streams, cutting of vegetation and excessive trampling of banks; pollution such as agricultural run-off. The presumed larval development sites tend to be highly localised, so they are vulnerable to elimination.

MANAGEMENT Retain any lush shaded marshy areas with stands of O. crocata, ensuring a relatively high stable water level in these and the continued presence of shading carr, trees etc.

LIMONIA MAGNICAUDA (Lundstroem)   VULNERABLE
                                                    TIPULIDAE

DISTRIBUTION .Only three known sites: Whitlaw Moss NNR, Roxburghshire (1976): Lochmaben, Dumfriesshire (1976) and Llyn Hafodol, Anglesey (1976, 1987).

HABITAT Quaking bog, especially in areas of bare wet peat among Agrostis stolonifera.

ECOLOGY Biology unknown. The larvae probably develop in saturated peat. Adults recorded in July and August.

STATUS A very recent addition to the British list and not listed in Shirt (1987). At the Anglesey site it was recorded in relative abundance.

THREAT The destruction of quaking bog through drainage and conversion to agriculture, intensive forestry, excessive trampling and peat cutting; mis-management of water levels with a subsequent loss of breeding sites and scrub invasion.

MANAGEMENT Ensure a high, stable water level and areas of bare wet peat and prevent any drying out and scrub invasion.

LIMONIA MASONI (Edwards)   RARE
                                                    TIPULIDAE

DISTRIBUTION Records highly dispersed in England (Surrey, Oxfordshire, Norfolk, Cambridgeshire, Leicestershire, Northamptonshire, Derbyshire, Cheshire), predominating in the Peak District.

HABITAT Calcareous woodland edges and scrub. There is an old record from Bagshot, Surrey which is in a non-calcareous area.

ECOLOGY Biology unknown. The larvae possibly develop in damp earth, leaf litter or wood mould. Adults recorded in May and June.

STATUS About a dozen known post 1960 sites mainly in Yorkshire, the Peak District of Derbyshire and the East Midlands.

THREAT The destruction of calcareous woods through clearance for intensive forestry or agriculture.

MANAGEMENT Maintain a scrub or herb rich border along woodland edges, preventing the encroachment of agriculture or conifer plantations right up to the wood. Retain all dead wood, old or diseased trees and any marshy areas as potential breeding sites.

LIMONIA OCCIDUA (Edwards)   NOTABLE
                                                    TIPULIDAE

DISTRIBUTION A northern species with records scattered widely in Scotland including Mull; also Durham, Yorkshire and Herefordshire in England.

HABITAT Seepages and bogs with rushes and other vegetation in upland areas, reaching altitudes of about 300m in Perthshire.

ECOLOGY Biology unknown. The larvae possibly develop in boggy soil or moss. Adults recorded in June and July.

STATUS About a dozen known post 1960 sites, mainly from Scotland, with two in Durham (High Force and Bowless Beck, both 1981) and Widdybank Pasture, Yorkshire (1981).

THREAT The destruction of bogs and seepages in upland areas through drainage for intensive forestry or agriculture.

MANAGEMENT Maintain a high, relatively stable water level in boggy areas, with natural patterns of seepage, and avoid trampling or overgrazing by animals.

LIMONIA OMISSINERVIS (de Meijere)   VULNERABLE
                                                    TIPULIDAE

DISTRIBUTION Only seven known sites: two along the Spey Valley near Aviemore, Elgin (1981 and 1911): Wentworth Pond, Yorkshire (1982); the River Usk at Newbridge, Monmouthshire (1972, 1973): Ross-on-Wye, Herefordshire (1973): River Clyde at Carmyle, Lanarkshire and the River Tay near Caputh, Perthshire (1977).

HABITAT Alluvial, usually sandy river banks within the shade of alders, willows or other trees.

ECOLOGY Biology unknown. The larvae probably develop in alluvial river banks. Adults recorded in July and August.

STATUS Apart from the 1911 specimen, all records are after 1972 when it was recognised as British. Though it may be more widespread, it does seem to be very localised even on its chosen rivers. It can occasionally occur in good numbers at sites along the River Spey and River Usk.

THREAT River improvement including the removal of trees and damage to the banks through excessive trampling etc., also pollution such as agricultural run-off.

MANAGEMENT Maintain the presence of undisturbed alluvial or sandy river banks with some trees for shade.

LIMONIA ORNATA (Meigen)

DISTRIBUTION Records widely dispersed in England and southern parts of Scotland as far north as Midlothian.

HABITAT In stands of butterbur Petasites hybridus along canals and rivers.

ECOLOGY The larvae have been reared from the decaying petioles of butterbur. Adults recorded mainly from May to early June, but extending to July.

STATUS About 10 known post 1960 sites in Surrey, Berkshire, Herefordshire, Wiltshire and Lanarkshire. Old records are comparatively numerous especially from the North Midlands and northern England though no recent records could be obtained. Status revised from RDB3 (Shirt 1987).

THREAT The degrading of river banks in calcareous areas through river improvement. This species was eliminated from one site as the result of mowing butterbur. Pollution such as agricultural run-off and excessive trampling of river banks could be a problem.

MANAGEMENT Maintain substantial stands of butterbur.

LIMONIA QUADRIMACULATA (Linnaeus)

DISTRIBUTION Records restricted to Epping Forest, Essex (1912); Windsor Forest, Berkshire (up to 1977) and at least four sites within the New Forest including Mark Ash (1973) and Burley Old Inclosure (1986).

HABITAT Ancient broadleaved woodland with old trees and stumps, especially beech Fagus.

ECOLOGY The larvae develop in the bracket fungi Inonotus hispidus on beech and Polyporus schweinitzii. Adults recorded from May to August.

STATUS Only three known post 1960 sites, though possibly fairly secure in the New Forest and Windsor. It may however be extinct at Epping Forest which is now degraded as the result of removal of many old trees and much of the fallen timber. This species is not listed in Shirt (1987).

THREAT The clearance of ancient woodland and removal of old or diseased trees and dead wood from within sites (which support the required fungi).

MANAGEMENT Retain any dead wood and old or diseased trees, ensuring continuity of these in the future.

LIMONIA RUFIVENTRIS (Strobl)

DISTRIBUTION Known from a small number of sites in Scotland: Bonawe nr. Taynuilt, Argyllshire (1919); Aviemore (1903) and Nethy Bridge (1906), Elgin: Arisaig (1981) and Clunes (1981), Westerness.

HABITAT Boggy ground and seepages.

ECOLOGY Biology unknown. The larvae probably develop in boggy ground or moss. Adults recorded in July and August.

STATUS Only two known post 1960 sites. The flight period has not been extensively covered by recording in the Highlands.

THREAT The destruction of bogs in Scotland through drainage for intensive forestry or agriculture, also peat cutting and pollution such as agricultural run-off.

MANAGEMENT Maintain a high, stable water level in boggy areas and natural patterns of seepage.

LIMONIA STIGMATICA (Meigen)

DISTRIBUTION A north-western species recorded widely in Scotland, including Rhum, North Uist, South Uist and Benbecula, North Wales (Montgomeryshire, Caernarvonshire, Denbighshire) and England (Herefordshire).

HABITAT Wet woodlands and boggy ground, usually in upland valleys.

ECOLOGY Biology unknown. The larvae probably develop in boggy ground or moss. Adults recorded from June to September.

STATUS Some 15 known post 1960 sites from widely throughout the known range including Wales and Herefordshire.

THREAT The destruction of wet woodlands and boggy habitat through drainage and clearance for intensive forestry or agriculture. Peat cutting could have a local effect in some parts of its range.

MANAGEMENT Maintain a high, stable water level in bogs and marshy areas.

LIMONIA STYLIFERA (Lackschewitz) VULNERABLE TIPULIDAE

DISTRIBUTION A number of sites in Perthshire: near White Bridge (1935), Lochan na Lairige (1932) and Meall Nan Tarmachan (1961); also Moor House NNR, Westmorland (1954-6) and Inchnadamph NNR, Sutherland (1986).

HABITAT Base rich flushes in uplands (up to 500m in Perthshire) and probably in association with calcareous outcrops, which would greatly restrict and localise the areas of suitable habitat.

ECOLOGY Biology unknown. The larvae possibly develop in marshy ground or moss. Adults recorded in June and July.

STATUS Only two known posts 1960 sites. There is no obvious reason why it should not still exist at Moor House and other parts of the Breadalbanes. Status revised from RDB3 (Shirt 1987).

THREAT The destruction of base rich marshy areas and flushes through drainage for intensive forestry or improved grazing; excessive disturbance through human trampling could provide a local problem.

MANAGEMENT Maintain a natural pattern of drainage in flushes and seepages and a high, stable water level in associated marshy areas.

LIMONIA TRIVITTATA (Schummel) NOTABLE TIPULIDAE

DISTRIBUTION A clumped distribution in England, Wales and Scotland, including Jura and the Isle of Barra.

HABITAT Wet woodlands on calcareous soils, especially beside rivers.

ECOLOGY Biology unknown but there seems to be a partial association with butterbur Petasites hybridus and larvae may develop in petioles or rootstocks. Adults recorded from June to September.

STATUS About 35 known post 1960 sites from widely throughout the known range. It can be fairly common at certain sites.

THREAT The destruction of the habitat through clearance for intensive forestry or agriculture; also river improvement schemes, excessive trampling or mowing of banks and pollution such as agricultural run-off.

MANAGEMENT Maintain sites in a natural state with substantial stands of butterbur.

LIMONIA UNISERIATA (Schiner) RARE TIPULIDAE

DISTRIBUTON Records scattered thinly in southern England (Somerset, Hampshire, Kent, Surrey, Middlesex, Hertfordshire, Berkshire, Huntingdonshire).

HABITAT Old broadleaved woodland and probably also parkland, coppice and hedgerow situations where old trees are present. There is a requirement for dead wood or old and diseased trees.

ECOLOGY Reared from a range of dead wood situations including very rotten elm and beech logs; from detritus beneath a dead bird in the cavity of an elm and from white rotted wood debris on a recently felled live beech. A record from a mature coppice of chestnut at Murston, Kent suggests dead wood of this species is also suitable, though at a good number of sites elm seems to be the main species used. Adults recorded from April to July.

STATUS About a dozen known post 1960 sites from widely within the known range, however it may now be extinct at many of its former sites following Dutch Elm Disease. Status revised from RDB2 (Shirt 1987).

THREAT The clearance of old broadleaved woodland and removal of old diseased trees and dead wood. The loss of elm has probably had serious deleterious consequences.

MANAGEMENT Retain any dead wood and old or diseased trees, and ensure continuity of these in the future.

LIMONIA VENTRALIS (Schummel) NOTABLE TIPULIDAE

DISTRIBUTION Records widely dispersed in England, Scotland, including the Hebrides and a number of sites in South Wales.

HABITAT Many records refer to brackish ditches on coastal levels, whilst others refer to inland locations at muddy sparsely vegetated margins of lakes and ponds. Whilst brackish conditions are obviously tolerated, its presence at inland sites suggests this is not essential and sparse emergent vegetation is probably a more essential feature. A record from a mature chestnut coppice in North Kent probably refers to a straggler from nearby coastal marshes.

ECOLOGY Larvae develop in brackish pools amongst vegetation. Adults recorded from May to October.

STATUS About 30 known post 1960 sites from widely throughout the known range. The greatest concentration of recent records are from the rather threatened North Kent marshes. Status revised from RDB3 (Shirt 1987).

THREAT The loss of wetlands through drainage for agriculture, intensive forestry or coastal developments; pollution such as agricultural run-off; mis-management of water levels with a loss of breeding sites and scrub invasion.

MANAGEMENT Maintain a high, relatively stable water level at sites. Employ rotational ditch or pond management where necessary, and note that it is possible that the trampling of ditch edges by cattle may be beneficial in producing muddy sparsely vegetated areas.

LIPSOTHRIX ECUCULLATA Edwards   RARE
TIPULIDAE

DISTRIBUTION Records widely dispersed in the Scottish Highlands within Stirlingshire, Perthshire, Easterness, Elgin, West Ross and Sutherland.

HABITAT Seepages in damp woods in highland districts, strongly avoiding acid sites.

ECOLOGY Biology unknown. The larvae of this genus normally develop in wet rotten wood. Adults recorded in June and July.

STATUS Of the nine known sites, eight are post 1960 and six of these were recorded by A. E. Stubbs, suggesting that this species may occur in more Scottish sites if specifically searched for. The comparative lack of records for the many well visited sites of Speyside is intriguing. Status revised from RDB2 (Shirt 1987).

THREAT The clearance of damp woodland for intensive forestry or agriculture. Also pollution such as agricultural run-off.

MANAGEMENT Maintain woods in a natural state with a high, relatively stable water level in marshy areas and around seepages, and retain any dead wood ensuring continuity of this resource in future.

LIPSOTHRIX ERRANS (Walker)   NOTABLE
TIPULIDAE

DISTRIBUTION Essentially a northern species, recorded widely in Scotland including Mull; also Durham (1898) and scattered localities in Wales (within Breconshire, Cardiganshire, Merionethshire, Denbighshire).

HABITAT Wooded streamsides in upland districts.

ECOLOGY Biology unknown. The larvae of this genus are generally assumed to develop in wet, rotten wood. Adults recorded from May to July.

STATUS Some 18 known post 1960 sites, widely scattered and with comparatively few older records.

THREAT The clearance of broadleaved woodland for agriculture or intensive forestry; also ditching of streams, excessive trampling of banks and pollution such as agricultural run-off.

MANAGEMENT Maintain wooded streamsides in a natural state, retaining any marshy areas and dead wood.

LIPSOTHRIX NIGRISTIGMA Edwards   ENDANGERED
TIPULIDAE

DISTRIBUTION Known only from a single specimen taken at Clayton-le-Dale, Lancashire on 1 June 1924.

HABITAT Unclear.

ECOLOGY Unclear. The larvae of this genus are generally thought to develop in wet, rotten wood associated with streams and marshy areas.

STATUS Only the single old record, which represents the type specimen. If not extinct it must be very rare.

THREAT Unclear other than destruction of the known site (the exact location of which is unknown).

MANAGEMENT Unclear.

MOLOPHILUS BIHAMATUS de Meijere   NOTABLE
TIPULIDAE

DISTRIBUTION Records widely dispersed in England (Hampshire, Sussex, Surrey, Berkshire, Norfolk, Huntingdonshire, Cambridgeshire, Westmorland, Yorkshire) and three post 1960 sites in Sutherland, Scotland.

HABITAT Usually wet alder carr.

ECOLOGY Biology unknown. The larvae possibly develop in damp soil or leaf litter. Adults recorded from May to July.

STATUS About a dozen known post 1960 sites scattered widely. This species appears to be somewhat elusive and possibly under recorded.

THREAT The destruction of alder carr through clearance and drainage for agriculture or intensive forestry. Also mis-management of water levels with a subsequent loss of breeding sites.

MANAGEMENT Maintain the carr in a natural state with a high, relatively stable water level.

MOLOPHILUS CORNIGER de Meijere NOTABLE TIPULIDAE

DISTRIBUTION Recorded widely in calcareous districts of England, Wales and parts of Scotland including Arran.

HABITAT Seepage woodland, usually alder carr in calcareous districts.

ECOLOGY Biology unknown. The larvae possibly develop in damp soil or leaf litter. Adults recorded from May to August.

STATUS About 20 known post 1960 sites scattered widely.

THREAT The destruction of the required habitat through clearance and drainage for intensive agriculture or forestry. Also mis-management of water levels with a subsequent loss of breeding sites.

MANAGEMENT Maintain carr and damp woodland in a natural state with a high, relatively stable water level.

MOLOPHILUS CZIZEKI Lackschewitz RARE TIPULIDAE

DISTRIBUTION Scattered records in upland areas of Scotland (Argyllshire, Perthshire, Aberdeenshire, Ross-shire), northern England (Lancashire, Westmorland) and Wales (Glamorganshire, Breconshire).

HABITAT Seepages in upland woods.

ECOLOGY Biology unknown. The larvae possibly develop in damp soil or leaf litter. Adults recorded in May and June.

STATUS Nine known post 1960 sites scattered widely.

THREAT The destruction of upland woods through clearance and for intensive forestry or agriculture.

MANAGEMENT Maintain woods in a natural state retaining any marshy areas and seepages.

MOLOPHILUS LACKSCHEWITZIANUS Alexander RARE TIPULIDAE

DISTRIBUTION Records widely dispersed in England (Devon, Surrey, Kent, Berkshire, Lancashire and Yorkshire); also Montgomeryshire in Wales.

HABITAT Usually heavily shaded clay woods with incised streams, occasionally in more open conditions.

ECOLOGY Biology unknown. The larvae possibly develop in damp soil or leaf litter. Adults recorded in May and June.

STATUS All nine sites are post 1960. This species was only described as new to science in 1952 and was not recognised as British until 1976. The apparent habitat preference is highly localised.

THREAT Habitat loss through clearance for agriculture or intensive forestry; ditching of streams and excessive trampling of banks; also pollution such as agricultural run-off.

MANAGEMENT Maintain sites in a natural and undisturbed condition, in particular retain incised stream banks which may provide the breeding site.

MOLOPHILUS NIGER Goetghebuer NOTABLE TIPULIDAE

DISTRIBUTION A clumped distribution in England (Devon, Somerset, Hampshire, Berkshire, Northamptonshire, Cheshire, Lancashire), Wales (Breconshire) and Scotland (Dunbartonshire, Rhum).

HABITAT Lushly vegetated streamsides in woods, usually in calcareous districts.

ECOLOGY Biology unknown. The larvae possibly develop in damp soil or vegetation beside streams. Adults found from April to June.

STATUS Only four known post 1960 records: Kinloch, Rhum (1960); Sydmonton Common, Hampshire (1973); Headley Ford, Berkshire (1973) and Ashclyst Wood, Devon (1978). Probably under recorded to some extent.

THREAT Clearance and drainage of damp woodland for agriculture or intensive forestry. Also canalisation of streams, excessive trampling of banks and pollution such as agricultural run-off.

MANAGEMENT Maintain a rich marginal vegetation along streamsides and retain shading influences.

MOLOPHILUS PROPINQUUS (Egger)

DISTRIBUTION Records scattered widely in England, Wales and Scotland, most numerous for Scotland and North Wales.

HABITAT Moist sandy banks of streams and ditches, either shaded or open.

ECOLOGY Larvae probably develop in wet sandy soil of the above locations. Adults recorded from May to July.

STATUS About 15 known post 1960 sites scattered widely.

THREAT Disturbance and drainage of sandy banks through canalisation and ditching; also excessive trampling of banks and pollution such as agricultural run-off.

MANAGEMENT Maintain sandy stream and ditch banks in a natural state free from excessive disturbance.

MOLOPHILUS VARIISPINUS Stary

DISTRIBUTION A northern and western species with 6 known sites: Nant Sere Wood (1976) and Cathedine Common (1976), Breconshire; Castle Eden Dene, Durham (1978), Den of Airlie, Angus (1981); Pass of Killiecrankie, Perthshire (1986) and Struy Oxbows, Easterness (1981).

HABITAT Damp woods.

ECOLOGY Biology unknown. The larvae are thought to develop in damp mud or sand. Adults recorded from June to August.

STATUS A recent addition to the British list (1977), with all six records recent. It was only formally described in 1971.

THREAT Drainage and clearance of sites for intensive forestry or agriculture.

MANAGEMENT Maintain habitat diversity in woods, retaining any marshy areas, seepages etc.

133

NEOLIMNOPHILA CARTERI (Tonnoir)

DISTRIBUTION Essentially northern with records widely dispersed in Scotland (Lanarkshire, Midlothian, East Ross, Rhum), northern England (Shropshire, Derbyshire, Cheshire, Lancashire, Westmorland, Yorkshire) also Flintshire in Wales and a very isolated record from Brockenhurst, Hampshire (1969).

HABITAT Damp woods with streams.

ECOLOGY Biology unknown. The larvae are thought to develop in damp soil. Adults recorded from May to July.

STATUS A decline seems apparent with only six known post 1960 sites in contrast to a relatively large number of old records. This could be in part due to relatively intense levels of recording in northern England in the earlier part of this century.

THREAT Drainage and clearance of damp woods for intensive forestry or agriculture; also ditching of streams, excessive trampling of banks and pollution such as agricultural run-off.

MANAGEMENT Maintain wooded streams in a natural state retaining any marshy areas and preventing any undue disturbance to banks.

NEOLIMNOPHILA PLACIDA (Meigen)

DISTRIBUTION Records widely dispersed in England (Kent, Hertfordshire, Nottinghamshire, Yorkshire).

HABITAT Damp woods with streams.

ECOLOGY Biology unknown. The larvae are thought to develop in damp soil. Adults recorded from May to September.

STATUS A poorly known species which is rather nondescript and liable to be under recorded, hence only given notable status.

THREAT Clearance and drainage of damp woods for intensive forestry or agriculture; also ditching of streams, excessive trampling of banks and pollution such as agricultural run-off.

MANAGEMENT Maintain streams in a natural state free from excessive disturbance, retaining any marshy areas.

NEPHROTOMA ACULEATA (Loew)

VULNERABLE
TIPULIDAE

DISTRIBUTION Records confined to a small area of the Scottish Highlands along Speyside in Elgin: Forres (1900), Nethy Bridge (1906), Aviemore (1903) and Logie (1903); also Tomintoul, Banffshire (1937).

HABITAT Abroad, this species has been recorded from willow scrub by rivers with sandy banks. These conditions are found on the River Spey and several of the other known locations.

ECOLOGY Biology unknown. The larvae probably develop in sandy alluvial material beneath herbaceous vegetation and shrubs. Adults recorded in August.

STATUS Last recorded in 1937. Not found on recent surveys despite earlier reports that it was locally common. The late and possibly short flight period may account for it being elusive since it seems unlikely that it could disappear from all its sites. Status revised from RDB3 (Shirt 1987).

THREAT Disturbance to sandy river banks through river improvement schemes, excessive trampling and removal of shading shrubs and trees.

MANAGEMENT Maintain sandy river riverbanks in an undisturbed state with some trees and shrubs for shade.

NEPHROTOMA CROCATA (Linnaeus)

RARE
TIPULIDAE

DISTRIBUTION Records widely dispersed in England, extending thinly into Wales and up to Midlothian in Scotland. Old records are particularly numerous for Yorkshire and Surrey.

HABITAT Requirements, unclear, heathy woods and fen woodland seem to be favoured.

ECOLOGY The larva has been found in damp soil. Adults recorded from May to August.

STATUS A very marked decline is obvious with 15 known post 1960 sites for this striking and unmistakeable cranefly. In the past it was quite frequent in southern counties, especially the Surrey heaths and parts of northern England, even locally abundant. Recent records are for a small number of sites in Yorkshire and sites in Cheshire, Northamptonshire, Norfolk, Lancashire, Warwickshire and Surrey.

THREAT Habitat loss to agriculture and intensive forestry; scrub invasion on heaths; drainage of any damp areas.

MANAGEMENT Uncertain other than careful management of sites where known to persist, maintaining a full range of conditions including a high, relatively stable water level in any marshy areas and preventing scrub invasion on heathland and in rides and clearings of woods.

NEPHROTOMA DORSALIS (Fabricius)

NOTABLE
TIPULIDAE

DISTRIBUTION Records widely dispersed in England, North Wales and Scotland, predominating in the north, though with a further stronghold in the New Forest.

HABITAT Sandy river banks, usually beside woodlands.

ECOLOGY The larva has been found in damp soil, possibly from river banks. Adults recorded from May to August.

STATUS Some 25 known post 1960 sites, over half from Scotland, others widely dispersed in England and Wales.

THREAT The loss or degrading of sandy river banks and removal of adjacent tree or shrub cover through river improvement schemes, and excessive trampling of banks; pollution such as agricultural run-off.

MANAGEMENT Maintain sandy river banks in a natural condition and retain marginal trees or shrubs.

NEPHROTOMA LUNULICORNIS (Schummel)

NOTABLE
TIPULIDAE

DISTRIBUTION Records widely dispersed in western and northern England (Somerset, Gloucestershire, Herefordshire, Cheshire, Lancashire, Yorkshire); also Scotland (Elgin) and Wales (Monmouthshire). A strong westerly bias is apparent.

HABITAT Sandy river banks with trees and scrub or in wooded stretches. There seems to be a preference for the stretches of rivers below the torrential upper reaches, though above the gentle sluggish sections. On the River Spey it is seemingly confined to the lower reaches, but where the flow is still fairly fast.

ECOLOGY The larvae probably develop in sandy alluvium beneath vegetation and leaf litter. Adults recorded from May to July (also October according to Coe).

STATUS Seven known post 1960 sites scattered widely. Status revised from RDB3 (Shirt 1987).

THREAT The destruction of riverside habitat on the middle sections of rivers through river improvement schemes, excessive trampling of banks, encroachment of agriculture and intensive forestry and pollution such as agricultural run-off.

MANAGEMENT Maintain sandy river banks in a natural state, free from excessive disturbance, with some trees or shrubs for shade.

NEPHROTOMA QUADRISTRIATA (Schummel) VULNERABLE TIPULIDAE

DISTRIBUTION Confined to major sand dune systems on the west coast of England and Wales, namely Newborough Warren NNR (1976) and Aberffraw (1987), Anglesey; Morfa Harlech NNR (1967, 1987) and Morfa Dyffryn NNR (1959) both in Merionethshire; Glamorgan Lower Peninsula (Oxwich NNR), Glamorganshire (1959 and possibly more recently); Braunton Burrows NNR, Devon (1923 and 1973).

HABITAT Sand dunes, usually at the rear margins of mobile dunes adjoining dune slacks.

ECOLOGY Biology unknown. The larvae possibly develop in the damp sand and vegetation of slacks. Adults recorded in July and August.

STATUS Only four known post 1960 sites. Whilst most of the sites are NNRs, none can claim to be free from recreational pressures. Status revised from RDB3 (Shirt 1987).

THREAT Recreational pressures with subsequent dune erosion and 'blow-outs'; lowering of water tables in slacks.

MANAGEMENT Ensure a full succession of vegetation types on dunes; maintain a high, relatively stable water level in slacks. Minimise recreational pressure using fences and boardwalks where necessary.

NEPHROTOMA SULLINGTONENSIS Edwards ENDANGERED TIPULIDAE

DISTRIBUTION Known from only one site, Sullington Warren, West Sussex (1938 and 1983).

HABITAT Heathland with pine woods. It was recently found beside a sandy path across a patch of heather with lichens. This patch is in a glade only 100m across, surrounded by pine. It is not known whether the insect is strictly confined to this type of habitat on the site.

ECOLOGY Biology unknown. The larvae probably develop in the soil. Adults present in June.

STATUS At the single known locality it was taken on two occasions in June 1938. The Warren was subject to several unsuccessful searches in the 1970s, but two males and a female were found on 4 June 1983. The area of available habitat is extremely small since pine now covers much of the site, the other remaining areas being mostly grassland. Southern heathland and pine woods have been well worked for craneflies, especially in the adjacent county of Surrey, so this appears to be a genuinely very rare insect.

THREAT The degrading of the known site through pine encroachment and accidental summer fires. The small area could be vulnerable to trampling.

MANAGEMENT Maintain Calluna heathland at the known site. Attempt to determine the precise habitat requirements of this species.

ORIMARGA JUVENILIS (Zetterstedt) NOTABLE TIPULIDAE

DISTRIBUTION A mainly northern species with records widely dispersed in Scotland including Mull and Rhum, more sparsely in England (Yorkshire, Lancashire, Berkshire, Isle of Wight and Devon) and two sites in Anglesey.

HABITAT Usually at boggy seepages with wet mud or peat with sparse vegetation.

ECOLOGY Biology unknown. The larvae are thought to inhabit wet peat. Adults recorded in June and July.

STATUS Some 17 known post 1960 sites, scattered widely though predominating in Scotland. Status revised from RDB3 (Shirt 1987).

THREAT Drainage of boggy seepages for intensive forestry or agriculture; excessive trampling and scrub invasion through lowering of the water table.

MANAGEMENT Maintain high and relatively stable water levels and a natural pattern of seepage.

ORIMARGA VIRGO (Zetterstedt) RARE TIPULIDAE

DISTRIBUTION Recorded widely in England (Devon, Dorset, Yorkshire, Westmorland) and Scotland (Ayrshire, Kintyre, Dunbartonshire, West Ross and Sutherland) and a number of recent records for North Wales (1987). A western bias is shown.

HABITAT Seepages, sometimes in association with small streamlets. There would appear to be a strong affinity with limestone and other base rich sites, in both shaded and open situations. Several of the sites are coastal cliffs.

ECOLOGY Biology unknown. The larvae are thought to live in wet soil or peat. Adults recorded in June and July.

STATUS Extremely local with about 10 known post 1960 sites scattered widely over the known range.

THREAT Drainage of seepages; ditching of small streams; conversion of sites to intensive forestry or agriculture.

MANAGEMENT Maintain seepages and small streams in a natural undisturbed state.

ORMOSIA ACICULATA Edwards

VULNERABLE
TIPULIDAE

DISTRIBUTION Only seven known sites, in northern England: Ingleborough (1921), Holmehouse Wood (1932) and Stonesdale (pre 1938) all in Yorkshire; Cotterill Clough, Cheshire (1923); and Scotland: Braidwood (pre 1938) and Gorge of Avon (pre 1938) both in Lanarkshire and Aviemore, Elgin (pre 1938).

HABITAT Unclear, possibly damp woodland.

ECOLOGY Biology unknown. The larvae possibly develop in soil or leaf litter. Adults recorded from April to June.

STATUS No recent records for this poorly known species suggesting it is now in a vulnerable position. Status revised from RDB3 (Shirt 1987).

THREAT Woodland clearance for intensive forestry or agriculture.

MANAGEMENT Maintain habitat diversity in woods, retaining any marshy areas, streams and dead wood as potential breeding sites.

ORMOSIA BICORNIS (de Meijere)

VULNERABLE
TIPULIDAE

DISTRIBUTION Recorded from Gloucestershire, Herefordshire, Oxfordshire, Hertfordshire, Kent, Huntingdonshire and Yorkshire.

HABITAT Broadleaved woodland on calcareous soil.

ECOLOGY Life history unknown. The larvae possibly develop in soil or leaf litter. Adults recorded in August and September.

STATUS Only three known post 1960 sites: Monks Wood NNR, Huntingdonshire (1967); Murston, Kent (1983) and Haugh Wood, Herefordshire (1981). Other recent records may also exist for the Herefordshire/Gloucestershire district. Status revised from RDB3 (Shirt 1987).

THREAT The clearance of calcareous woods for agriculture or intensive forestry.

MANAGEMENT Maintain habitat diversity in woods retaining any marshy areas, streams and dead wood as potential breeding sites.

ORMOSIA STAEGERIANA Alexander

NOTABLE
TIPULIDAE

DISTRIBUTION The majority of records are from the Central Highlands of Scotland (Easterness, Elgin, Banffshire, Perthshire and Aberdeenshire) where it is locally frequent. Recorded more sparsely in other parts of Scotland (Ross & Cromarty, Midlothian, Isle of Lewis), northern England (Durham and Yorkshire) and North Wales (Denbighshire). An old record from Somerset seems dubious.

HABITAT Boggy flushes in woods.

ECOLOGY Biology unknown. The larvae are thought to live in soil or leaf litter. Adults recorded from June to September.

STATUS About 20 known post 1960 sites, all from the Central Highlands except for one from High Force, Yorkshire (1981).

THREAT The destruction of damp, boggy woodland through clearance or drainage for intensive forestry or agriculture.

MANAGEMENT Maintain habitat diversity in woods, retaining boggy flushes.

PARADELPHOMYIA ECALCARATA (Edwards)

VULNERABLE
TIPULIDAE

DISTRIBUTION Only three known records: Pandy, Denbighshire (1972-79); Llangollen, Flintshire (1914) and Brendon, Devon (pre 1938).

HABITAT Wet woodlands with seepages and small streams in calcareous districts.

ECOLOGY Biology unknown. The larvae possibly develop in mud. Adults recorded in June.

STATUS Only a single post 1960 record though the known distribution of this species corresponds to an under recorded area of Britain. Status revised from RDB3 (Shirt 1987).

THREAT Drainage and clearance of wet woodlands for intensive forestry or agriculture; pollution such as agricultural run-off.

MANAGEMENT Maintain habitat diversity in woods, retaining marshy areas around seepages and along streams.

PARADELPHOMYIA FUSCULA (Loew)

DISTRIBUTION Scattered records in England (Devon, Sussex, Gloucestershire, Shropshire, Yorkshire), Wales (Breconshire, Montgomeryshire, Merionethshire) and Scotland (Dunfriesshire, Elgin, Easterness, Arran).

HABITAT Associated with small shaded streams.

ECOLOGY Biology unknown. The larvae possibly develop in shaded streamside mud. Adults recorded from August to November.

STATUS About 15 known post 1960 sites, mainly from Wales and Scotland with 2 sites in Gloucestershire and 4 in Devon. Status revised from RDB3 (Shirt 1987).

THREAT The degrading of streamside habitats through ditching and the effects of adjacent agriculture or intensive forestry; also pollution such as agricultural run-off.

MANAGEMENT Maintain stream margins in a natural state, retaining shading trees and shrubs.

PARADELPHOMYIA NIELSENI (Kuntze)

DISTRIBUTION Records widely dispersed in England (Devon, Dorset, Sussex, Kent, Shropshire, Cheshire), Wales (Breconshire, Caernarvonshire, Merionethshire) and Scotland (Elgin, Easterness, Westerness).

HABITAT Seepages and streamlets, usually in woods.

ECOLOGY The larvae probably develop in moist sediment or moss at the edge of streams. Adults recorded from July to October.

STATUS About a dozen known post 1960 sites, widely scattered. It may be under recorded in some parts of its range such as West Scotland. Status revised from RDB3 (Shirt 1987).

THREAT Drainage and clearance of woods for intensive forestry or agriculture.

MANAGEMENT Maintain habitat diversity in woods, retaining streams, boggy areas and seepages.

PEDICIA LUCIDIPENNIS (Edwards)

DISTRIBUTION Mainly recorded from the Central Highlands of Scotland (Perthshire, Aberdeenshire, Elgin, Banffshire, Easterness, Westerness, Argyllshire) also from Wales (Cardiganshire, Caernarvonshire).

HABITAT Small streams and flushes in upland areas.

ECOLOGY Biology unknown. The larvae are possibly semi-aquatic, developing in damp mud or moss beside streams or flushes. Adults recorded from June to August.

STATUS Nine known post 1960 sites, mainly from Scotland, one from the Llynfant Valley, Cardiganshire (1970). Status revised from RDB3 (Shirt 1987).

THREAT The destruction of the above habitat through ditching, drainage and conversion to agriculture or intensive forestry.

MANAGEMENT Maintain small streams and flushes in a natural and undisturbed condition retaining any associated marshy areas.

PEDICIA UNICOLOR (Schummel)

DISTRIBUTION Records widely dispersed in Scotland including Rhum and Mull, northern England and North Wales with isolated records in Monmouthshire, Hampshire and Norfolk.

HABITAT Small streams and flushes, usually in shaded situations. Upland areas seem preferred though there are some lowland sites.

ECOLOGY Larva apparently found in marshy soil. Adults recorded from April to June (a record for September seems dubious).

STATUS About 25 known post 1960 sites, mainly from Scotland and North Wales though records exist for Neatishead, Norfolk (1963) and Cwm Coedycerrig, Monmouthshire (1973). It seems to have disappeared from the New Forest where it was taken on several occasions at the start of the century.

THREAT The loss of the above habitat to intensive forestry and agriculture and through ditching of streams, pollution such as agricultural run-off and the removal of shading influences.

MANAGEMENT Maintain streamsides and flushes in a natural and undisturbed state, retaining any elements of shade.

PHALACROCERA REPLICATA (Linnaeus)

DISTRIBUTION Records widely dispersed in England, Wales and Scotland. Records particularly frequent in northern England.

HABITAT Mossy pools, either with Sphagnum or other semi-aquatic mosses, and in both fen and bog.

ECOLOGY The aquatic camouflaged larvae develop in mosses such as Sphagnum and Hypnum. Adults recorded from April to August.

STATUS About 20 known post 1960 sites, scattered widely, though a decline seems apparent, particularly in northern England where past records are widespread and numerous, yet with only five post 1960 sites. This could be, in part, due to relatively high levels of cranefly recording in this area before 1960. Status revised from RDB3 (Shirt 1987).

THREAT Destruction of the above habitat, through drainage and conversion to agriculture or intensive forestry; pollution such as agricultural run-off; trampling of water margins.

MANAGEMENT Maintain a high, relatively stable water level to retain the mossy breeding sites and prevent their drying out.

PILARIA FUSCIPENNIS (Meigen)

DISTRIBUTION Very local in southern counties from Cornwall to Kent, with additional sites in Suffolk, Wales (Breconshire, Cardiganshire), northern England (Yorkshire) and a single site in Argyllshire (Loch Awe, 1973).

HABITAT Bare wet peat in alder carr and damp woods.

ECOLOGY The larvae have been reared from marshy mud or peat. Adults recorded from April to August.

STATUS About 25 known post 1960 sites scattered widely over southern England and Wales.

THREAT Drainage and clearance of carr and damp woodland for intensive forestry and agriculture; pollution such as agricultural run-off; mis-management of water levels with a loss of breeding sites and scrub invasion.

MANAGEMENT Maintain a high, relatively stable water level and retain areas of bare wet peat.

PILARIA MERIDIANA (Staeger)

DISTRIBUTION Essentially a northern and western species with records particularly numerous for the Scottish Highlands; also a number of sites in Wales; Whixall Moss, Shropshire (1937) and Horning Ferry within Bure NNR, Norfolk (pre 1938).

HABITAT Bare wet peat or mud in alder carr and other wet woods, more rarely in open situations. Usually on fairly acid sites.

ECOLOGY Biology unknown. The larvae probably develop in wet mud. Adults recorded from May to August.

STATUS About 20 known post 1960 sites, all from Scotland or Wales.

THREAT Drainage of wetland areas for agricultural improvement or afforestation; pollution such as agricultural run-off; lowering of water levels through mis-management with a subsequent loss of bare wet peat or mud.

MANAGEMENT Maintain a high, relatively stable water level, ensuring areas of bare mud or peat. Shaded conditions may be preferred so retain areas of carr and damp woodland.

PILARIA SCUTELLATA (Staeger)

DISTRIBUTION Records widely dispersed in England (Somerset, Sussex, Surrey, Kent, Essex, Suffolk, Norfolk, Shropshire, Cheshire), Scotland (Dumfriesshire, Kircudbrightshire, Roxburghshire, Angus, Elgin) and Anglesey in Wales. Records particularly numerous for the Surrey heaths and North Kent marshes.

HABITAT Associated with semi-bare humic mud or peat, usually on open sites but occasionally in carr. It tends to be associated with eutrophic sites on acid soils or poor fen.

ECOLOGY Larvae semi-aquatic, probably developing in wet mud. Adults recorded from May to October.

STATUS About 25 known post 1960 sites scattered widely over the known range.

THREAT Drainage of sites for agriculture or intensive forestry; pollution such as agricultural run-off; complete or excessive clearance of marginal vegetation such as through ditching of streams; mis-management of water levels with a loss of semi-bare mud and subsequent scrub invasion.

MANAGEMENT Maintain a high, relatively stable water level in marshes, bogs, carr and by ponds. The presence of sparsely vegetation mud/peat is important. It is possible that limited trampling of ditch and pond edges by cattle is useful in producing muddy areas.

PRIONOCERA PUBESCENS Loew

VULNERABLE
TIPULIDAE

DISTRIBUTION Twelve known sites dispersed in England, Wales and Scotland: Thursley NNR, Surrey (post 1960); Bristol area, Gloucestershire (1920's?); Brockenhurst, Hampshire (1897); Abbots Moss (1943) and Flaxmere (1941) both Cheshire; Ford Valley (1983) and Austwick Moss (1938) both Yorkshire; Cors y Llyn NNR, Radnorshire; Esgyn Bottom, Pembrokeshire (1987); Kirkconnell, Kirkcudbrightshire (1971); Balerno, Midlothian (1913); Dalfaber Bog, Elgin (1981).

HABITAT Basin and valley mire bogs, especially areas of Sphagnum/Juncus grading into Carex nigra/Menyanthes, or Molinia into small Sphagnum pools.

ECOLOGY Biology unknown, though larvae probably semi-aquatic in the mosses or peat of pools and ditches. Adults recorded in May and June.

STATUS Six post 1960 sites of which two are NNRs. The localised nature of the sites and their rapid loss in recent decades places this species in a vulnerable position. Status revised from RDB1 (Shirt 1987).

THREAT Drainage of bogs for agriculture or intensive forestry; pollution such as agricultural run-off; peat cutting in some areas. The Dalfaber Bog site has deteriorated through pollution and test drilling next to a building site and is now due to become a recreational lake.

MANAGEMENT Maintain a high, relatively stable water level with a particular emphasis on the transition zones outlined above. Retain any ditches and ponds.

PRIONOCERA SUBSERRICORNIS (Zetterstedt)

VULNERABLE
TIPULIDAE

DISTRIBUTION Mainly recorded from Norfolk: East Walton Common (1989), Thompson Common (1985) Woodbastick NNR (1987), Alderfen Broad (1987) and Great Catfield Fen (1920, 1987); subsequently it has been located at Woodwalton Fen, Huntingdonshire (1989) and Groby Pool, Leicestershire (1989).

HABITAT Ancient fenland, with most records referring to ditches or pools filled with wet, black organic material and beneath the shade of carr. Such locations are likely to be mildly base rich or neutral, but not acidic. A number of the known sites are 'pingo' systems.

ECOLOGY Larvae likely to develop in the black organic material of the above locations. Adults recorded from June to August and have been observed visiting angelica flowers in the midday sun, as unusual habit for a tipulid.

STATUS Modern records from all its known sites. Thompson Common, Catfield Fen and Alderfen Broad are County Trust Reserves and SSSI's; East Walton Common is a SSSI; Woodbastwick and Woodwalton Fen are NNRs. This species is also rare in Europe. Status revised from RDB1 (Shirt 1987).

THREAT The destruction of wetlands, particularly in East Anglia, through drainage for agriculture or intensive forestry; pollution such as agricultural run-off; removal of shading carr; mis-management of water levels which could lead to a loss of breeding sites and scrub invasion.

MANAGEMENT Maintain a high, relatively stable water level and retain any ponds and ditches, especially those filled with black organic material beneath the shade of carr.

RHABDOMASTIX HILARIS Edwards

RARE
TIPULIDAE

DISTRIBUTION Records predominating in the Central Highlands of Scotland (Easterness, Elgin, Aberdeenshire and Perthshire); also Moor House NNR, Westmorland (1954-6); Newbridge (River Usk), Monmouthshire (1972) and Fyning Moor (River Rother), West Sussex (1974).

HABITAT Banks of rivers where sand shoals are present.

ECOLOGY Biology unknown. The larvae possibly develop in the wet sand of river banks. Adults recorded from June to August.

STATUS Some eight known post 1960 sites, four in Elgin, either along the Spey or its tributaries, the others widely dispersed (Herefordshire, Monmouthshire, Sussex, Aberdeenshire).

THREAT River improvement schemes, pollution such as agricultural run-off and excessive trampling of sand banks.

MANAGEMENT Maintain areas of exposed sand along sandy river banks and prevent any excessive disturbance of these. Retain some trees and shrubs for shade.

RHABDOMASTIX INCLINATA Edwards

VULNERABLE
TIPULIDAE

DISTRIBUTION Only three known localities: Knucklas, Radnorshire (1975); Glen Quoich, Aberdeenshire (1977) and Mulgrave Woods, Yorkshire (1937).

HABITAT The Radnorshire record refers to an alder-lined small stream with grassy seepages on Ludlow rocks. The Aberdeenshire record refers to a partly wooded stream flowing from the Cairngorms.

ECOLOGY Biology unknown. The larvae possibly develop in the wet sand of river banks. Adults recorded from June to September.

STATUS Rather poorly known, with only two relatively recent records and not known from the Spey or other Scottish rivers sampled. Status revised from RDB3 (Shirt 1987).

THREAT River improvement schemes and excessive trampling of banks; pollution such as agricultural run-off; afforestation right up to river banks.

MANAGEMENT Maintain the presence of any sandy river banks and prevent any undue disturbance to these. Retain some shrubs and trees for shade.

SCLEROPROCTA PENTAGONALIS (Loew)

DISTRIBUTION .About seven known sites in Herefordshire, Gloucestershire, Monmouthshire, Flintshire, Derbyshire, Lancashire, Yorkshire and Dumfriesshire.

HABITAT Wet woodland.

ECOLOGY The larvae have been reared through from the fungus Piptoporus betulinus. Adults recorded from May to July.

STATUS Three known post 1960 sites: Cusop Dingle, Herefordshire (1985); Wye Valley, Gloucestershire/Monmouthshire (1982) and Tynron, Dumfriesshire (1972). There has been some confusion surrounding the nomenclature of this species. In Edwards (1938) this species was called Ormosia danica and his S. pentagonalis was actually S. sororcula.

THREAT Clearance of woodland for agriculture or intensive forestry; removal of any dead wood and old or diseased trees which support the host fungi.

MANAGEMENT Maintain habitat diversity in woodlands, retaining any dead wood and old or diseased trees and ensuring continuity of these in the future.

SCLEROPROCTA SORORCULA (Zetterstedt)

DISTRIBUTION Records widely dispersed in England, Wales and Scotland (including Arran and Mull).

HABITAT Wet woodlands.

ECOLOGY Biology unknown. Related species develop in fungi. Adults recorded in May and June.

STATUS About 25 known, widely scattered post 1960 sites. There has been some confusion surrounding the nomenclature of this species. In Edwards (1938) this species was called S. pentagonalis. Status revised from RDB3 (Shirt 1987).

THREAT Clearance of woods for agriculture or intensive forestry.

MANAGEMENT Maintain habitat diversity in woodlands, retaining any marshy areas, streams, dead wood and old or diseased trees which may provide breeding sites.

TASIOCERA COLLINI Freeman

DISTRIBUTION A single record from Chippenham Fen NNR, Cambridgeshire taken on 25 July 1950.

HABITAT The site consists of various fenland types and woodland. The species was taken around a dead poplar.

ECOLOGY Biology unknown. The above observation could suggest a development in dead wood.

STATUS The known site is an NNR and the lack of recent information suggests this species is now very rare.

THREAT Breaks in the continuity of suitable poplar dead wood, if indeed that is the true requirement. There is currently plenty of dead wood of other tree species on the site.

MANAGEMENT Maintain habitat diversity in wet woods, retaining good range of dead wood and ensuring its future continuity.

TASIOCERA JENKINSONI Freeman

DISTRIBUTION Only two Sussex records: Crowborough (14 August 1906) and Rogate (about 1975).

HABITAT Seepage alder carr.

ECOLOGY Biology unknown. Adults recorded in August.

STATUS Only a single post 1960 site suggesting it is now critically rare.

THREAT Destruction of the known sites through drainage and clearance for afforestation or agriculture; also pollution such as agricultural run-off and mis-management of water levels with a loss of potential breeding sites through scrub invasion.

MANAGEMENT Maintain a high, relatively stable water level, and ensure the presence of some carr, but do not allow scrub invasion.

TASIOCERA LAMINATA Freeman
NOTABLE
TIPULIDAE

DISTRIBUTION Known records include Yorkshire, Devon and Cornwall in England and several sites in North Wales, though other records have been reported.

HABITAT Wet woods.

ECOLOGY Biology unknown. Adults recorded in July.

STATUS A poorly known species which is likely to have been considerably under recorded due to its small size. It was taken at a handful of sites in the late 1970s and several sites in North Wales during 1987.

THREAT Unclear other than the drainage and clearance of wet woods for agriculture or intensive forestry.

MANAGEMENT Maintain habitat diversity in wet woods, retaining any marshy areas, streams, dead wood and old or diseased trees, any of which may support breeding sites.

THAUMASTOPTERA CALCEATA Mik
NOTABLE
TIPULIDAE

DISTRIBUTION Recorded widely in England and Wales extending as far north as Yorkshire though with a strong southerly bias.

HABITAT Seepage alder carr, rarely in Phragmites.

ECOLOGY The larvae develop in wet leaf litter and mud where they are case-makers. Adults recorded from May to July.

STATUS About 30 known post 1960 sites widely scattered over the known range.

THREAT The destruction of seepage alder carr through clearance and drainage for agriculture or intensive forestry; also pollution such as agricultural run-off and mis-management of water levels with a loss of breeding sites and scrub invasion.

MANAGEMENT Maintain a high, relatively stable water level in areas of carr, but do not allow scrub invasion.

TIPULA ALPINA Loew
RARE
TIPULIDAE

DISTRIBUTION Nine known sites mostly concentrated in the Morecambe Bay area of Westmorland and Lancashire and along the Wye Valley in Gloucestershire and Monmouthshire. Additionally reported from Morfa Bychan, Caernarvonshire; Burton Pidsea, Yorkshire and a site in Kent.

HABITAT Limestone woods.

ECOLOGY The larvae have been bred from soil under moss. Adults recorded from May to July.

STATUS Only post 1960 records: Wye Valley, Gloucestershire (1982); Whitbarrow (1970s) and Silverdale (post 1960) in Lancashire and the Kent site (1960s).

THREAT The destruction of the above habitat through clearance for agriculture or intensive forestry.

MANAGEMENT Maintain habitat diversity in woods, retaining situations with a rich and varied moss flora.

TIPULA BISTILATA Lundstroem
VULNERABLE
TIPULIDAE

DISTRIBUTION Recorded from about half a dozen sites along the Speyside region of the central Highlands: Aviemore, near Kinrara (1949, 1982), River Findhorn (1982), Nethy Bridge (1923) and Alvie SSSI (including Kinrara) (1976).

HABITAT Shaded sandy river banks.

ECOLOGY Biology unknown. The larvae are thought to develop in sandy soil along river banks. Adults recorded in June.

STATUS Four post 1960 sites confined to a rather small area and suggesting this species is in a vulnerable position.

THREAT Disturbance to sandy river banks through river improvement schemes, excessive trampling and removal of riverside trees and woodland.

MANAGEMENT Maintain sandy river banks in an undisturbed condition with trees for shading.

TIPULA CHEETHAMI Edwards NOTABLE TIPULIDAE

DISTRIBUTION A clumped distribution in Scotland and north-west England extending as far south as Cheshire and Breconshire in Wales. It is particularly well established on parts of the Inner Hebrides.

HABITAT Lowland woods and on open moorland where sheltered wet moss occurs at vertical seepages and beside streams, springs or small waterfalls. It can occur up to 900m. There seems to be a rather strong association with calcareous conditions, which could account for its local distribution and its comparative frequency on the base rich volcanic rocks of the Inner Hebrides. Records from the Cairngorms could refer to small pockets of base-rich rock within an area of acidic granite.

ECOLOGY Larvae develop in mosses such as Rhynchostegium riparioides or occasionally liverworts on wet rock faces in streams, and waterfalls, even where the current is fast. Adults recorded from May to July.

STATUS About 15 known post 1960 sites from widely throughout Scotland, also from Rake Beck, Yorkshire (1976) and Nant Bwrefwr, Breconshire (1964). Status revised from RDB3 (Shirt 1987).

THREAT River improvement schemes, ditching of seepages and streams, excessive trampling, drainage and other direct and indirect effects of moorland improvement for agriculture and afforestation; pollution such as agricultural run-off.

MANAGEMENT Maintain the mossy breeding sites in an undisturbed condition, preventing any change of water quality.

TIPULA COERULESCENS Lackschewitz RARE TIPULIDAE

DISTRIBUTION Scattered records in northern England (Westmorland and Yorkshire) and Scotland (Kirkcudbrightshire, Dumfriesshire, Easterness and Elgin).

HABITAT Small flushes and vegetated banks of streams and rivers, possibly preferring calcareous conditions, though known from Aviemore, Elgin where such conditions are scarce. It occurs at over 600m in the Pennines.

ECOLOGY The larvae live in or along the banks of small streams. Adults recorded in May and early June with a record from August.

STATUS Only two known post 1960 sites: Moorhouse NNR, Westmorland (1975) and a site in Dumfriesshire (1977). The early flight period of the adult may have led to it being somewhat overlooked.

THREAT Drainage of marshy areas around springs and flushes, ditching of streams and river improvements; pollution such as agricultural run-off; indirect effects of agricultural improvement and afforestation.

MANAGEMENT Maintain the flushes and stream margins, where larvae develop, in an undisturbed condition.

TIPULA DILATATA Schummel VULNERABLE TIPULIDAE

DISTRIBUTION Known from three Scottish sites: Pass of Killiecrankie (1 August 1975) and Blackspout Waterfall, Pitlochry (31 July 1976) both in Perthshire and River Spey, Aviemore, Elgin (August 1981).

HABITAT Sandy river banks with alders.

ECOLOGY Biology unknown. The larvae probably develop in the sand or soil of the above location. Adults recorded in July and August.

STATUS A recent addition to the British list (1977), which may prove to be a little more widespread in the future.

THREAT River improvement schemes, excessive trampling of banks and clearance of riverside trees for agriculture or intensive forestry.

MANAGEMENT Maintain riverside vegetation, trees and sandy banks in a natural undisturbed condition.

TIPULA GIMMERTHALI Lackschewitz RARE TIPULIDAE

DISTRIBUTION Known from a small number of upland sites: Moorhouse NNR, Westmorland (1954-6 and 1976-8); Pentlands, Midlothian (1945); Ben Venue, Perthshire (1966) and Glen Luss, Dumfriesshire (1966).

HABITAT Base rich streamsides and flushes above 300m.

ECOLOGY Biology unknown. The larvae probably develop in damp soil or moss. Adults recorded in October. Females are wingless which must greatly limit the dispersal powers of this species.

STATUS Poorly known and probably under recorded due to the late flight period of the adult. There is an interesting report of a grouse having over 400 specimens in its crop (Butterfield and Coulson, 1975) suggesting that it can be locally abundant if only for a short period. Other recorders remark on its extremely localised occurrence within a site. Status revised from RDB2 (Shirt 1987).

THREAT Drainage of sites for agricultural improvement and afforestation; ditching of streams and excessive trampling of banks.

MANAGEMENT Maintain upland streams and flushes in a natural undisturbed condition.

TIPULA GRISESCENS Zetterstedt RARE TIPULIDAE

DISTRIBUTION Upland areas in northern England (Shropshire, Cheshire, Lancashire, Westmorland, Yorkshire, particularly the Pennines) and very sparingly in Scotland (Dumbartonshire, Dumfriesshire, Midlothian, Perthshire, Easterness, Sutherland).

HABITAT Upland peat bogs, exceeding heights of 700m in Perthshire.

ECOLOGY The larvae have been reared from the moss Hypnum and it is probable that Sphagnum is also used. Adults recorded from April to early June; this is a spring species, its emergence time depending on the warmth of a given season and on altitude.

STATUS Some six known post 1960 sites lying within Easterness, Perthshire, Shropshire, Lancashire, Westmorland and Dumfriesshire. The particularly early flight period within some comparatively under recorded parts of Britain have probably led to it being overlooked.

THREAT Drainage of bogs for intensive forestry or agriculture; excessive trampling; peat cutting in some areas; mis-management of water levels with a loss of breeding sites and scrub invasion.

MANAGEMENT Maintain bogs in a natural and undisturbed condition with a high, relatively stable water level.

TIPULA HELVOLA Loew NOTABLE TIPULIDAE

DISTRIBUTION Southern England from Kent to Cornwall and as far north as Wiltshire and Essex, with several sites in North Wales (all within Merionethshire).

HABITAT Dry broadleaved woodland.

ECOLOGY Biology unknown. The larvae are thought to develop in dry soil. Adults recorded in July and August.

STATUS Seventeen known post 1960 sites but there are very few old records. The drab appearance of this species combined with the unusual choice of habitat for a cranefly has probably led to it being overlooked in the past and only the recent recording effort has allowed a more full understanding of the habitat requirements of this species.

THREAT Woodland clearance for agriculture or intensive forestry.

MANAGEMENT Maintain habitat diversity in woodlands, retaining any marshy areas, dead wood, streams etc., to provide a range of possible breeding sites.

TIPULA HOLOPTERA Edwards NOTABLE TIPULIDAE

DISTRIBUTION A clumped distribution with numerous records for North Wales (Merionethshire and Caernarvonshire) extending down to Cardiganshire and within England known from a small number of sites: Arne, Dorset; Hothfield NR, Kent; Cadnam and Latchmoor Brook, Hampshire; Tranmire, Yorkshire (all recent) and old records from sites in Warwickshire, Hampshire and Sussex.

HABITAT Boggy flushes with coarse herbage such as Juncus acutiflorus.

ECOLOGY Biology unknown. The larvae possibly develop in moss or beneath turf as in some related species. Adults recorded in October.

STATUS 17 known post 1960 sites, with very few older records and it would seem that the late adult flight period, in relatively under recorded parts of the country, has led to its being overlooked until recently. It does appear to be very local even within a favourable district. T. holoptera appears to be unrecorded outside the British Isles. Status revised from RDB3 (Shirt 1987).

THREAT Drainage for intensive forestry or agriculture; pollution such as agricultural run off; excessive trampling; mis-management of water levels with a loss of breeding sites and scrub invasion.

MANAGEMENT Maintain a high and relatively stable water level in marshy areas and prevent scrub invasion.

TIPULA HORTORUM Linnaeus RARE TIPULIDAE

DISTRIBUTION Records widely scattered in England (Hampshire, Sussex, Surrey, Berkshire, Oxfordshire, Northamptonshire, Lancashire, Westmorland, Yorkshire) and Scotland (Perthshire).

HABITAT Old broadleaved woodlands.

ECOLOGY Biology unknown. The larvae may be dependant on dead wood, or alternatively live in soil. Adults recorded from April to June.

STATUS About a dozen known post 1960 sites, scattered widely. Older records tend to be erroneous and require checking.

THREAT Clearance of woodland for agriculture and intensive forestry, also removal of dead wood and old or diseased trees which may support breeding sites.

MANAGEMENT Maintain habitat diversity in woodland, including a range of dead wood niches, old trees and damp areas within the site.

TIPULA LIMBATA Zetterstedt

DISTRIBUTION A northern species with a handful of sites in Scotland (within Easterness, Kirkcudbrightshire, Elgin and the Glasgow area), also Westmorland and Yorkshire.

HABITAT Boggy flushes in woodland (in the Spey Valley) and upon high level moorland (in the Pennines).

ECOLOGY Biology unknown. The larvae possibly develop in boggy soil. Adults recorded in August and September.

STATUS Nine known post 1960 sites: Rothiemurchus, Easterness (1981); Aviemore area (1966) and Craigellachie NNR (1978), Elgin (the latter two may refer to the same general area); Crianlarich, Perthshire (1986); Kirkconnel, Kirkudbrightshire (1971) and four sites on the High Pennines: Widdybank Fell, Cow Green, Sunbiggin and Tranmire (all 1970's).

THREAT Habitat loss, especially through drainage and afforestation.

MANAGEMENT Maintain the presence of undisturbed boggy flushes.

TIPULA LIVIDA Wulp

DISTRIBUTION Records widely dispersed in southern England extending as far north as Yorkshire and into North Wales.

HABITAT Woodlands or heathland besides clumps of trees. The sites typically have dry soils, as on the clay cappings on downs or on heaths (however, on heaths several finds were close to water).

ECOLOGY The whitish larva has been reared from damp soil and detritus in woodland, and has also been found in soil under dog's mercury <u>Mercurialis</u> <u>perenne</u>. Adults recorded from June to August.

STATUS About a dozen known widely scattered post 1960 sites. This species was first discovered in Britain as a larva in 1952 though some older specimens have been located in collections. Status revised from RDB3 (Shirt 1987).

THREAT Clearance of woodland and heathland for intensive forestry or agriculture; drainage of any damp areas; mis-management of heathland with subsequent scrub invasion.

MANAGEMENT Maintain rides and clearings in woods and use traditional management of heathland to produce a mosaic of vegetation types including limited scrub and copses. Retain any marshy areas as potential breeding sites.

TIPULA LURIDIROSTRIS Schummel

DISTRIBUTION Only four known sites: Glen Nant NNR, Argyllshire (1976); Tynron, Dumfriesshire (1952); Exeter, Devon (1954, 1955) and Mark Ash, Hampshire (1936).

HABITAT Oakwoods, especially in damp western situations (though Mark Ash is now mainly beech).

ECOLOGY The larvae have been reported to occur in debris amongst epiphytes growing on oak trees. Adults recorded from June to August.

STATUS Only the single post 1960 site which is an NNR. The arboreal life-style may have led to it being under recorded. However, since western oak woods have been sampled on many occasions during the flight period without yielding specimens, it remains likely that this is a genuinely rare insect.

THREAT The clearance of oakwoods for agriculture or intensive forestry, especially western sessile oakwoods which are rich in an epiphyte flora. Air pollution is a possible problem, perhaps including acid rain.

MANAGEMENT Maintain a good age structure of trees in woodlands and do not remove epiphytes or accumulations of organic material from old trees.

TIPULA MARGINATA Meigen

DISTRIBUTION A disjunct distribution. In the south it is known from at least six sites within Hampshire, two in Dorset, three in Surrey, one in Suffolk and one in Sussex. In Scotland it is known from two Speyside sites: Insh, Easterness and Aviemore, Elgin.

HABITAT Fens, damp heathland and carr, where saturated peat is exposed amongst tall vegetation. One Hampshire site is at the margins of a chalk river, the Test. Adults often confined to within a few square yards.

ECOLOGY Biology unknown. The larvae probably develop in the mud or peat of the above locations. Adults recorded from June to August.

STATUS About a dozen known post 1960 sites, widely scattered. Only two older records. Its strongholds seem to lie in the New Forest and on the Surrey heaths. The substantial loss of damp heathland and boggy heathland pools through the decline in heathland management and peat cutting will almost certainly have been accompanied by a decline in this species, even at the two strongholds.

THREAT Drainage of sites for agriculture or afforestation; excessive trampling of sensitive peat or <u>Sphagnum</u> areas; mis-management of water levels and the cessation of traditional heathland management with a loss of breeding sites and subsequent scrub invasion; pollution such as agricultural run-off.

MANAGEMENT Maintain a high and relatively stable water level and ensure the presence of small patches of bare peat or mud.

DISTRIBUTION Only two old records: New Forest, Hampshire (28 May 1896) and Chickerell, Dorset (turn of century).

HABITAT Uncertain, possibly old broadleaved woodland.

ECOLOGY Uncertain.

STATUS No recent information. If not extinct in Britain it must be extremely rare.

THREAT Uncertain other than overgrazing and degrading of the New Forest through afforestation and agricultural reclamation.

MANAGEMENT Uncertain, but prevention of excessive grazing by ponies is almost certainly required. Retain dead wood as a potential breeding site.

TIPULA NODICORNIS Meigen

RARE
TIPULIDAE

DISTRIBUTION Restricted to the east coast of Scotland and the Spey Valley, with records for Elgin, Easterness, Easter-Ross, Sutherland and Midlothian.

HABITAT Records include sandy river banks, coastal dunes and coastal shingle. Whilst bare or sparsely vegetated areas are clearly the requirement more precise preferences are unclear.

ECOLOGY The yellowish larva develops in sandy soil. Adults recorded from June to October.

STATUS Eight known, widely scattered post 1960 sites: Stow, Midlothian (1962); Dorback Burn, Abernethy (1982); Alvie SSSI (1976? and Culbin Sands (1982, with a long history prior to this date), Elgin; Morrich Mor, East Ross (1976); Cuthill Links (1976) and Ferrytown (1984), Sutherland. This is the T. juncea of Coe et al. (1950).

THREAT Coastal development, recreational pressure on dunes and coastal sites; afforestation or agricultural reclamation; river improvement, gravel extraction and excessive trampling of sandy banks; pollution such as agricultural run-off.

MANAGEMENT Maintain areas of sparsely vegetated sand and shingle along river banks and on dunes, preventing excessive disturbance.

DISTRIBUTION A northern and western species recorded in northern England (Yorkshire, Durham, Northumberland), Scotland (Perthshire, Elgin and Westerness and Rhum) and Wales (Merionethshire and Monmouthshire/Gloucestershire).

HABITAT Broadleaved valley woods in upland areas, usually within the proximity of streams.

ECOLOGY Biology unknown, larvae presumed to be in soil or decaying wood. Adults recorded from May to August.

STATUS Seven known post 1960 sites from widely throughout the known range. This is the T. rubripes of Coe (1950) and his T. nubeculosa is T. hortorum. Old records should therefore be treated with caution.

THREAT Woodland clearance for agriculture and afforestation; ditching of streams and drainage of marshy areas.

MANAGEMENT Maintain habitat diversity in broadleaved woodlands, retaining any marshy areas and dead wood as potential breeding sites.

TIPULA PELIOSTIGMA Schummel

NOTABLE
TIPULIDAE

DISTRIBUTION Recorded widely in southern England, perhaps predominating in East Anglia, extending to Yorkshire in the north.

HABITAT Woods and hedgerows.

ECOLOGY Reared from birds nests including robin and blackbird, but it is not clear whether this is a major or subsidiary larval habitat and there are other records referring to their occurrence in damp woodland soil. Adults recorded from May to August.

STATUS Some seven known and widely scattered post 1960 sites. Probably under recorded to some extent, especially as it occurs in very low numbers and is most usually found in rather undistinguished places. Nest-utilising species are often canopy dwellers as adults. Status revised from RDB3 (Shirt 1987).

THREAT Clearance of woodland and hedgerows.

MANAGEMENT Maintain woodland and hedgerows in a condition suitable for the nesting of small birds, particularly through the retaining of any large, over-mature trees.

DISTRIBUTION Records scattered widely in southern England as far north as Herefordshire, Oxfordshire and Hertfordshire, predominating in the south-west.

HABITAT Broadleaved woodland, with a requirement for dead wood.

ECOLOGY The larvae develop beneath the bark of dead wood, even in small branches lying on wet soil. Basden reared this species from the nest of a song thrush, though this was probably coincidental and influenced by nearby dead wood situations. Adults recorded from April to July.

STATUS About a dozen known post 1960 sites, four in Devon, the others widely scattered (Somerset, Wiltshire, Hampshire, Hertfordshire). Status revised from RDB2 (Shirt 1987).

THREAT Clearance of woodland for intensive forestry and agriculture. Removal of old or diseased trees and dead wood.

MANAGEMENT Retain any dead wood and old or diseased trees, ensuring continuity of these in the future.

TIPULA SERRULIFERA Alexander   ENDANGERED
TIPULIDAE

DISTRIBUTION Only three known sites: Wyre Forest, Worcestershire (1892); Pentlands, Midlothian (1945) and Yarlsey, Yorkshire (recent).

HABITAT At the Pentlands site it was confined to a small area of grassy heath beside a small burn in a steep-sided glen. The recent Yorkshire record is from moorland.

ECOLOGY Biology unknown. The larvae possibly develop in the soil. Adults recorded in August and September.

STATUS A very poorly known species with only the single recent record suggesting it is now very rare.

THREAT Destruction of the known sites through afforestation and agricultural reclamation.

MANAGEMENT Employ traditional moorland management to produce a mosaic of vegetation types. Retain any marshy areas.

TIPULA PSEUDOVARIIPENNIS Czizek   NOTABLE
TIPULIDAE

DISTRIBUTION A local, mainly southern, species with northern records felt to be rather dubious.

HABITAT Mainly recorded from broadleaved woods on chalk, though there are a few records from localities with sandy soils.

ECOLOGY Biology unknown. Adults recorded in May and June.

STATUS At least eight modern sites, though the accuracy of all records may require checking in the future. The females of the subgenus to which this species belongs are much more variable than originally thought and it is felt on the basis of males that this is an essentially southern species and that records from the midlands northwards are possibly based on misinterpreted females.

THREAT Clearance of woodland for intensive forestry or agriculture.

MANAGEMENT Maintain habitat diversity in woodlands, retaining any dead wood, streams and marshy areas, any of which may support breeding sites.

TIPULA SARAJEVENSIS Strobl   ENDANGERED
TIPULIDAE

DISTRIBUTION Only a single old record for a female taken at Mark Ash (New Forest), Hampshire on 1 July 1901.

HABITAT Probably old broadleaved woodland.

ECOLOGY Unknown.

STATUS Possibly extinct or, if not, very rare.

THREAT Degrading of the New Forest area through the removal of dead wood, old diseased trees and overgrazing by ponies.

MANAGEMENT Maintain habitat diversity including small valley bogs, and retain any old or diseased trees and dead wood which may possibly support the larval development site.

TIPULA SIEBKEI Zetterstedt
ENDANGERED
TIPULIDAE

DISTRIBUTION Only a single record of a male taken on 26 June 1953 at Mark Ash in the New Forest (Hampshire).

HABITAT Old broadleaved woodland, with a requirement for dead wood.

ECOLOGY On the continent, larvae have been reported from the rotting wood of aspen *Populus tremula*.

STATUS Only the single old record suggesting this species is very rare if not extinct. Aspen is not currently present at Mark Ash but it may be that other trees are used.

THREAT The degrading of the New Forest through removal of old trees and dead wood and overgrazing leading to a highly reduced ground flora.

MANAGEMENT Retain any old or diseased trees and dead wood ensuring continuity of these in the future. It is probably too late to consider the value of aspen since if the species has survived at all it will be associated with the dead wood of other tree species.

TIPULA TRUNCORUM Meigen
NOTABLE
TIPULIDAE

DISTRIBUTION Records widely dispersed in England (Surrey, Hertfordshire, Oxfordshire, Lincolnshire, Cheshire, Lancashire, Westmorland, Yorkshire, Durham), Wales (Glamorganshire, Breconshire) and Scotland (Elgin, Easterness, Aberdeenshire) with no obvious biases.

HABITAT Woodland, though preferences most unclear.

ECOLOGY The larva apparently develops in damp soil or moss in woods. Adults recorded from June to August.

STATUS Four known post 1960 sites: Juniper Hall, Surrey (1979); Shotover, Oxfordshire (1975-80); Banks of Nant y Capel, Glamorganshire (1973) and Copley, Durham (1976). It appears to be elusive rather than just rare. In the Alps it was obtained most easily by throwing stones into the foliage of spruce trees in order to flush specimens out. In Britain it has been taken almost as often in light traps as by all other methods. Status revised from RDB3 (Shirt 1987).

THREAT Uncertain, other than the loss of semi-natural woodland through clearance for agriculture and intensive forestry.

MANAGEMENT Uncertain, other than maintaining habitat diversity within woodland.

TIPULA YERBURYI Edwards
NOTABLE
TIPULIDAE

DISTRIBUTION A southern species with a clumped distribution; cites extending as far north as Yorkshire, and into Wales. It seems comparatively frequent in south-west England and to a lesser extent in North Wales and the New Forest.

HABITAT Wet, usually acid woods, and in southern England a preference is shown for sallow carr on heathland.

ECOLOGY Biology unknown. The larvae possibly live in wet soil. Adults recorded from May to July.

STATUS About 30 widely scattered post 1960 sites nine of which are within Devon, four in Cornwall and four in Hampshire, reflecting the south westerly bias. Abroad, this species is restricted to eastern Europe and a significant proportion of its world population seems to lie within the British Isles.

THREAT Habitat drainage and clearance for afforestation and agricultural reclamation. Mis-management of water levels in damp heathland with subsequent loss of breeding sites and scrub invasion.

MANAGEMENT Maintain a high and relatively stable water level in wet heathland carr and marshy areas in woods. Prevent carr from reverting to scrub through a lowering of the water table.

TRIOGMA TRISULCATA (Schummel)
RARE
TIPULIDAE

DISTRIBUTION Southern Scotland (Selkirkshire, Renfrewshire, Dumfriesshire, Kirkcudbrightshire, Perthshire), northern England (Yorkshire, Lancashire); North Wales (Merionethshire, Caernarvonshire).

HABITAT Seepage bog and upland streams.

ECOLOGY The camouflaged larvae have been reared from the aquatic moss *Acrocladium cuspidatum* and have also been found in mountain streams living amongst the stems of *Fontinalis*, to which they clung firmly by means of two strong caudal hooks. Adults recorded in May, a very short flight period being apparent.

STATUS Some six known and widely scattered post 1960 sites. Status revised from RDB2 (Shirt 1987).

THREAT Drainage of bogs and seepages for afforestation, ditching of streams and excessive trampling of their banks.

MANAGEMENT Maintain sites in a natural and undisturbed state with a high and relatively stable water level in marshy areas to sustain the mossy breeding sites.

SOLVA MACULATA (Meigen)

VULNERABLE
XYLOMYIIDAE

DISTRIBUTION Southern England with about half a dozen sites in the New Forest, Hampshire also the Windsor Forest area of Berkshire (including Silwood and Virginia Water); Ruislip Woods and Finchley, Middlesex and Epping Forest, Essex.

HABITAT Old broadleaved woodland, with a requirement for dead wood and old or diseased trees.

ECOLOGY The larvae develop in the decaying wood and rot holes of a range of old, diseased and dead trees, mainly beech, but including oak and ash. Adults recorded from May to July. Larvae and puparia appear to be much more easily found than adults and may occur in large numbers within the confined area of the substrate where development takes place.

STATUS A very restricted insect, seemingly confined to a small number of old woods in southern England. Three known post 1960 sites: Mallard Wood, Hampshire (1977); Windsor Forest, Berkshire (1966, 1977); Epping Forest, Essex (1975). All sites experience dead wood removal and it seems to have seriously declined in the New Forest.

THREAT Clearance of old woodland for agriculture, intensive forestry and urbanisation. Removal of any dead wood and old or diseased trees.

MANAGEMENT Retain any dead wood and old or diseased trees, ensuring continuity of these in the future.

SOLVA MARGINATA (Meigen)

NOTABLE
XYLOMYIIDAE

DISTRIBUTION Essentially southern England, though with scattered records as far north as Yorkshire.

HABITAT Old broadleaved woodland, occasionally more open habitats such as parkland, heathland or fens where there has been continuity of old or diseased trees.

ECOLOGY Larvae develop in the rotten wood or beneath sappy bark of a range of broadleaved trees, especially poplar, but also including sycamore, oak, ash and walnut. Fallen trees are preferred, though it would appear that live trees with some dead bark can be exploited. Adults recorded from May to August, usually resting on foliage. Larvae and puparia appear to be much more easily found than adults and may occur in large numbers within the confined area of the substrate where development takes place.

STATUS Fairly regular in southern old woods with about 25 known post 1960 sites. Possibly under recorded as an adult, searching for larvae and puparia may be a better way of obtaining records. Status revised from RDB2 (Shirt 1987).

THREAT The clearance of old woods for agriculture or intensive forestry and removal of the post mature trees or dead trees.

MANAGEMENT Retain any post mature or dead trees within a site, ensuring continuity of these in the future.

XYLOPHAGUS CINCTUS Degeer

DISTRIBUTION Scattered records in the Central Highlands of Scotland within Perthshire, Aberdeenshire, Easterness, Elgin and West Ross.

HABITAT Ancient coniferous woodland as found in the Caledonian pine forests, with a requirement for dead pine trees and stumps.

ECOLOGY Larvae develop in the dead wood or beneath the bark of Scots pine in association with beetle larvae such as Acanthocinus aedilis and Rhagium species (Ceramhycidae). The fly larvae are said to feed on freshly dead beetle larvae rather than living or decayed ones. Adults recorded from April to June and may be found resting on the bark of dead pines.

STATUS A very rare and restricted species with six known post 1960 sites: Ballochbuie, Aberdeenshire (1966); Balcladaich (1962), Loch Garten area (1986, 1987) and Rothiemurchus (1984, 1987), Easterness; Black Wood of Rannoch, Perthshire (1974); Beinn Eighe NNR, West Ross (1989). Searching for larvae and pupae beneath bark is probably the most efficient way of recording this species. Not listed in Shirt (1987).

THREAT The destruction of Caledonian pine forest, removal of dead trees and stumps within such sites and replacement with intensive forestry (which does not provide breeding sites).

MANAGEMENT Retain areas of Caledonian pine forest and any old trees (in particular old and large ones), dead trees and stumps, ensuring continuity of these in the future. Grazing by deer appears to be hindering pine regeneration in some sites and fencing areas or protection of young trees may be necessary.

XYLOPHAGUS JUNKI Szilady

DISTRIBUTION Only recorded from a single site in the Scottish Highlands: Glenmore Forest (near Aviemore), Elgin (June 1913).

HABITAT Ancient Caledonian pine forest with a probable requirement for old trees, dead trees or dead wood.

ECOLOGY Larvae possibly developing in the dead wood of Scots pine.

STATUS Only the single old record and it may now be extinct, as mature pines were removed from the only known site shortly after the record.

THREAT Destruction of native pine forest, either through removal of old trees and dead wood or the conversion to commercial forestry which does not provide suitable pines for larval development.

MANAGEMENT Retain old and diseased trees (in particular old and large ones) and dead wood, ensuring continuity of these in the future. Grazing by deer appears to be hindering pine regeneration in some sites and fencing areas or protection of young trees may be necessary.

INDEX

The species listed in this index are those mentioned in Volume one. Species for which accounts are present are indicated in bold type.

Appendix 1 Nationally rare and nationally scarce species listed in checklist order.

Trichoceridae

Diazosma hirtipennis (Siebke)	Notable
Trichocera maculipennis Meigen	Notable

Tipulidae

Arctoconopa melampodia (Loew)	RDB 2
Cheilotrichia imbuta (Meigen)	Notable
Ctenophora atrata (Linnaeus)	Notable
Ctenophora flaveolata (Fabricius)	RDB 2
Ctenophora nigricornis Meigen	RDB 3
Ctenophora ornata Meigen	RDB 1
Ctenophora pectinicornis (Linnaeus)	Notable
Dactylolabis sexmaculata (Macquart)	Notable
Dactylolabis transversa (Meigen)	Notable
Dicranoptycha fuscescens (Schummel)	RDB 1
Dicranota gracilipes Wahlgren	Notable
Dicranota guerini Zetterstedt	Notable
Dicranota robusta Lundstroem	Notable
Dicranota simulans Lackschewitz	RDB 3
Diogma glabrata (Meigen)	Notable
Elliptera omissa Schiner	RDB K
Erioptera bivittata (Loew)	RDB 2
Erioptera limbata Loew	RDB 2
Erioptera meigeni (Zetterstedt)	RDB 3
Erioptera meijerei Edwards	RDB 2
Erioptera nielseni de Meijere	Notable
Erioptera nigripalpis Goetghebuer	RDB 3
Erioptera pusilla (Schiner)	RDB 1
Erioptera scotica Edwards	RDB 1
Erioptera sordida Zetterstedt	RDB 3
Gnophomyia elsneri Stary	RDB 1
Gnophomyia viridipennis (Gimmerthal)	Notable
Gonomyia abbreviata Tjeder	RDB 3
Gonomyia alboscutellata (von Roser)	RDB 1
Gonomyia bifida Tonnoir	Notable
Gonomyia bradleyi Edwards	RDB 2
Gonomyia connexa Loew	RDB 1
Gonomyia conoviensis Barnes	Notable
Gonomyia edwardsii	RDB K
Gonomyia limbata	RDB 1
Gonomyia punctata Edwards	RDB 2
Gonomyia sexguttata (Dale)	RDB 1
Helius pallirostris Edwards	Notable
Limnophila abdominalis Staeger	Notable
Limnophila apicata (Loew)	Notable
Limnophila fasciata (Linnaeus)	RDB 1
Limnophila glabricula (Meigen)	Notable
Limnophila heterogyna Bergroth	RDB 1
Limnophila mundata (Loew)	Notable
Limnophila pictipennis (Meigen)	RDB 2
Limnophila pulchella (Meigen)	Notable
Limnophila trimaculata (Zetterstedt)	Notable
Limnophila verralli (Bergroth)	Notable
Limonia annulata (Linnaeus)	RDB 3
Limonia aperta (Wahlgren)	RDB 1
Limonia aquosa (Verrall)	Notable
Limonia bezzii (Alexander & Leonard)	RDB 2
Limonia caledonica (Edwards)	Notable
Limonia complicata (de Meijere)	Notable
Limonia consimilis (Zetterstedt)	RDB 3
Limonia ctenophora (Loew)	RDB 2
Limonia danica (Kuntze)	RDB 3
Limonia distendens (Lundstroem)	Notable
Limonia frontalis (Staeger)	RDB 1
Limonia goritiensis (Mik)	RDB 3
Limonia halterata Osten Sacken	RDB K
Limonia halterella (Edwards)	Notable
Limonia inusta (Meigen)	Notable
Limonia lucida (de Meijere)	Notable
Limonia magnicauda	RDB 2
Limonia masoni (Edwards)	RDB 3
Limonia occidua (Edwards)	Notable
Limonia omissinervis (de Meijere)	RDB 2
Limonia ornata (Meigen)	Notable
Limonia quadrimaculata (Linnaeus)	RDB 2
Limonia rufiventris (Strobl)	RDB 3
Limonia stigmatica (Meigen)	Notable
Limonia stylifera (Lackschewitz)	RDB 2
Limonia trivittata (Schummel)	Notable
Limonia uniseriata (Schiner)	RDB 3
Limonia ventralis (Schummel)	Notable
Lipsothrix ecucullata Edwards	RDB 3
Lipsothrix errans (Walker)	Notable
Lipsothrix nigristigma Edwards	RDB 1
Molophilus bihamatus de Meijere	Notable
Molophilus corniger de Meijere	Notable
Molophilus czizeki Lackschewitz	RDB 3
Molophilus lackschewitzianus Alexander	RDB 3
Molophilus niger Goetghebuer	Notable
Molophilus propinquus (Egger)	Notable
Molophilus variispinus Stary	Notable
Neolimnophila carteri (Tonnoir)	Notable
Neolimnophila placida (Meigen)	Notable
Nephrotoma aculeata (Loew)	RDB 2
Nephrotoma crocata (Linnaeus)	RDB 3
Nephrotoma dorsalis (Fabricius)	Notable
Nephrotoma lunulicornis (Schummel)	Notable
Nephrotoma quadristriata (Schummel)	RDB 2
Nephrotoma sullingtonensis Edwards	RDB 1
Orimarga juvenilis (Zetterstedt)	Notable
Orimarga virgo (Zetterstedt)	RDB 3
Ormosia aciculata Edwards	RDB 2
Ormosia bicornis (de Meijere)	RDB 2
Ormosia staegeriana Alexander	Notable
Paradelphomyia ecalcarata (Edwards)	RDB 2
Paradelphomyia fuscula (Loew)	Notable
Paradelphomyia nielseni (Kuntze)	Notable
Pedicia lucidipennis (Edwards)	Notable
Pedicia unicolor (Schummel)	Notable
Phalacrocera replicata (Linnaeus)	Notable
Pilaria fuscipennis (Meigen)	Notable
Pilaria meridiana (Staeger)	Notable
Pilaria scutellata (Staeger)	Notable
Prionocera pubescens Loew	RDB 2
Prionocera subserricornis (Zetterstedt)	RDB 2
Rhabdomastix hilaris Edwards	RDB 3
Rhabdomastix inclinata Edwards	RDB 2
Scleroprocta pentagonalis (Loew)	RDB 3
Scleroprocta sororcula (Zetterstedt)	Notable
Tasiocera collini Freeman	RDB 1
Tasiocera fuscescens (Lackschewitz)	RDB 1
Tasiocera jenkinsoni Freeman	RDB 1
Tasiocera laminata Freeman	Notable
Thaumastoptera calceata Mik	Notable
Tipula alpina Loew	RDB 3
Tipula bistilata Lundstroem	RDB 2
Tipula cheethami Edwards	Notable
Tipula coerulescens Lackschewitz	RDB 3
Tipula dilatata Shummel	RDB 2
Tipula gimmerthali Lackschewitz	RDB 3

Tipula grisescens	RDB 3	*Allodiopsis ingeniosa* Kidd	Notable
Tipula helvola Loew	Notable	*Allodiopsis maculosa* (Meigen)	Notable
Tipula holoptera Edwards	Notable	*Allodiopsis rufilatera* (Edwards)	RDB 2
Tipula hortorum Linnaeus	RDB 3	*Anaclileia dispar* (Winnertz)	Notable
Tipula limbata Zetterstedt	RDB 3	*Anatella alpina* Plassman	RDB 3
Tipula livida Wulp	Notable	*Anatella ankeli* Plassman	RDB 3
Tipula luridirostris Schummel	RDB 3	*Anatella dampfi* Landrock	RDB 3
Tipula marginata Meigen	RDB 3	*Anatella lenis* Dziedzicki	Notable
Tipula mutila Wahlgren	RDB 1	*Anatella pseudogibba* Plassmann	RDB 1
Tipula nodicornis Meigen	RDB 3	*Asindulum nigrum* Latreille	RDB 2
Tipula nubeculosa Meigen	Notable	*Azana anomala* (Staeger)	Notable
Tipula peliostigma Schummel	Notable	*Boletina digitata* Lundstroem	RDB 2
Tipula pseudovariipennis Czizek	Notable	*Boletina dispecta* Dziedzicki	Notable
Tipula sarajevensis Strobl	RDB 1	*Boletina groenlandica* Staeger	RDB 3
Tipula selene	RDB 3	*Boletina moravica* Landrock	Notable
Tipula serrulifera Alexander	RDB 1	*Boletina nasuta* (Haliday)	RDB 3
Tipula siebkei Zetterstedt	RDB 1	*Boletina nigrofusca* Dziedzicki	RDB 2
Tipula truncorum Meigen	Notable	*Boletina nitida* Grzegorzek	Notable
Tipula yerburyi Edwards	Notable	*Boletina pallidula* Edwards	Notable
Triogma trisulcata (Schummel)	RDB 3	*Boletina pectinunguis* Edwards	RDB 1
		Boletina rejecta Edwards	Notable
Ptychopteridae		*Boletina silvatica* Dziedzicki	RDB 1
		Boletina villosa Landrock	RDB 3
Ptychoptera longicauda (Tonnoir)	Notable	*Bolitophila basicornis* (Mayer)	Notable
		Bolitophila bimaculata Zetterstedt	RDB 2
Dixidae		*Bolitophila fumida* Edwards	RDB 1
		Bolitophila glabrata Loew	Notable
Dixa maculata Meigen	Notable	*Bolitophila rossica* Landrock	Notable
Dixella attica Pandazis	Notable	*Brachypeza armata* Winnertz	RDB 2
Dixella filicornis Edwards	Notable	*Brachypeza bisignata* Winnertz	Notable
Dixella obscura	Notable	*Brevicornu boreale* (Lundstroem)	Notable
Dixella serotina Meigen	Notable	*Brevicornu fennicum* Landrock	RDB 2
		Brevicornu foliatum (Edwards)	RDB 3
Culicidae		*Brevicornu griseolum* (Zetterstedt)	RDB 1
		Brevicornu kingi (Edwards)	RDB 3
Aedes communis (Degeer)	RDB K	*Brevicornu nigrofuscum* (Lundstroem)	Notable
Aedes dorsalis (Meigen)	RDB 3	*Brevicornu proximum* (Staeger)	Notable
Aedes flavescens (Muller)	RDB 2	*Brevicornu serenum* Winnertz	RDB 3
Aedes leucomelas (Meigen)	RDB K	*Coelosia silvatica* Landrock	Notable
Aedes sticticus (Meigen)	RDB K	*Cordyla insons* Lastovaska & Matile	RDB 2
Anopheles algeriensis Theobald	RDB K	*Cordyla nitidula* Edwards	Notable
Culiseta longiareolata (Macquart)	RDB K	*Diadocidia valida* Mik, 1874	RDB 2
Orthopodomyia pulcripalpis (Rondani)	RDB 3	*Ditomyia fasciata* (Meigen)	Notable
		Docosia carbonaria Edwards	Notable
Thaumaleidae		*Docosia fuscipes* (Roser)	Notable
		Docosia marionella Mik	RDB 1
Thaumalea truncata Edwards	Notable	*Docosia pallipes* Edwards	Notable
		Docosia setosa	Notable
Ceratopogonidae		*Docosia sp. indet.* of Hudson et. al. (1980)	RDB 3
		Dynatosoma cochleare Strobl	RDB 2
Dasyhelea saxicola (Edwards, 1929)	RDB 2	*Dynatosoma nigromaculatum* Lundstroem	RDB 3
		Dziedzickia marginata (Dziedzicki))	Notable
Anisopodidae		*Ectrepesthoneura colyeri* Chandler	RDB 2
		Ectrepesthoneura pubescens (Zetterstedt)	RDB 1
Mycetobia pallipes Meigen	Notable	*Epicypta limnophila* Chandler	Notable
		Eudicrana nigriceps (Lundstroem)	RDB 1
Mycetophilidae		*Exechia cincta* Winnertz	RDB 3
		Exechia dizona Edwards	RDB 1
Acnemia amoena Winnertz	RDB 2	*Exechia exigua* Lundstroem	Notable
Acnemia longipes Winnertz	Notable	*Exechia lucidula* (Zetterstedt)	RDB 2
Allodia angulata Lundstroem	RDB 2	*Exechia lundstroemi* Landrock	RDB K
Allodia barbata (Lundstroem)	Notable	*Exechia pectinivalva* Stackelberg	RDB 3
Allodia czernyi (Landrock)	RDB 2	*Exechia pseudofestiva*	Notable
Allodia embla Hackman	RDB 3	*Exechia sororcula* Lachschewitz	RDB 3
Allodia neglecta Edwards	Notable	*Exechia sp. nov.*	RDB 1
Allodia pistillata (Lundstroem)	Notable	*Exechiopsis crucigera* (Lundstroem)	Notable
Allodia retracta Plassman	RDB 2	*Exechiopsis dryaspagensis* Chandler	RDB 1
Allodia silvatica Landrock	Notable	*Exechiopsis dumitrescae* Burghele-Balace	Notable
Allodia triangularis Strobl	RDB 3	*Exechiopsis fimbriata* (Lundstroem)	Notable

Exechiopsis furcata (Lundstroem)	Notable	*Mycomya parva* (Dziedzicki)	Notable
Exechiopsis jenkinsoni (Edwards)	Notable	*Mycomya pectinifera* Edwards	RDB 3
Exechiopsis ligulata (Lundstroem)	Notable	*Mycomya permixta* Vaisanen, 1984	RDB 1
Exechiopsis magnicauda (Lundstroem)	RDB 2	*Mycomya punctata* (Meigen)	RDB 1
Exechiopsis membranacea (Lundstroem)	Notable	*Mycomya rosalba* Hutson	RDB 1
Exechiopsis pollicata (Edwards)	Notable	*Mycomya shermani* Garrett, 1924	RDB 2
Exechiopsis pseudindecisa	Notable	*Mycomya trivittata* (Zettertstedt, 1838)	Notable
Gnoriste bilineata Zetterstedt	Notable	*Mycomya vittiventris* (Zetterstedt)	RDB 2
Gnoriste longirostris Siebke	RDB 2	*Neoempheria bimaculata*	RDB 2
Grzegorzekia collaris (Meigen)	RDB 3	*Neoempheria lineola* (Meigen)	RDB 1
Keroplatus testaceus Dalman	Notable	*Neoempheria striata* (Meigen, 1818)	RDB 1
Leia bifasciata Gimmerthal	Notable	*Neoempheria winnertzi* Edwards, 1913	RDB 1
Leia longiseta Barendrecht	RDB 2	*Neoplatyura biumbrata* (Edwards, 1913)	RDB 2
Leia piffardi Edwards	Notable	*Neuratelia nigricornis* Edwards	Notable
Macrocera aterrima Stackelberg	RDB 3	*Palaedocosia flava* (Edwards)	RDB 1
Macrocera crassicornis Winnertz	Notable	*Palaeodocosia alpicola* (Strobl)	RDB K
Macrocera estonica Landrock	Notable	*Phronia caliginosa* Dziedzecki	RDB 1
Macrocera fascipennis Staeger	RDB 3	*Phronia disgrega* Dziedzicki	Notable
Macrocera fastuosa Loew	RDB 1	*Phronia egregia* Dziedzecki	RDB 3
Macrocera inversa Loew, 1869	RDB 2	*Phronia egregia*	Notable
Macrocera longibrachiata Landrock	RDB 1	*Phronia electa* Dziedzecki	RDB 2
Macrocera maculata Meigen	Notable	*Phronia interstincta* Dziedzicki	RDB 3
Macrocera nana Macquart, 1826	Notable	*Phronia longelamellata* Strobl	RDB 3
Macrocera propleuralis Edwards	RDB 1	*Phronia mutabilis* Dziedzicki	RDB 1
Macrocera tusca Loew	Notable	*Phronia persimilis* Hackman	RDB 2
Macrocera zetterstedti Lundstroem	RDB 1	*Phronia silvatica* Dziedzicki	RDB 1
Manota unifurcata Lundstroem	RDB 2	*Phronia sp. nov.*	RDB 1
Megalopelma nigroclavatum (Strobl)	Notable	*Phronia sudetica* Dziedzicki	RDB 2
Megophtalmidia crassicornis (Curtis)	Notable	*Pseudexechia aurivernica* Chandler	RDB 3
Monocentrota favonii Chandler	RDB 1	*Pseudexechia parallela* (Edwards)	Extinct
Mycetophila abbreviata Landrock	RDB 3	*Pseudorymosia fovea* (Dziedzicki)	RDB 3
Mycetophila autumnalis Lundstroem	RDB 3	*Pyratula perpusilla* (Edwards, 1913)	RDB 3
Mycetophila bialorussica Dziedzicki	RDB 3	*Rocetelion humerale* (Zetterstedt, 1850)	RDB 1
Mycetophila bohemica (Lastovka)	RDB 2	*Rutylapa ruficornis* (Zetterstedt, 1851)	RDB 1
Mycetophila caudata Staeger	RDB 2	*Rymosia acta* Dziedzicki	RDB 2
Mycetophila confusa Dziedzicki	RDB 3	*Rymosia affinis* Winnertz	RDB 2
Mycetophila czizeki (Landrock)	RDB 3	*Rymosia armata* Lackschewitz	RDB 3
Mycetophila dziedzickii	RDB 3	*Rymosia britteni* Edwards	RDB 2
Mycetophila freyi Lundstroem	Notable	*Rymosia connexa* Winnertz	RDB 2
Mycetophila gratiosa Winnertz	RDB 1	*Rymosia placida* Winnertz	Notable
Mycetophila hetschkoi Landrock	Notable	*Rymosia setiger* Dziedzicki	Notable
Mycetophila immaculata (Dziedzicki)	RDB 3	*Rymosia sp. nov.*	RDB 1
Mycetophila lapponica Lundstroem	RDB 2	*Rymosia spinipes* Winnertz	Notable
Mycetophila lastovkia Caspers	RDB 2	*Rymosia winnertzi* Barendrecht	Notable
Mycetophila lubomirskii Dziedzicki	RDB 1	*Sceptonia concolor* Winnertz	RDB 3
Mycetophila magnicauda Strobl	Notable	*Sceptonia costata* (Wulp)	Notable
Mycetophila mitis Johannsen	Notable	*Sceptonia flavipuncta* Edwards	RDB 3
Mycetophila mohilevensis Dziedzicki	RDB 2	*Sceptonia fuscipalpis* Edwards	Notable
Mycetophila morosa Winnertz	RDB 2	*Sceptonia humerella* Edwards	RDB 2
Mycetophila schnabli (Dziedzicki)	RDB 1	*Sceptonia tenuis* Edwards	RDB 1
Mycetophila scotica Edwards	RDB 2	*Sciophila adamsi* Edwards	RDB 1
Mycetophila signata Meigen	Notable	*Sciophila antiqua* Chandler	RDB 1
Mycetophila sp. nov.	RDB 2	*Sciophila buxtoni* Freeman	RDB 2
Mycetophila stolida Walker	Notable	*Sciophila cliftoni* Edwards	Extinct
Mycetophila strigata Staeger	Notable	*Sciophila fenestella* Curtis	Notable
Mycetophila strigatoides (Landrock)	RDB 2	*Sciophila fridolini* Stackelberg	RDB 1
Mycetophila v-nigrum Lundstroem	RDB 2	*Sciophila geniculata* Zetterstedt	Notable
Mycomya britteni Kidd	RDB 2	*Sciophila interrupta* (Winnertz)	RDB 1
Mycomya clavigera	RDB 2	*Sciophila limbatella* Zetterstedt	RDB 1
Mycomya collini Edwards	RDB 2	*Sciophila nigronitida* Landrock	Notable
Mycomya digitifera Edwards	RDB 2	*Sciophila nonnisilva* Hutson	Notable
Mycomya flavicollis (Zetterstedt)	Notable	*Sciophila ochracea* Walker	RDB 1
Mycomya fuscata (Winnertz)	RDB 3	*Sciophila plurisetosa* Edwards	RDB 2
Mycomya griseovittata (Zetterstedt, 1852)	RDB 3	*Sciophila quadriterga* Hutson	RDB 1
Mycomya insignis (Winnertz, 1863)	RDB 2	*Sciophila rufa* Meigen	Notable
Mycomya lambi Edwards	RDB 3	*Sciophila sp. nov.*	RDB 1
Mycomya nigricornis (Zetterstedt, 1852)	RDB 3	*Sciophila varia* (Winnertz)	RDB 1
Mycomya occultans (Zetterstedt, 1852)	RDB 1	*Syntemma nitidula* Edwards	RDB 3
Mycomya ornata (Meigen)	RDB 3	*Syntemna stylata* Hutson	RDB 1

158

Tarnania dziedzickii (Edwards)	RDB 2	**Tabanidae**	
Tarnania tarnanii (Dziedzicki)	RDB 3		
Trichonta bicolor Landrock	RDB 1	*Atylotus fulvus* (Meigen)	Notable
Trichonta clavigera Lundstrom	Notable	*Atylotus latistriatus* (Brauer)	RDB 3
Trichonta flavicauda Lundstroem	RDB 1	*Atylotus plebeius* (Fallen)	RDB 1
Trichonta fragilis	RDB 3	*Atylotus rusticus* (Linnaeus)	RDB 1
Trichonta fragilis Gagne	RDB 3	*Chrysops sepulchralis* (Fabricius)	RDB 1
Trichonta fusca Landrock	RDB 1	*Haematopota bigoti* Gobert	RDB 3
Trichonta icenica Edwards	RDB 3	*Haematopota grandis* Meigen	RDB 3
Trichonta nigritula Edwards	RDB 1	*Hybomitra ciureai* Seguy	RDB 3
Trichonta pulchra Gagne	RDB 1	*Hybomitra expollicata* (Pandelle)	RDB 2
Trichonta sp. nov.	RDB 1	*Hybomitra lurida* (Fallen)	RDB 3
Trichonta vulcani (Dziedzicki)	Notable	*Hybomitra micans* (Meigen)	RDB 2
Urytalpa atriceps (Edwards, 1913)	RDB 3	*Hybomitra muhlfeldi* (Brauer)	RDB 3
Urytalpa macrocera (Edwards, 1913)	RDB 1	*Tabanus bovinus* Linnaeus	RDB K
		Tabanus cordiger Meigen	Notable
Stratiomyidae		*Tabanus glaucopis* Meigen	RDB 3
		Tabanus miki Brauer	RDB K
Beris clavipes (Linnaeus)	Notable		
Beris fuscipes Meigen	Notable	**Asilidae**	
Chorisops nagatomii Rozkosny	Notable		
Clitellaria ephippium (Fabricius)	Extinct	*Asilus crabroniformis* Linnaeus	Notable
Eupachygaster tarsalis (Zetterstedt)	Notable	*Dasypogon diadema* Fabricius	RDB 1
Neopachygaster meromelaena (Austen)	Notable	*Dioctria cothurnata* Meigen	RDB 3
Odontomyia angulata (Panzer)	RDB 1	*Dioctria oelandica* (Linnaeus)	Notable
Odontomyia argentata (Fabricius)	RDB 2	*Epitriptus arthriticus* (Zeller)	RDB 1
Odontomyia hydroleon (L., 1758)	RDB 1	*Epitriptus cowini* Hobby	RDB K
Odontomyia ornata (Linnaeus)	RDB 2	*Eutolmus rufibarbis* (Meigen)	RDB 3
Odontomyia tigrina (Fabricius)	Notable	*Laphria flava* (Linnaeus)	RDB 3
Oxycera analis Meigen	RDB 2	*Laphria gilva* (Linnaeus)	RDB K
Oxycera dives Loew	RDB 3	*Laphria marginata* (Linnaeus)	Notable
Oxycera leonina (Panzer, 1798)	RDB 1	*Lasiopogon cinctus* (Fabricius)	Notable
Oxycera morrisii Curtis	Notable	*Machimus rusticus* (Meigen)	RDB 2
Oxycera pardalina Meigen	Notable	*Neoitamus cothurnatus* (Meigen)	RDB 1
Oxycera pygmaea (Fallen)	Notable	*Pamponerus germanicus* (Linnaeus)	RDB 3
Oxycera terminata Meigen	RDB 2	*Rhadiurgus variabilis* (Zetterstedt)	RDB 3
Oxycera varipes Loew, 1870	RDB 1		
Stratiomys chamaeleon	RDB 1	**Therevidae**	
Stratiomys longicornis	RDB 2		
Stratiomys potamida	Notable	*Dialineura anilis* (Linnaeus)	RDB 3
Stratiomys singularior (Harris)	Notable	*Psilocephala melaleuca* (Loew)	RDB 1
Vanoyia tenuicornis (Macquart)	Notable	*Psilocephala rustica* (Panzer)	RDB 3
Zabrachia minutissima (Zetterstedt)	Notable	*Thereva fulva* (Meigen)	RDB 3
		Thereva handlirschi Krober	RDB 3
Xylomyidae		*Thereva inornata* Verrall	RDB 3
		Thereva lunulata Zetterstedt	RDB 3
Solva maculata (Meigen)	RDB 2	*Thereva plebeia* (Linnaeus)	Notable
Solva marginata (Meigen)	Notable	*Thereva strigata* Fabricius	RDB 3
Solva varia (Meigen)	Extinct	*Thereva valida* Loew	RDB 3
Xylophagidae		**Scenopinidae**	
Xylophagus cinctus Degeer	RDB 3	*Scenopinus niger* (Degeer)	Notable
Xylophagus junki Szilady	RDB 1		
		Acroceridae	
Rhagionidae			
		Ogcodes gibbosus (Linnaeus)	Notable
Atrichops crassipes (Meigen)	RDB 3	*Ogcodes pallipes* Latreille	Notable
Chrysopilus erythrophthalmus Loew	RDB 2		
Chrysopilus laetus (Zetterstedt)	RDB 1	**Bombyliidae**	
Ptiolina atra Staeger	Notable		
Ptiolina obscura (Fallen)	Notable	*Bombylius canescens* Mikan	Notable
Rhagio annulatus Degeer	RDB 3	*Bombylius discolor* Mikan	Notable
Rhagio strigosus (Meigen)	RDB 3	*Bombylius minor* Linnaeus	RDB 2
Spania nigra Meigen	Notable	*Phthiria pulicaria*	Notable
Symphoromyia immaculata (Meizen)	Notable	*Thyridanthrax fenestratus* (Fallen)	RDB 3
		Villa cingulata (Meigen)	RDB 1
		Villa circumdata (Meigen)	RDB 2

Empididae

Athalia sp. indet.	RDB 1
Bicellaria halterata Collin	Notable
Bicellaria mera Collin	Notable
Chelifera angusta Collin	Notable
Chelifera aperticauda Collin	Notable
Chelifera astigma Collin	RDB 1
Chelifera concinnicauda Collin	Notable
Chelifera monostigma (Meigen)	Notable
Chelifera subangusta Collin	Notable
Chersodromia cursitans (Zetterstedt)	Notable
Chersodromia speculifera Haliday	Notable
Clinocera nivalis (Zetterstedt)	RDB 3
Clinocera tenella (Wahlberg)	RDB 3
Clinocera wesmaelii (Macquart)	Notable
Dolichocephala ocellata (Costa)	RDB 3
Drapetis arcuata Loew	Notable
Drapetis convergens Collin	RDB K
Drapetis curvipes (Meigen)	Notable
Drapetis infitialis Collin	Notable
Drapetis setigera Loew	RDB 3
Drapetis simulans Collin	Notable
Dryodromia testacea (Rondani)	Notable
Empis decora Meigen	Notable
Empis laetabilis Collin	RDB 3
Empis limata Collin	RDB 1
Empis melaena Bezzi	RDB 1
Empis picipes Meigen	Notable
Empis prodromus Loew	RDB 1
Empis rufiventris Meigen	Notable
Empis volucris Meigen	Notable
Empis woodi Collin	RDB 3
Euthyneura albipennis	RDB 1
Euthyneura gyllenhali (Zetterstedt)	Notable
Euthyneura halidayi Collin	Notable
Euthyneura inermis Becker	RDB 1
Heleodromia irwini	RDB 1
Hemerodromia adulatoria Collin	Notable
Hemerodromia laudatoria Collin	Notable
Hemerodromia melangyna Collin	RDB 2
Hilara abdominalis Zetterstedt	Notable
Hilara aeronetha Mik	RDB 1
Hilara albipennis von Roser	Notable
Hilara albitarsis von Roser	Notable
Hilara albiventris von Roser	Notable
Hilara apta Collin	Notable
Hilara barbipes Frey	RDB 3
Hilara biseta Collin	Notable
Hilara brevivittata Macquart	RDB 3
Hilara clypeata Meigen	Notable
Hilara discoidalis Lundbeck	Notable
Hilara gallica (Meigen)	RDB 1
Hilara germanica Engel	Notable
Hilara hirta Strobl	RDB 2
Hilara hirtella Collin	RDB 2
Hilara implicata Collin	Notable
Hilara lugubris (Zetterstedt)	Notable
Hilara medeterifrons Collin	RDB 2
Hilara media Collin	Notable
Hilara merula Collin	RDB 1
Hilara morata Collin	Notable
Hilara nigrohirta Collin	Notable
Hilara pilosopectinata Strobl	RDB 1
Hilara platyura Loew	Notable
Hilara primula Collin	Notable
Hilara quadriseta Collin	RDB 3
Hilara recedens Walker	RDB 3
Hilara scrobiculata Loew	Notable
Hilara setosa Collin	RDB 2
Hilara submaura Collin	RDB 1
Hilara woodi Collin	Notable
Hormopeza obliterata Zetterstedt	RDB 1
Leptopeza borealis Zetterstedt	RDB 2
Microphorus anomalus (Meigen)	Notable
Ocydromia melanopleura Loew	Notable
Oedalea apicalis Loew	Notable
Oedalea oriunda Collin	RDB 1
Oedalea ringdahli Chvala	RDB 1
Oedalea tibialis Macquart	Notable
Oedalea zetterstedti Collin	Notable
Platypalpus aeneus (Macquart)	RDB 3
Platypalpus albicornis (Zetterstedt)	Notable
Platypalpus albiseta (Panzer)	Notable
Platypalpus albocapillatus (Fallen)	Notable
Platypalpus alter (Collin)	RDB 3
Platypalpus analis (Meigen)	RDB 1
Platypalpus aristatus (Collin)	Notable
Platypalpus articulatoides	Notable
Platypalpus articulatus Macquart	Notable
Platypalpus aurantiacus (Collin)	RDB 3
Platypalpus carteri (Collin)	RDB 2
Platypalpus confinis (Zetterstedt)	RDB 3
Platypalpus cothurnatus Macquart	Notable
Platypalpus cryptospina Frey	Notable
Platypalpus difficilis Frey	Notable
Platypalpus divisus Walker	Notable
Platypalpus ecalceatus (Zetterstedt)	Notable
Platypalpus excisus (Becker)	RDB 3
Platypalpus incertus (Collin)	Notable
Platypalpus inexpectatus Smith & Chvala	RDB 1
Platypalpus infectus (Collin)	RDB 2
Platypalpus ingenuus (Collin)	RDB 2
Platypalpus interpolus (Collin)	RDB 3
Platypalpus leucothrix (Strobl)	Notable
Platypalpus longimanus (Corti)	RDB 1
Platypalpus luteolus (Collin)	RDB 3
Platypalpus macula (Zetterstedt)	Notable
Platypalpus melancholicus (Collin)	RDB 3
Platypalpus mikii (Becker)	RDB 3
Platypalpus niger (Meigen)	Notable
Platypalpus niveiseta Zetterstedt	RDB 3
Platypalpus ochrocera (Collin)	RDB 1
Platypalpus pallidicoxa Frey	RDB 2
Platypalpus pallidiseta	RDB 1
Platypalpus politus (Collin)	Notable
Platypalpus praecinctus (Collin)	Notable
Platypalpus pseudociliaris Strobl	Notable
Platypalpus pulicarius (Meigen)	Notable
Platypalpus pygialis Chvala	RDB 1
Platypalpus rapidus (Meigen)	RDB 3
Platypalpus ruficornis (von Roser)	Notable
Platypalpus stabilis (Collin)	Notable
Platypalpus stigma (Collin)	Notable
Platypalpus stigmatellus (Zetterstedt)	Notable
Platypalpus subtilis (Collin)	RDB 3
Platypalpus sylvicola (Collin)	RDB 3
Platypalpus tonsus (Collin)	Notable
Platypalpus tuomikoskii Chvala	RDB 3
Platypalpus unicus Collin	RDB 2
Ragas unica Walker	Notable
Rhamphomyia aethiops Zetterstedt	RDB 3
Rhamphomyia albidiventris Strobl	RDB 1
Rhamphomyia albitarsis Collin	Notable
Rhamphomyia albosegmentata Zett.	Notable
Rhamphomyia breviventris Frey	RDB 1
Rhamphomyia caliginosa Collin	Notable
Rhamphomyia culicina (Fallen)	Notable

Rhamphomyia curvula Frey	Notable	*Dolichopus agilis* Meigen	RDB 2
Rhamphomyia hirtula Zetterstedt	RDB 3	*Dolichopus andalusiacus* Strobl	RDB 3
Rhamphomyia ignobilis Zetterstedt	RDB 1	*Dolichopus arbustorum* Stannius	RDB 3
Rhamphomyia lamellata Collin	Notable	*Dolichopus argyrotarsis* Wahlberg	Notable
Rhamphomyia marginata (Fabricius)	RDB K	*Dolichopus caligatus* Wahlberg	Notable
Rhamphomyia micropyga Collin	Notable	*Dolichopus cilifemoratus* Macquart	RDB K
Rhamphomyia morio Zetterstedt	Notable	*Dolichopus laticola* Verrall	RDB 1
Rhamphomyia murina Collin	RDB 2	*Dolichopus latipennis* Fallen	RDB 3
Rhamphomyia nitidula Zetterstedt	Notable	*Dolichopus linearis* Meigen	Notable
Rhamphomyia obscura Zetterstedt	Notable	*Dolichopus lineatocornis* Zetterstedt	RDB 1
Rhamphomyia physoprocta Frey	RDB 1	*Dolichopus maculipennis* Zetterstedt	RDB 2
Rhamphomyia plumipes (Meigen)	RDB 3	*Dolichopus mediicornis* Verrall	RDB 2
Rhamphomyia sulcatina Collin	Notable	*Dolichopus melanopus* Meigen	Extinct
Rhamphomyia tibialis Meigen	Notable	*Dolichopus migrans* Zetterstedt	RDB 3
Rhamphomyia trigemina Oldenburg	RDB 1	*Dolichopus nigripes* Fallen	RDB 1
Rhamphomyia vesiculosa (Fallen)	RDB 1	*Dolichopus notatus* Staeger	Notable
Stilpon lunata (Haliday)	Notable	*Dolichopus plumitarsis* Fallen	RDB 1
Stilpon sublunata Collin	Notable	*Dolichopus signifer* Haliday	RDB 2
Symballophthalmus dissimilis (Fallen)	Notable	*Dolichopus strigipes* Verrall	Notable
Symballophthalmus pictipes (Becker)	RDB 3	*Dolichopus virgultorum* Haliday	Notable
Symballophthalmus scapularis	Notable	*Hercostomus angustifrons* (Staeger)	RDB 2
Syndyas nigripes (Zetterstedt)	RDB 2	*Hercostomus chalybeus* (Wiedemann)	Notable
Syneches muscarius (Fabricius)	RDB 1	*Hercostomus fulvicaudis* (Haliday)	RDB 3
Tachydromia acklandi Chvala	RDB 2	*Hercostomus nigrilamellatus* (Macquart)	Notable
Tachydromia connexa Meigen	RDB 3	*Hercostomus nigrocoerulea* Latreille	Notable
Tachydromia costalis (von Roser)	RDB 3	*Hercostomus plagiatus* (Loew)	Notable
Tachydromia halidayi (Collin)	RDB 3	*Hercostomus praetextatus* (Haliday)	Notable
Tachydromia halterata (Collin)	RDB 2	*Hercostomus sahlbergi* (Zetterstedt)	RDB 1
Tachydromia lundstroemi Frey	RDB 1	*Hydrophorus rufibarbis* Gerstaecker	Notable
Tachydromia terricola	RDB 1	*Hydrophorus viridis* (Meigen)	RDB 3
Tachydromia woodi (Collin)	RDB 2	*Hypophyllus discipes* (Ahrens)	Notable
Tachypeza fuscipennis (Fallen)	Notable	*Lamprochromus elegans* (Meigen)	Notable
Tachypeza heeri Zetterstedt	RDB 2	*Medetera ambigua* (Zetterstedt)	Notable
Tachypeza truncorum (Fallen)	RDB 3	*Medetera borealis* Thuneberg	RDB 2
Trichina opaca Loew	Notable	*Medetera cuspidata* Collin	RDB 3
Trichina pallipes (Zetterstedt)	Notable	*Medetera excellens* Frey	RDB 2
Weidemannia impudica Mik	RDB 1	*Medetera infumata* Loew	RDB 3
Weidemannia lamellata (Loew)	RDB 1	*Medetera inspissata* Collin	RDB 3
Wiedemannia lota Walker	Notable	*Medetera jugalis* Collin	Notable
Wiedemannia phantasma Mik	RDB 3	*Medetera melancholica* Lundbeck	RDB 3
		Medetera nitida (Macquart)	Notable
Dolichopodidae		*Medetera obscura* (Zetterstedt)	Notable
		Medetera oscillans Allen	RDB 3
Achalcus melanotrichus Mik	Notable	*Medetera parenti* Stackleberg	RDB K
Acropsilus niger (Loew)	RDB 1	*Medetera petrophila* Kowarz	Notable
Aphrosylus mitis Verrall	RDB 3	*Medetera pinicola* Kowarz	Notable
Aphrosylus raptor Haliday	Notable	*Medetera striata* Parent	RDB 3
Argyra atriceps Loew	Notable	*Medetera unisetosa* Collin	RDB 3
Argyra auricollis (Meigen)	RDB 2	*Melanostolus melancholicus* (Loew)	RDB 3
Argyra elongata (Zetterstedt)	RDB 3	*Micromorphus albipes* (Zetterstedt)	Notable
Argyra grata Loew	RDB 2	*Nematoproctus distendens* (Meigen)	RDB 2
Campsicnemus compeditus Loew	Notable	*Neurigona abdominalis* (Fallen)	RDB 1
Campsicnemus magius (Loew)	RDB 3	*Neurigona suturalis* (Fallen)	Notable
Campsicnemus marginatus Loew	Notable	*Orthoceratium lacustre* (Scopoli)	Notable
Campsicnemus pectinulatus Loew	Notable	*Poecilobothrus ducalis* (Loew)	RDB 2
Campsicnemus pusillus (Meigen)	Notable	*Poecilobothrus majesticus* Fonseca	RDB 1
Chrysotimus concinnus (Zetterstedt)	Notable	*Poecilobothrus principalis* (Loew)	Notable
Chrysotus angulicornis Kowarz	Notable	*Rhaphium antennatum* Carlier	Notable
Chrysotus collini Parent	Notable	*Rhaphium auctum* (Loew)	Notable
Chrysotus kowarzi Lundbeck	Notable	*Rhaphium fascipes* (Meigen)	Notable
Chrysotus melampodius Loew	Notable	*Rhaphium fractum* Loew	Notable
Chrysotus monochaetus Kowarz	Notable	*Rhaphium gravipes* Haliday	Notable
Chrysotus palustris Verrall	Notable	*Rhaphium lanceolatum* Loew	Notable
Chrysotus suavis Loew	Notable	*Rhaphium micans* (Meigen)	Notable
Chrysotus verralli Parent	RDB 3	*Rhaphium nasutum* (Fallen)	Notable
Cyturella albosetosa (Strobl)	RDB 1	*Rhaphium patulum* (Raddatz)	Notable
Diaphorus hoffmannseggii Meigen	RDB 1	*Rhaphium pectinatum* (Loew)	Extinct
Diaphorus winthemi Meigen	RDB 1	*Rhaphium penicillatum* Loew	RDB 2
Dolichopus acuticornis Wiedemann	Notable	*Rhaphium rivale* (Loew)	Notable

Schoenophilus versutus (Haliday)	Notable	*Chalarus griseus* Coe	Notable
Sciapus contristans (Wiedemann)	Notable	*Chalarus parmenteri* Coe	Notable
Sciapus heteropygus Parent	RDB 1	*Dorylomorpha beckeri* Aczel	Notable
Sciapus laetus (Meigen)	Notable	*Dorylomorpha clavifemora* Coe	RDB 1
Sciapus loewi (Becker)	Notable	*Dorylomorpha hungarica* (Aczel)	Notable
Sympycnus spiculatus Gerstaecker	Notable	*Dorylomorpha infirmata* (Collin)	Notable
Symtormon macula Parent	RDB 3	*Eudorylas arcanus* Coe	Notable
Syntormon filiger Verrall	Notable	*Eudorylas dissimilis* Coe	RDB 1
Syntormon mikii Strobl	RDB 2	*Eudorylas halteratus* (Meigen)	Notable
Syntormon spicatus (Loew)	Notable	*Eudorylas horridus* (Becker)	Notable
Syntormon zelleri (Loew)	Notable	*Eudorylas inferus* Collin	Notable
Systenus bipartitus (Loew)	RDB 3	*Eudorylas jenkinsoni* Coe	Notable
Systenus leucurus Loew	Notable	*Eudorylas kowarzi* (Becker)	Notable
Systenus pallipes (von Roser)	Notable	*Eudorylas melanostolus* (Becker)	Notable
Systenus scholtzii (Loew)	Notable	*Eudorylas montium* (Becker)	Notable
Systenus tener Loew	RDB 3	*Eudorylas obliquus* Coe	Notable
Tachytrechus consobrinus (Haliday)	Notable	*Eudorylas restrictus* Coe	RDB 1
Tachytrechus ripicola Loew	RDB 3	*Eudorylas ruralis* (Meigen)	RDB 1
Telmaturgus tumidulus (Raddatz)	RDB 3	*Eudorylas terminalis* (Thomson)	RDB 2
Thinophilus ruficornis (Haliday)	Notable	*Eudorylas unicolor* (Zetterstedt)	Notable
Thrypticus cuneatus (Becker)	RDB 1	*Eudorylas zermattensis* (Becker)	Notable
Thrypticus divisus (Strobl)	RDB 3	*Nephrocerus flavicornis* Zetterstedt	Notable
Thrypticus laetus Verrall	Notable	*Nephrocerus scutellatus* Macquart	RDB 1
Thrypticus nigricauda Wood	Notable	*Pipunculus fonsecai* Coe	Notable
Thrypticus pollinosus Verrall	Notable	*Pipunculus phaeton* Coe	Notable
Thrypticus tarsalis Parent	RDB 3	*Pipunculus zugmayeriae* Kowarz	Notable
		Tomosvaryella cilitarsis (Strobl)	Notable
Lonchopteridae		*Tomosvaryella minima* (Becker)	RDB 3
		Tomosvaryella palliditarsis (Collin)	Notable
Lonchoptera meijeri Collin, 1938	Notable		
Lonchoptera nigrociliata Duda	Notable	**Syrphidae**	
Lonchoptera nitidifrons Strobl	Notable		
Lonchoptera scutellata Stein, P.	Notable	*Anasimyia interpuncta* (Harris)	RDB 3
		Anasimyia lunulata (Meigen)	Notable
Phoridae		*Blera fallax* (Linnaeus)	RDB 1
		Brachyopa bicolor (Fallen)	RDB 3
Aenigmatias brevifrons Schmitz	RDB K	*Brachyopa insensilis* Collin	Notable
Aenigmatias franzi Schmitz	RDB K	*Brachyopa pilosa* Collin	Notable
Aenigmatias lubbocki (Verrall)	RDB K	*Brachypalpus laphriformis* (Fallen)	Notable
Phora obscura (Zetterstedt)	RDB K	*Caliprobola speciosa* (Rossi)	RDB 1
Phora praepandens Schmitz	RDB K	*Callicera aenea* (Fabricius)	RDB 3
Plectanocnema nudipes (Becker)	RDB K	*Callicera rufa* Schummel	RDB 3
Triphleba excisa (Lundbeck)	RDB K	*Callicera spinolae* Rondani	RDB 1
Triphleba flexipalpis Schmitz	RDB K	*Chalcosyrphus eunotus* (Loew)	RDB 2
Triphleba smithi Disney	RDB K	*Chamaesyrphus caledonicus* Collin	RDB 1
Woodiphora retroversa (Wood)	RDB K	*Chamaesyrphus scaevoides* (Fallen)	RDB 3
		Cheilosia barbata Loew	Notable
Platypezidae		*Cheilosia carbonaria* Egger	Notable
		Cheilosia chrysocoma (Meigen)	RDB 3
Agathomyia collini Verrall	RDB 2	*Cheilosia cynocephala* Loew	Notable
Agathomyia elegantula (Fallen)	Notable	*Cheilosia mutabilis* (Fallen)	Notable
Agathomyia falleni (Zetterstedt)	RDB 3	*Cheilosia nebulosa* Verrall	RDB 3
Agathomyia species 1	Notable	*Cheilosia nigripes* (Meigen)	RDB 3
Agathomyia species 2	Notable	*Cheilosia pubera* (Zetterstedt)	Notable
Atelestus dissonans Collin	Notable	*Cheilosia sahlbergi* Becker	RDB 2
Callomyia dives Zetterstedt	Notable	*Cheilosia semifasciata* Becker	RDB 3
Callomyia elegans Meigen	RDB 2	*Cheilosia soror* (Zett.)	Notable
Microsania straeleni Collart	RDB 3	*Cheilosia species B* Stubbs	RDB 1
Platypeza hirticeps Verrall	Notable	*Cheilosia velutina* Loew	Notable
Seri obscuripennis (Oldenburg)	RDB 2	*Chrysogaster macquarti* Loew	Notable
		Chrysotoxum elegans Loew	RDB 3
Pipunculidae		*Chrysotoxum octomaculatum* Curtis	RDB 2
		Chrysotoxum vernale Loew	RDB 1
Cephalops carinatus (Verrall)	Notable	*Criorhina asilica* (Fallen)	Notable
Cephalops curtifrons Coe	RDB 1	*Criorhina ranunculi* (Panzer)	Notable
Cephalops oberon Coe	Notable	*Didea alneti* (Fallen)	RDB 1
Cephalops perspicuus (de Meijere)	RDB 2	*Didea fasciata* Macquart	Notable
Chalarus argenteus Coe	Notable	*Didea intermedia* Loew	Notable
Chalarus basalis Loew	Notable	*Doros conopseus* (Fabricius)	RDB 2

Epistophella euchroma (Kowarz)	RDB 3	**Conopidae**	
Epistrophe diaphana (Zetterstedt)	Notable		
Eristalis cryptarum (Fabricius)	RDB 2	*Conops strigata* Wiedemann	Notable
Eristalis rupium Fabricius	Notable	*Conops vesicularis* Linnaeus	Notable
Eumerus ornatus Meigen	Notable	*Leopoldius brevirostris* (Germar)	RDB 2
Eumerus sabulonum (Fallen)	Notable	*Leopoldius signatus* (Wiedemann)	Notable
Ferdinandea ruficornis (Fabricius)	Notable	*Myopa curtirostris* Krober	RDB 3
Hammerschmidtia ferruginea (Fallen)	RDB 1	*Myopa extricata* Collin	RDB 3
Helophilus groenlandicus (Fabricius)	RDB 2	*Myopa fasciata* Meigen	RDB 3
Lejogaster splendida (Meigen)	Notable	*Myopa occulta* Wiedemann	RDB 1
Lejops vittata (Meigen)	RDB 2	*Myopa polystigma* Rondani	RDB 3
Mallota cimbiciformis (Fallen)	Notable	*Myopa strandi* Duda	RDB 3
Megasyrphus annulipes (Zetterstedt)	Notable	*Myopa vicaria* Walker	RDB 2
Melangyna barbifrons (Fallen)	Notable	*Physocephala nigra* (Degeer)	RDB 3
Melangyna ericarum (Collin)	RDB 3	*Sicus abdominalis* Krober	RDB 1
Melangyna guttata (Fallen)	Notable	*Thecophora fulvipes* Robineau-Desvoidyi	Notable
Melangyna triangulifera (Zetterstedt)	Notable	*Zodion cinereum* (Fabricius)	Notable
Melanostoma dubium (Zetterstedt)	Notable	*Zodion notatum* Meigen	RDB 3
Melanostoma species A Stubbs	Notable		
Metasyrphus lapponicus (Zetterstedt)	Notable	**Tephritidae**	
Metasyrphus latilunulatus (Collin)	Notable		
Metasyrphus nielseni Dusek & Laska	Notable	*Acanthiophilus helianthi* (Rossi)	Notable
Metasyrphus nitens (Zetterstedt)	Notable	*Acinia corniculata* (Zetterstedt)	RDB 1
Microdon devius (Linnaeus)	RDB 2	*Campiglossa argyrocephala* (Loew)	RDB 3
Microdon eggeri Mik	Notable	*Campiglossa grandinata* (Rondani)	RDB 2
Microdon mutabilis (L.)	Notable	*Chaetorellia ioricata* (Rondani)	RDB 2
Myolepta luteola (Gmelin)	Notable	*Chetostoma curvinerve* Rondani	RDB 2
Myolepta potens (Harris)	RDB 1	*Cryptaciura rotundiventris* (Fal.)	Notable
Neoascia geniculata (Meigen)	Notable	*Dioxyna bidentis* (Robineau-Desvoidy	Notable
Neoascia interrupta (Meigen)	Notable	*Euphranta toxoneura* (Loew)	Notable
Neoascia obliqua Coe	Notable	*Goniglossum wiedemanni* (Meigen)	Notable
Neocnemodon brevidens (Egger)	Notable	*Icterica westermanni* (Mg.)	Notable
Neocnemodon latitarsis (Egger)	Notable	*Myopites eximia* Seguy	RDB 3
Neocnemodon pubescens Delucchi & Psch	Notable	*Myopites inulaedyssentericae* Blot	RDB 3
Neocnemodon verrucula (Collin)	Notable	*Orellia falcata* (Scopoli)	Notable
Orthonevra brevicornis Loew	Notable	*Oxyna flavipennis* (Loew)	Notable
Orthonevra geniculata Meigen	Notable	*Oxyna nebulosa* (Wiedemann)	RDB 3
Paragus albifrons (Fallen)	RDB 2	*Paroxyna absinthii*	Notable
Paragus tibialis (Fal.)	Notable	*Paroxyna lhommei* Hering	RDB 1
Parasyrphus nigritarsis (Zetterstedt)	RDB 1	*Paroxyna producta*	Notable
Parhelophilus consimilis (Malm)	RDB 2	*Paroxyna solidagensis* White	Notable
Pelecocera tricincta Meigen	RDB 3	*Platyparea discoidea* (Fabricius)	RDB 2
Pipiza lugubris (Fabricius)	Notable	*Rhagoletis meigenii* (Loew)	Extinct
Pipizella maculipennis (Meigen)	RDB 3	*Tephritis praecox* (Loew)	RDB 1
Pipizella virens (Fabricius)	Notable	*Tephritis sp. nov.*	RDB K
Platycheirus discimanus Loew	Notable	*Terellia vectensis* (Collin)	RDB 3
Platycheirus immarginatus (Zetterstedt)	Notable	*Terellia winthemi* (Mg.)	RDB 3
Platycheirus melanopsis Loew	RDB 3	*Trupanea amoena* Frauenfeld	RDB 2
Platycheirus perpallidus Verrall	Notable	*Urophora cuspidata* (Mg.)	Notable
Platycheirus podagratus (Zetterstedt)	Notable	*Urophora solstitialis*	RDB 3
Platycheirus sticticus (Meigen)	Notable	*Urophora spoliata* (Haliday)	RDB 3
Pocota personata (Harris)	RDB 2	*Vidalia cornuta* (Scopoli)	RDB 3
Psilota anthracina Meigen	RDB 2	*Vidalia spinifrons* Schroeder	RDB 3
Rhingia rostrata (Linnaeus)	RDB 3		
Sphaerophoria loewi Zetterstedt	RDB 2	**Otitidae**	
Sphaerophoria virgata Goeldlin de Tie	Notable		
Sphegina verecunda Collin	Notable	*Dorycera graminum* (Fabricius)	RDB 3
Triglyphus primus Loew	Notable	*Herina oscillans* (Meigen)	RDB 3
Volucella inanis (Linnaeus)	Notable	*Herina paludum* (Fallen)	RDB 3
Volucella inflata (Fabricius)	Notable	*Herina palustris* (Meigen)	Notable
Volucella zonaria (Poda)	Notable	*Homocephala albitarsis* Zetterstedt	RDB 1
Xanthandrus comtus (Harris)	Notable	*Homocephala bipunctata* (Loew)	RDB K
Xylota abiens Meigen	Notable	*Melieria cana* (Loew)	Notable
Xylota coeruleiventris Zetterstedt	Notable	*Melieria picta* (Mg)	Notable
Xylota florum (Fabricius)	Notable	*Myennis octopunctata* (Coquebert)	RDB 2
Xylota tarda Meigen	Notable	*Tetanops myopinus* Fallen	Notable
Xylota xanthocnema Collin	Notable	*Ulidia erythrophthalma* Meigen	RDB 3

Micropezidae

Calobata stylifera Loew	RDB 3
Micropeza lateralis Meigen	Notable
Rainieria calceata (Fallen)	RDB 1
Pseudopomyza atrimana Meigen	RDB 1

Megamerinidae

Megamerina dolium (Fabricius)	Notable

Tanypezidae

Strongylophthalmyia ustulata (Zetterstedt)	RDB 1
Tanypeza longimana Fallen	RDB 2

Psilidae

Chyliza extenuatum (Rossi)	RDB 3
Chyliza fuscipennis (Robineau-Desvoidy)	Notable
Chyliza nova Collin	Notable
Chyliza vittata Meigen	Notable
Loxocera nigrifrons Macquart	RDB 2
Psila clunalis Collin	Notable
Psila luteola Collin	RDB 3

Chamaemyiidae

Acrometopia wahlbergi (Zetterstedt)	RDB 2
Chamaemyia elegans Panzer	Notable
Chamaemyia fasciata Loew	Notable
Chamaemyia paludosa Collin	RDB 2
Leucopis griseola (Fallen)	Notable
Leucopis morgei Smith	RDB K
Leucopis silesiaca Eggers	Notable
Parochthiphila coronata (Loew)	RDB 1
Parochthiphila spectabilis (Loew)	RDB 1

Lauxaniidae

Aulogastromyia anisodactyla (Loew)	Notable
Cnemacantha muscaria (Fallen)	RDB 3
Homoneura consobrina (Zetterstedt)	Notable
Homoneura interstincta (Fallen)	RDB 3
Homoneura limnea (Becker)	RDB 2
Homoneura tesquae (Becker)	Notable
Lyciella laeta (Zetterstedt)	RDB 3
Minettia dissimilis Collin	RDB 3
Minettia flaviventris (Costa)	RDB 3
Sapromyza albiceps Fallen	Notable
Sapromyza basalis Zetterstedt	Notable
Sapromyza bipunctata Meigen	Notable
Sapromyza obsoleta Fallen	Notable
Sapromyza opaca Becker	Notable
Sapromyza zetterstedti Hendel	Notable

Heleomyzidae

Borboropsis puberula (Zetterstedt)	RDB 1
Chaetomus confusus (Wahlgren)	Notable
Chaetomus flavotestaceus (Zett.)	Notable
Eccoptemera pallescens (Meigen)	Notable
Eccoptomera ornata Loew	Notable
Heleomyza captiosa Gorodkov	RDB K
Morpholeria dudai (Czerny)	RDB 3
Neoleria propinqua Collin	Notable
Neossos nidicola (Frey)	RDB 3
Oecothea praecox Loew	Notable
Oldenbergiella brumalis Czerny	RDB 1

Schroederella iners (Meigen)	RDB K
Scoliocentra scutellaris (Zett.)	RDB 3
Suillia dawnae Withers	RDB K
Suillia dumicola (Collin)	Notable
Suillia oxyphora (Mik)	RDB 2
Suillia vaginata (Loew)	Notable
Trixoscelis marginella (Fallen)	Notable

Chryomyidae

Aphaniosoma propinquans Collin	RDB 1
Aphaniosoma socium Collin	RDB 1

Sepsidae

Meroplius minutus Wiedemann	RDB 3
Nemopoda pectinulata Loew	Notable
Sepsis biflexuosa Strobl	Notable
Sepsis nigripes Meigen	RDB 3
Themira biloba Andersson	RDB K
Themira germanica Duda	Notable
Themira gracilis (Zetterstedt)	Notable
Themira nigricornis (Meigen)	RDB 3

Sciomyzidae

Antichaeta analis (Meigen)	RDB 3
Antichaeta brevipennis (Zetterstedt)	RDB 2
Antichaeta obliviosa Enderlein	RDB 2
Colobaea bifasciella (Fallen)	Notable
Colobaea distincta (Meigen)	Notable
Colobaea pectoralis (Zetterstedt)	RDB 2
Colobaea punctata (Lundbeck)	Notable
Dichetophora finlandica Verbeke	RDB 3
Dictya umbrarum (Linnaeus)	Notable
Ectinocera borealis (Zetterstedt)	RDB 3
Pelidnoptera nigripennis (Fabricius)	Notable
Pherbellia annulipes (Zetterstedt)	Notable
Pherbellia argyra Verbeke	RDB 2
Pherbellia brunnipes Meigen	Notable
Pherbellia dorsata (Zetterstedt)	Notable
Pherbellia griseola (Fallen)	Notable
Pherbellia grisescens (Meigen)	Notable
Pherbellia knutsoni Verbeke	RDB 3
Pherbellia nana (Fallen)	Notable
Psacadina verbekei Rozkonsky	Notable
Psacadina vittigera (Schiner)	RDB 2
Psacadina zernyi Mayer	RDB 2
Pteromicra glabricula (Fallen)	Notable
Pteromicra leucopeza (Meigen)	RDB 2
Pteromicra pectorosa (Hendel)	RDB 2
Renocera striata (Meigen)	Notable
Salticella fasciata (Meigen)	RDB 2
Sciomyza dryomyzina Zetterstedt	RDB 2
Sciomyza simplex Fallen	Notable
Tetanocera freyi Stackelberg	RDB 3
Tetanocera phyllophora Melander	Notable
Tetanocera punctifrons Rondani	Notable

Pallopteridae

Eurygnathomyia bicolor (Zetterstedt)	RDB 1
Palloptera ambusta (Meigen)	RDB 3
Palloptera laetabilis Loew	RDB 2
Palloptera usta (Meigen)	RDB 3

Lonchaeidae

Dasiops occultus Collin	Notable
Dasiops spatiosus (Becker)	Notable
Dasiops trichosternalis Morge	Notable
Earomyia schistopyga Collin	Notable
Lonchaea britteni Collin	Notable
Lonchaea collini Hackman	Notable
Lonchaea corusca Czerny	Notable
Lonchaea hirticeps Zetterstedt	Notable
Lonchaea laxa Collin	Notable
Lonchaea nitens (Bigot)	Notable
Lonchaea palposa Zetterstedt	Notable
Lonchaea peregrina Becker	Notable
Lonchaea ultima Collin	Notable

Neottiophilidae

Actenoptera hilarella (Zetterstedt)	RDB 3

Piophilidae

Centrophlebomya furcata (Fabricius)	RDB 1
Piophila signata (Fallen)	RDB 2

Opomyzidae

Geomyza angustipennis Zetterstedt	RDB 3
Geomyza apicalis (Meigen)	Notable
Geomyza breviseta (Czerny)	Notable
Geomyza hendeli Czerny	RDB 3
Geomyza majuscula (Loew)	Notable
Geomyza venusta (Meigen)	Notable
Opomyza lineatopunctata von Roser	Notable
Opomyza punctata Haliday	Notable
Opomyza punctella Fallen	RDB 3

Clusiidae

Clusiodes apicalis (Zetterstedt)	Notable
Clusiodes caledonica (Collin)	Notable
Clusiodes geomyzina (Fallen)	RDB 3
Heteromeringia nigrimana (Loew)	RDB 1
Paraclusia tigrina (Fallen)	RDB 2

Odiniidae

Odinia hendeli Collin	RDB 2
Odinia maculata (Meigen)	RDB 3
Odinia meijerei Collin	Notable
Odinia ornata (Zett.)	RDB 2
Odinia pomona Cogan	RDB 1
Odinia xanthocera Collin	RDB 2

Carniidae

Meonura freta Collin	RDB K
Meonura lacteipennis (Fallen)	RDB 3
Meonura minutissima (Zetterstedt)	Notable
Meonura neglecta Collin	RDB 3
Meonura prima Becker	Notable
Meonura triangularis Collin	Notable

Acartophthalmidae

Acartophthalmus bicolor Oldenberg	RDB 3

Periscelididae

Periscelis annulata (Fallen)	Notable
Periscelis annulipes Loew	RDB K
Periscelis nigra (Zetterstedt)	RDB 1
Periscelis winnertzi Egger	RDB 1

Aulacigastridae

Aulacigaster leucopeza (Meigen)	Notable
Stenomicra cogani Irwin	RDB 3
Stenomicra delicata (Collin)	RDB 2

Anthomyzidae

Anagnota bicolor (Meigen)	Notable
Anagnota collini Czerny	RDB 2
Anthomyza bifasciata Wood	Notable

Asteiidae

Asteia elegantula Zetterstedt	RDB 2
Astiosoma rufifrons Duda	RDB 2

Ephydridae

Athyroglossa ordinata Becker	RDB 1
Nostima semialata (Collin)	RDB K
Ochthera manicata	RDB 3
Ochthera schembrii Rondani	RDB 1
Parydroptera discomyzina Collin	RDB 2
Psilopa marginella Fallen	Notable
Scatella callosicosta Bezzi	RDB 2
Scatella crassicosta Becker	RDB 2
Scatella fusca Macquart	Extinct

Diastatidae

Diastata vagans Loew	Notable

Drosophilidae

Acletoxenus formosus (Loew)	RDB 3
Amiota albilabris Zett.	RDB 2
Amiota alboguttata (Wahlberg)	Notable
Amiota basdeni Fonseca	RDB 2
Amiota variegata (Fallen)	RDB 1
Chymomyza costata (Zetterstedt)	Notable
Chymomyza distincta (Egger)	RDB K
Stegana coleoptrata (Scopoli)	Notable
Stegana hypoleuca Meigen	RDB K
Stegana longifibula Takada	RDB 3
Stegana nigrithorax Strobl	Notable

Milichiidae

Leptometopa niveipennis (Strobl)	RDB K
Madiza britanica Hennig	RDB 2
Madiza pachymera Becker	RDB 3

Tethinidae

Tethina incisuralis (Macquart)	RDB K
Tethina simplex (Collin)	RDB K

Agromyzidae

Metopomyza ornata (Meigen)	Notable
Phytomyza orobanchia Kaltenbach	Notable

165

Chloropidae

Aphanotrigonum meijerei (Duda)	RDB 2
Calamoncosis aspistylina Duda	RDB K
Cetema myopina (Loew)	Notable
Cetema transversa Collin	RDB K
Chlorops adjuncta	Notable
Chlorops citrinella (Zetterstedt)	RDB K
Chlorops gracilis Meigen	Notable
Chlorops laeta Meigen	Notable
Chlorops planifrons Loew	Notable
Chlorops rufina (Zetterstedt)	Notable
Chlorops triangularis Becker	Notable
Chlorops troglodytes (Zetterstedt)	Notable
Chlorops varsoviensis Becker	Notable
Conioscinella zetterstedti	RDB K
Crassivenula brachyptera	RDB 3
Cryptonevra consimilis (Collin)	RDB 2
Cryptonevra nigritarsis	Notable
Dicraeus napaeus Collin	RDB K
Dicraeus raptus (Haliday)	Notable
Dicraeus scibilis Collin	Notable
Dicraeus styriacus (Strobl)	Notable
Dicraeus tibialis (Macquart)	Notable
Dicraeus vallaris Collin	Notable
Elachiptera pubescens (Thalhammar)	Notable
Elachiptera rufifrons Duda	RDB 3
Elachiptera uniseta Collin	Notable
Epichlorops puncticollis (Zetterstedt)	Notable
Eribolus gracilior (de Meijere)	Notable
Eribolus nana (Zetterstedt)	Notable
Eribolus slesvicensis (Becker)	Notable
Eurina lurida Meigen	RDB 3
Eutropha fulvifrons (Haliday)	Notable
Fiebrigella palposa (Fallen)	Notable
Fiebrigella parcepilosa (Collin)	RDB K
Gampsocera inornata Corti	RDB K
Gaurax brittanicus Deeming	RDB K
Gaurax niger (Czerny)	RDB K
Incertella scotica (Collin)	Notable
Lasiamba baliola Collin	Notable
Lasiamba brevibucca Duda	Notable
Lipara rufitarsis (Loew)	Notable
Lipara similis Schiner	RDB 2
Melanochaeta capreolus (Haliday)	Notable
Melanum fumipenne Loew	RDB K
Meromyza coronoseta Hubicka	Notable
Meromyza curvinervis Zetterstedt	RDB K
Meromyza hispanica	RDB K
Meromyza laeta Meigen	RDB K
Meromyza mosquensis Fedoseeva	Notable
Meromyza pluriseta Peterfi	Notable
Meromyza sp. indet.	Notable
Oscinella angularis Collin	Notable
Oscinella angustipennis Duda	Notable
Oscinomorpha arcuata (Duda)	Notable
Oscinomorpha sordissima (Strobl)	Notable
Oscinosoma gilvipes	Notable
Platycephala umbraculata (Fabricius)	RDB 2
Polyodaspis sulcicollis (Meigen)	RDB 1
Pseudopachychaeta approximatonervis (Zett.)	Notable
Pseudopachychaeta heleocharis	Notable
Pseudopachychaeta ruficeps	Notable
Rhopalopterum atricilla (Zetterstedt)	Notable
Rhopalopterum brunneipennis Besch. & Lansb.	RDB K
Rhopalopterum crucicarinatus Besch. & Lansb.	RDB K
Rhopalopterum femorale (Collin)	Notable
Siphonella oscinina (Fallen)	Notable
Siphunculina aenea (Macquart)	RDB 3

Speccafrons halophila Duda	Notable
Thaumatomyia rufa (Macquart)	Notable
Trachysiphonella carinfacies Narchuk	RDB K
Trachysiphonella pygmaea (Meigen)	Notable
Trachysiphonella ruficeps (Macquart)	Notable
Trachysiphonella scutellata (von Roser)	Notable

Oestrididae

Cephenemyia auribarbis (Mg.)	Notable
Hypoderma bovis (Linnaeus)	RDB 2
Hypoderma diana Brauer	RDB 3
Hypoderma lineatum (Villers)	RDB 2
Oestrus ovis Linnaeus	RDB 3
Pharyngomyia picta (Meigen)	Extinct

Gasterophilidae

Gasterophilus haemorrhoidalis (Linnaeus)	RDB 1
Gasterophilus intestinalis (Degeer)	Notable
Gasterophilus nasalis (Linnaeus)	RDB 1
Gasterophilus pecorum (Fabricius)	RDB 1

Tachinidae

Actia exoleta (Meigen)	RDB 1
Actia nudibasis Stein	RDB K
Anthomyiopsis nigrisquama (Zetterstedt)	RDB 3
Asiphona verralli (Wainwright)	RDB 2
Bactromyia aurulenta (Meigen)	RDB 3
Belida angelicae (Meigen)	RDB 1
Brachicheta strigata (Meigen)	Notable
Carcelia excisa (Fallen)	RDB 2
Carcelia intermedia (Herting)	RDB 1
Ceromya monstrosicornis (Stein)	RDB 2
Ceromya silacea (Meigen)	RDB 1
Chrysosomopsis auratus (Fallen)	RDB 1
Clemelis pullata (Meigen)	RDB 1
Cylindromyia brassicaria (Fabricius)	RDB 1
Dionaea aurifrons (Meigen)	RDB 1
Diplostichus janithrix (Hartig)	RDB 3
Drino lota (Meigen)	Notable
Eloceria delecta (Meigen)	Notable
Elodia ambulatoria (Meigen)	RDB 3
Ernestia puparum (Fabricius)	RDB 2
Erycia furibunda (Zetterstedt)	RDB 2
Erynnia ocypterata Fallen	RDB 2
Estheria bohemani Rondani	RDB 1
Eurithia conjugata (Zett.)	Notable
Eurysthaea scutellaris (Robineau-Desvoidy	RDB 1
Evibrissa vittata (Meigen)	RDB 3
Exorista glossatorum (Rondani)	RDB 2
Freraea gagatea Robineau-Desvoidy	RDB 3
Frontina laeta (Meigen)	RDB 3
Germaria angustata (Zetterstedt)	RDB 2
Germaria ruficeps (Fallen)	RDB 1
Gonia capitata (Degeer)	RDB 2
Gonia divisa Mg	RDB 3
Goniocera versicolor (Fallen)	RDB 2
Graphogaster brunnescens Villeneuve	RDB 3
Gymnosoma globosum (Fabricius)	RDB 1
Gymnosoma nitens (Meigen)	RDB 1
Gymnosoma rotundatum (Linnaeus)	RDB 3
Hemimacquartia paradoxa Brauer and Berg	RDB 1
Huebneria affinis (Fallen)	RDB 1
Hyalurgus lucidus (Meigen)	RDB 3
Labigastera forcipata (Meigen)	RDB 1
Leskia aurea (Fallen)	RDB 1
Leucostoma simplex (Fallen)	RDB 3

Linnaemya comta (Fallen)	RDB 3
Lithophasia hyalipennis (Fallen)	Extinct
Lophosia fasciata Meigen	Notable
Meigenia majuscula (Rondani)	RDB 2
Mintho rufiventris (Fal.)	Notable
Nemoraea pellucida (Meigen)	RDB 2
Opesia cana (Meigen)	RDB 3
Parasetigena silvestris (Robineau-Desvoidy	RDB 2
Peleteria rubescens Robineau-Desvoidyi	Extinct
Peribaea fissicornis (Strobl)	Notable
Periscepsia prunaria (Rondani)	RDB K
Phania thoracica (Meigen)	RDB 3
Phebellia nigripalpis Robineau-Desvoidyi	RDB 2
Phebellia stulta (Zetterstedt)	Extinct
Policheta unicolor (Fallen)	RDB 2
Redtenbacheria insignis Egger	RDB 2
Rhaphiochaeta breviseta (Zetterstedt)	RDB 1
Rhinotachina modesta (Meigen)	RDB 2
Rondania fasciata (Macquart)	Notable
Staurochaeta albocingulata (Fallen)	RDB K
Stomatomyia acuminata (Rondani)	RDB 2
Subclytia rotundiventris (Fallen)	RDB 3
Tachina magnicornis (Zetterstedt)	RDB K
Thecocarcelia acutangula (Macqart)	RDB 2
Thelymorpha marmorata (F)	Notable
Tlephusa diligens (Zetterstedt)	RDB 3
Trichopareia seria (Meigen)	RDB 2
Wagneria costata (Fallen)	RDB 2
Wagneria gagatea Robineau-Desvoidyi	RDB 3
Xylotachina diluta (Meigen)	RDB 1
Zophomyia temula (Scopoli)	Notable

Rhinophoridae

Angioneura acerba (Meigen)	RDB 1
Angioneura cyrtoneurina (Zetterstedt)	RDB 2

Sarcophagidae

Agria affinis (Fallen)	RDB 1
Agria mamillata (Pandelle)	RDB 3
Angiometopa ruralis (Fallen)	RDB 1
Blaesoxipha erythrura (Meigen)	RDB 3
Blaesoxipha gladiatrix (Pandelle)	Notable
Blaesoxipha rossica Villeneuve	RDB 3
Macronychia griseola (Fallen)	RDB 3
Macronychia polyodon (Meigen)	RDB 3
Macronychia ungulans (Pandelle)	Notable
Miltogramma germari Meigen	RDB 3
Pterella grisea (Meigen)	Notable
Sarcophaga arcipes Pandelle	Notable
Sarcophaga ebrachiata Pandelle	RDB 3
Sarcophaga exuberans Pandelle	RDB 1
Sarcophaga laciniata Pandelle	Notable
Sarcophaga similis Meade	Notable
Sarcophaga villeneuvei Bottcher	RDB 3
Sarcophila latifrons (Fallen)	Notable

Calliphoridae

Calliphora alpina (Zetterstedt)	RDB 3
Calliphora loewi Enderlein	Notable
Calliphora uralensis Villeneuve	RDB 3
Eggisops pecchiolii Rondani	Notable
Pseudonesia puberula (Zetterstedt)	Notable

Scathophagidae

Acanthocnema glaucescens (Loew)	Notable
Acanthocnema nigrimana (Zetterstedt)	RDB 3
Cordilura aemula Collin	RDB 3
Cordilura atrata Zetterstedt	Notable
Cordilura hyalinipennis Ringdahl	RDB 1
Cordilura picipes Mg.	RDB 3
Cordilura rufimana Meigen	Notable
Cordilura similis Siebke	RDB 3
Cosmetopus dentimanus (Zetterstedt)	RDB 1
Ernoneura argus (Zetterstedt)	RDB 2
Gimnomera tarsea (Fallen)	Notable
Gonatherus planiceps (Fallen)	RDB 3
Microprosopa pallidicauda (Zetterstedt)	RDB 3
Nanna brevifrons (Zetterstedt)	Notable
Norellia spinipes Robineau-Desvoidyi	Notable
Parallelomma paridis Hering	RDB 2
Parallelomma vittatum (Meigen)	Notable
Scathophaga decipiens Haliday	Notable
Scathophaga pictipennis Oldenburg	RDB 3
Scathophaga scybalaria (Linnaeus)	Notable
Scathophaga tinctinervis (Becker)	RDB 2

Anthomyiidae

Chirosia aberrans Collin	RDB K
Chirosia montana Pokorny	RDB K
Delia caledonica Fonseca	RDB K
Delia flavogrisea (Ringdahl)	RDB K
Delia hirtitibia (Stein)	RDB K
Delia pilifemur (Ringdahl)	RDB K
Delia tarsifimbria (Pandelle)	RDB K
Delia tumidula Ringdahl	RDB K
Egle subarctica Huckett, 1965	RDB K
Eremomyia anderssoni Hennig	RDB K
Eustalomyia hilaris (Fal.)	RDB 3
Eustalomyia vittipes (Zetterstedt)	Notable
Hydrophoria spiniclunis (Pandelle)	RDB K
Paraprosalpia albipennis (Ringdahl)	RDB K
Pegohylemyia apiciseta (Ringdahl)	RDB K
Pegohylemyia flavisquama (Stein)	RDB K
Pegohylemyia norvegica Ringdahl	RDB K
Pegohylemyia sanctimarci (Czerny)	RDB K
Pegomya argyrocephala (Meigen)	RDB K
Phorbia atrogrisea Tiensuu	Notable
Phorbia longipilis (Pandelle)	RDB K
Phorbia nuditibia Fonseca	RDB K
Pseudomyopina moriens (Zetterstedt)	RDB K

Fanniidae

Fannia atripes Stein	RDB K
Fannia carbonaria (Meigen)	Notable
Fannia clara Collin	Notable
Fannia collini Fonseca	RDB K
Fannia coracula Collin	Notable
Fannia gotlandica Ringdahl	Notable
Fannia hirticeps (Stein)	RDB K
Fannia hirundinis Ringdahl	RDB K
Fannia immutica Collin	Notable
Fannia latipalpis (Stein)	RDB K
Fannia lineata Stein	RDB K
Fannia melania (Dufour)	Notable
Fannia metallipennis (Zetterstedt)	Notable
Fannia nidica Collin	Notable
Fannia nigra Malloch	Notable
Fannia norvegica Ringdahl	Notable
Fannia novalis Pont	RDB K

Fannia ornata (Meigen)	RDB K
Fannia pseudonorvegica Fonseca	RDB K
Fannia ringdahlana Collin	Notable
Fannia speciosa (Villeneuve)	Notable
Fannia subatripes Fonseca	RDB K
Fannia subpubescens Collin	Notable
Fannia tuberculata (Zetterstedt)	Notable
Fannia umbratica Collin	RDB K
Fannia verrallii (Stein)	Notable
Fannia vespertilionis Ringdahl	Notable
Piezura boletorum (Rondani)	RDB K

Muscidae

Caricea brachialis (Rondani)	RDB 3
Caricea falculata Collin	Notable
Caricea pallipalpis (Zetterstedt)	Notable
Caricea rubricornis (Zetterstedt)	RDB 3
Caricea spuria (Zetterstedt)	Notable
Coenosia atra Meigen	Notable
Coenosia brevisquama Fonseca	RDB K
Coenosia campestris (R-D)	Notable
Coenosia dubiosa Hennig	RDB K
Coenosia flavimana (Zett.)	RDB 3
Coenosia paludis Tiensuu	RDB 3
Coenosia pudorosa Collin	Notable
Coenosia pulicaria (Zetterstedt)	Notable
Coenosia pygmaea (Zetterstedt)	Notable
Coenosia stigmatica Wood	RDB 3
Coenosia trilineella (Zetterstedt)	Notable
Coenosia verralli Collin	Notable
Coenosia vibrissata Collin	RDB 3
Dexiopsis lacustris Karl	Notable
Dexiopsis minutalis (Zetterstedt)	Notable
Helina abdominalis (Zetterstedt)	Notable
Helina annosa (Zetterstedt)	RDB 3
Helina arctata Collin	Notable
Helina calceata (Rondani)	Notable
Helina cilipes (Schnabl and Dz	RDB 1
Helina concolor (Czerny)	RDB 3
Helina cothurnata (Rondani)	RDB 3
Helina crinita Collin	RDB 2
Helina flagripes (Rondani)	RDB 3
Helina intermedia (Villeneuve)	RDB 2
Helina parcepilosa (Stein)	RDB 2
Helina pubescens (Stein)	RDB 3
Helina pulchella (Ringdahl)	RDB 3
Helina quadrinotata (Meigen)	RDB 3
Helina vicina (Czerny)	Notable
Hydrotaea basdeni Collin	RDB 3
Hydrotaea borussica Stein	Notable
Hydrotaea cinerea Robineau-Desvoidyi	Notable
Hydrotaea glabricula (Fallen)	RDB 3
Hydrotaea meridionalis Portschinsky	RDB 3
Hydrotaea nidicola Malloch	RDB 3
Hydrotaea pandellei Stein	RDB K
Hydrotaea parva Meade	Notable
Hydrotaea pilipes Stein	Notable
Hydrotaea pilitibia Stein	RDB 3
Hydrotaea velutina Robineau-Desvoidyi	RDB 2
Limnophora nigripes (Robineau-Desvoidy	Notable
Limnophora scrupulosa (Zetterstedt)	Notable

Limnophora uniseta Stein	Notable
Lispe caesia Meigen	Notable
Lispe consanguinea Loew	RDB 2
Lispe hydromyzina Fallen	Extinct
Lispe loewi Ringdahl	Notable
Lispe nana Macquart	Notable
Lispe uliginosa Fallen	Notable
Mydaea deserta (Zetterstedt)	Notable
Mydaea maculiventris	RDB 3
Mydaea obscurella Malloch	RDB 2
Neolimnophora maritima (Roder)	RDB 2
Neolimnophora virgo (Villeneuve)	RDB 3
Orchisia costata (Meigen)	RDB 2
Phaonia amabilis (Mg)	RDB 2
Phaonia apicalis Stein	RDB 2
Phaonia atriceps	Notable
Phaonia bitincta (Rondani)	RDB 3
Phaonia canescens Stein	RDB 3
Phaonia colbrani Collin	RDB K
Phaonia consobrina (Zetterstedt)	Notable
Phaonia exoleta (Meigen)	RDB 3
Phaonia falleni Michelsen	Notable
Phaonia fusca (Meade)	RDB 3
Phaonia gracilis Stein	RDB 1
Phaonia jaroschewskii (Schnabl)	RDB 2
Phaonia laeta (Fal.)	RDB 3
Phaonia latipalpis Schnabl	RDB 2
Phaonia lugubris (Meigen)	Notable
Phaonia mediterranea Hennig	Notable
Phaonia nymphaearum R-D	RDB 2
Phaonia pratensis (Robineau-Desvoidy	Notable
Phaonia pullata (Czerny)	RDB K
Phaonia scutellata (Zetterstedt)	Extinct
Phaonia siebecki Schnabl & Dzeidzicki	Notable
Phaonia subfuscinervis (Zetterstedt)	Notable
Phaonia zugmayeriae Schnabl	Notable
Polietes steinii (Ringdahl)	RDB 1
Potamia setifemur (Stein)	RDB 1
Pyrellia rapax (Harris)	RDB 2
Spilogona alpica (Zetterstedt)	RDB K
Spilogona baltica (Ringdahl)	Notable
Spilogona biseriata (Stein)	Notable
Spilogona depressiuscula (Zetterstedt)	RDB 3
Spilogona griseola (Collin)	RDB 3
Spilogona litorea (Fallen)	RDB 3
Spilogona scutulata (Schnabl and Dz	RDB 3
Spilogona septemnotata (Zetterstedt)	RDB 3
Spilogona setigera (Stein)	Notable
Spilogona triangulifera (Zetterstedt)	Notable
Spilogona trianguligera (Zetterstedt)	RDB 3
Thricops aculeipes (Zetterstedt)	Notable
Thricops albibasalis (Zetterstedt)	Notable
Thricops foveolatus (Zett.)	Notable
Thricops hirtulus (Zett.)	Notable
Thricops innocuus (Zett.)	Notable
Thricops separ (Zetterstedt)	RDB 2

Hippoboscidae

Hippobosca equina Linnaeus	RDB K

Appendix 2 Nationally rare and nationally scarce species listed in alphabetic order.

Acanthiophilus helianthi (Rossi)	Notable	*Aphanotrigonum meijerei* (Duda)	RDB 2
Acanthocnema glaucescens (Loew)	Notable	*Aphrosylus mitis* Verrall	RDB 3
Acanthocnema nigrimana (Zetterstedt)	RDB 3	*Aphrosylus raptor* Haliday	Notable
Acartophthalmus bicolor Oldenberg	RDB 3	*Arctoconopa melampodia* (Loew)	RDB 2
Achalcus melanotrichus Mik	Notable	*Argyra atriceps* Loew	Notable
Acinia corniculata (Zetterstedt)	RDB 1	*Argyra auricollis* (Meigen)	RDB 2
Acletoxenus formosus (Loew)	RDB 3	*Argyra elongata* (Zetterstedt)	RDB 3
Acnemia amoena Winnertz	RDB 2	*Argyra grata* Loew	RDB 2
Acnemia longipes Winnertz	Notable	*Asilus crabroniformis* Linnaeus	Notable
Acrometopia wahlbergi (Zetterstedt)	RDB 2	*Asindulum nigrum* Latreille	RDB 2
Acropsilus niger (Loew)	RDB 1	*Asiphona verralli* (Wainwright)	RDB 2
Actenoptera hilarella (Zetterstedt)	RDB 3	*Asteia elegantula* Zetterstedt	RDB 2
Actia exoleta (Meigen)	RDB 1	*Astiosoma rufifrons* Duda	RDB 2
Actia nudibasis Stein	RDB K	*Atelestus dissonans* Collin	Notable
Aedes communis (Degeer)	RDB K	*Athalia sp. indet.*	RDB 1
Aedes dorsalis (Meigen)	RDB 3	*Athyroglossa ordinata* Becker	RDB 1
Aedes flavescens (Muller)	RDB 2	*Atrichops crassipes* (Meigen)	RDB 3
Aedes leucomelas (Meigen)	RDB K	*Atylotus fulvus* (Meigen)	Notable
Aedes sticticus (Meigen)	RDB K	*Atylotus latistriatus* (Brauer)	RDB 3
Aenigmatias brevifrons Schmitz	RDB K	*Atylotus plebeius* (Fallen)	RDB 1
Aenigmatias franzi Schmitz	RDB K	*Atylotus rusticus* (Linnaeus)	RDB 1
Aenigmatias lubbocki (Verrall)	RDB K	*Aulacigaster leucopeza* (Meigen)	Notable
Agathomyia collini Verrall	RDB 2	*Aulogastromyia anisodactyla* (Loew)	Notable
Agathomyia elegantula (Fallen)	Notable	*Azana anomala* (Staeger)	Notable
Agathomyia falleni (Zetterstedt)	RDB 3		
Agathomyia species 1	Notable	*Bactromyia aurulenta* (Meigen)	RDB 3
Agathomyia species 2	Notable	*Belida angelicae* (Meigen)	RDB 1
Agria affinis (Fallen)	RDB 1	*Beris clavipes* (Linnaeus)	Notable
Agria mamillata (Pandelle)	RDB 3	*Beris fuscipes* Meigen	Notable
Allodia angulata Lundstroem	RDB 2	*Bicellaria halterata* Collin	Notable
Allodia barbata (Lundstroem)	Notable	*Bicellaria mera* Collin	Notable
Allodia czernyi (Landrock)	RDB 2	*Blaesoxipha erythrura* (Meigen)	RDB 3
Allodia embla Hackman	RDB 3	*Blaesoxipha gladiatrix* (Pandelle)	Notable
Allodia neglecta Edwards	Notable	*Blaesoxipha rossica* Villeneuve	RDB 3
Allodia pistillata (Lundstroem)	Notable	*Blera fallax* (Linnaeus)	RDB 1
Allodia retracta Plassman	RDB 2	*Boletina digitata* Lundstroem	RDB 2
Allodia silvatica Landrock	Notable	*Boletina dispecta* Dziedzicki	Notable
Allodia triangularis Strobl	RDB 3	*Boletina groenlandica* Staeger	RDB 3
Allodiopsis ingeniosa Kidd	Notable	*Boletina moravica* Landrock	Notable
Allodiopsis maculosa (Meigen)	Notable	*Boletina nasuta* (Haliday)	RDB 3
Allodiopsis rufilatera (Edwards)	RDB 2	*Boletina nigrofusca* Dziedzicki	RDB 2
Amiota albilabris Zett.	RDB 2	*Boletina nitida* Grzegorzek	Notable
Amiota alboguttata (Wahlberg)	Notable	*Boletina pallidula* Edwards	Notable
Amiota basdeni Fonseca	RDB 2	*Boletina pectinunguis* Edwards	RDB 1
Amiota variegata (Fallen)	RDB 1	*Boletina rejecta* Edwards	Notable
Anaclileia dispar (Winnertz)	Notable	*Boletina silvatica* Dziedzicki	RDB 1
Anagnota bicolor (Meigen)	Notable	*Boletina villosa* Landrock	RDB 3
Anagnota collini Czerny	RDB 2	*Bolitophila basicornis* (Mayer)	Notable
Anasimyia interpuncta (Harris)	RDB 3	*Bolitophila bimaculata* Zetterstedt	RDB 2
Anasimyia lunulata (Meigen)	Notable	*Bolitophila fumida* Edwards	RDB 1
Anatella alpina Plassman	RDB 3	*Bolitophila glabrata* Loew	Notable
Anatella ankeli Plassman	RDB 3	*Bolitophila rossica* Landrock	Notable
Anatella dampfi Landrock	RDB 3	*Bombylius canescens* Mikan	Notable
Anatella lenis Dziedzicki	Notable	*Bombylius discolor* Mikan	Notable
Anatella pseudogibba Plassmann	RDB 1	*Bombylius minor* Linnaeus	RDB 2
Angiometopa ruralis (Fallen)	RDB 1	*Borboropsis puberula* (Zetterstedt)	RDB 1
Angioneura acerba (Meigen)	RDB 1	*Brachicheta strigata* (Meigen)	Notable
Angioneura cyrtoneurina (Zetterstedt)	RDB 2	*Brachyopa bicolor* (Fallen)	RDB 3
Anopheles algeriensis Theobald	RDB K	*Brachyopa insensilis* Collin	Notable
Anthomyiopsis nigrisquama (Zetterstedt)	RDB 3	*Brachyopa pilosa* Collin	Notable
Anthomyza bifasciata Wood	Notable	*Brachypalpus laphriformis* (Fallen)	Notable
Antichaeta analis (Meigen)	RDB 3	*Brachypeza armata* Winnertz	RDB 2
Antichaeta brevipennis (Zetterstedt)	RDB 2	*Brachypeza bisignata* Winnertz	Notable
Antichaeta obliviosa Enderlein	RDB 2	*Brevicornu boreale* (Lundstroem)	Notable
Aphaniosoma propinquans Collin	RDB 1	*Brevicornu fennicum* Landrock	RDB 2
Aphaniosoma socium Collin	RDB 1	*Brevicornu foliatum* (Edwards)	RDB 3

Brevicornu griseolum (Zetterstedt)	RDB 1
Brevicornu kingi (Edwards)	RDB 3
Brevicornu nigrofuscum (Lundstroem)	Notable
Brevicornu proximum (Staeger)	Notable
Brevicornu serenum Winnertz	RDB 3
Calamoncosis aspistylina Duda	RDB K
Caliprobola speciosa (Rossi)	RDB 1
Callicera aenea (Fabricius)	RDB 3
Callicera rufa Schummel	RDB 3
Callicera spinolae Rondani	RDB 1
Calliphora alpina (Zetterstedt)	RDB 3
Calliphora loewi Enderlein	Notable
Calliphora uralensis Villeneuve	RDB 3
Callomyia dives Zetterstedt	Notable
Callomyia elegans Meigen	RDB 2
Calobata stylifera Loew	RDB 3
Campiglossa argyrocephala (Loew)	RDB 3
Campiglossa grandinata (Rondani)	RDB 2
Campsicnemus compeditus Loew	Notable
Campsicnemus magius (Loew)	RDB 3
Campsicnemus marginatus Loew	Notable
Campsicnemus pectinulatus Loew	Notable
Campsicnemus pusillus (Meigen)	Notable
Carcelia excisa (Fallen)	RDB 2
Carcelia intermedia (Herting)	RDB 1
Caricea brachialis (Rondani)	RDB 3
Caricea falculata Collin	Notable
Caricea pallipalpis (Zetterstedt)	Notable
Caricea rubricornis (Zetterstedt)	RDB 3
Caricea spuria (Zetterstedt)	Notable
Centrophlebomya furcata (Fabricius)	RDB 1
Cephalops carinatus (Verrall)	Notable
Cephalops curtifrons Coe	RDB 1
Cephalops oberon Coe	Notable
Cephalops perspicuus (de Meijere)	RDB 2
Cephenemyia auribarbis (Mg.)	Notable
Ceromya monstrosicornis (Stein)	RDB 2
Ceromya silacea (Meigen)	RDB 1
Cetema myopina (Loew)	Notable
Cetema transversa Collin	RDB K
Chaetomus confusus (Wahlgren)	Notable
Chaetomus flavotestaceus (Zett.)	Notable
Chaetorellia ioricata (Rondani)	RDB 2
Chalarus argenteus Coe	Notable
Chalarus basalis Loew	Notable
Chalarus griseus Coe	Notable
Chalarus parmenteri Coe	Notable
Chalcosyrphus eunotus (Loew)	RDB 2
Chamaemyia elegans Panzer	Notable
Chamaemyia fasciata Loew	Notable
Chamaemyia paludosa Collin	RDB 2
Chamaesyrphus caledonicus Collin	RDB 1
Chamaesyrphus scaevoides (Fallen)	RDB 3
Cheilosia barbata Loew	Notable
Cheilosia carbonaria Egger	Notable
Cheilosia chrysocoma (Meigen)	RDB 3
Cheilosia cynocephala Loew	Notable
Cheilosia mutabilis (Fallen)	Notable
Cheilosia nebulosa Verrall	RDB 3
Cheilosia nigripes (Meigen)	RDB 3
Cheilosia pubera (Zetterstedt)	Notable
Cheilosia sahlbergi Becker	RDB 2
Cheilosia semifasciata Becker	RDB 3
Cheilosia soror (Zett.)	Notable
Cheilosia species B Stubbs	RDB 1
Cheilosia velutina Loew	Notable
Cheilotrichia imbuta (Meigen)	Notable
Chelifera angusta Collin	Notable
Chelifera aperticauda Collin	Notable
Chelifera astigma Collin	RDB 1
Chelifera concinnicauda Collin	Notable
Chelifera monostigma (Meigen)	Notable
Chelifera subangusta Collin	Notable
Chersodromia cursitans (Zetterstedt)	Notable
Chersodromia speculifera Haliday	Notable
Chetostoma curvinerve Rondani	RDB 2
Chirosia aberrans Collin	RDB K
Chirosia montana Pokorny	RDB K
Chlorops adjuncta	Notable
Chlorops citrinella (Zetterstedt)	RDB K
Chlorops gracilis Meigen	Notable
Chlorops laeta Meigen	Notable
Chlorops planifrons Loew	Notable
Chlorops rufina (Zetterstedt)	Notable
Chlorops triangularis Becker	Notable
Chlorops troglodytes (Zetterstedt)	Notable
Chlorops varsoviensis Becker	Notable
Chorisops nagatomii Rozkosny	Notable
Chrysogaster macquarti Loew	Notable
Chrysopilus erythrophthalmus Loew	RDB 2
Chrysopilus laetus (Zetterstedt)	RDB 1
Chrysops sepulchralis (Fabricius)	RDB 1
Chrysosomopsis auratus (Fallen)	RDB 1
Chrysotimus concinnus (Zetterstedt)	Notable
Chrysotoxum elegans Loew	RDB 3
Chrysotoxum octomaculatum Curtis	RDB 2
Chrysotoxum vernale Loew	RDB 1
Chrysotus angulicornis Kowarz	Notable
Chrysotus collini Parent	Notable
Chrysotus kowarzi Lundbeck	Notable
Chrysotus melampodius Loew	Notable
Chrysotus monochaetus Kowarz	Notable
Chrysotus palustris Verrall	Notable
Chrysotus suavis Loew	Notable
Chrysotus verralli Parent	RDB 3
Chyliza extenuatum (Rossi)	RDB 3
Chyliza fuscipennis (Robineau-Desvoidy)	Notable
Chyliza nova Collin	Notable
Chyliza vittata Meigen	Notable
Chymomyza costata (Zetterstedt)	Notable
Chymomyza distincta (Egger)	RDB K
Clemelis pullata (Meigen)	RDB 1
Clinocera nivalis (Zetterstedt)	RDB 3
Clinocera tenella (Wahlberg)	RDB 3
Clinocera wesmaelii (Macquart)	Notable
Clitellaria ephippium (Fabricius)	Extinct
Clusiodes apicalis (Zetterstedt)	Notable
Clusiodes caledonica (Collin)	Notable
Clusiodes geomyzina (Fallen)	RDB 3
Cnemacantha muscaria (Fallen)	RDB 3
Coelosia silvatica Landrock	Notable
Coenosia atra Meigen	Notable
Coenosia brevisquama Fonseca	RDB K
Coenosia campestris (R-D)	Notable
Coenosia dubiosa Hennig	RDB K
Coenosia flavimana (Zett.)	RDB 3
Coenosia paludis Tiensuu	RDB 3
Coenosia pudorosa Collin	Notable
Coenosia pulicaria (Zetterstedt)	Notable
Coenosia pygmaea (Zetterstedt)	Notable
Coenosia stigmatica Wood	RDB 3
Coenosia trilineella (Zetterstedt)	Notable
Coenosia verralli Collin	Notable
Coenosia vibrissata Collin	RDB 3
Colobaea bifasciella (Fallen)	Notable
Colobaea distincta (Meigen)	Notable
Colobaea pectoralis (Zetterstedt)	RDB 2

Colobaea punctata (Lundbeck)	Notable	Dioxyna bidentis (Robineau-Desvoidy	Notable
Conioscinella zetterstedti	RDB K	Diplostichus janithrix (Hartig)	RDB 3
Conops strigata Wiedemann	Notable	Ditomyia fasciata (Meigen)	Notable
Conops vesicularis Linnaeus	Notable	Dixa maculata Meigen	Notable
Cordilura aemula Collin	RDB 3	Dixella attica Pandazis	Notable
Cordilura atrata Zetterstedt	Notable	Dixella filicornis Edwards	Notable
Cordilura hyalinipennis Ringdahl	RDB 1	Dixella obscura	Notable
Cordilura picipes Mg.	RDB 3	Dixella serotina Meigen	Notable
Cordilura rufimana Meigen	Notable	Docosia carbonaria Edwards	Notable
Cordilura similis Siebke	RDB 3	Docosia fuscipes (Roser)	Notable
Cordyla insons Lastovaska & Matile	RDB 2	Docosia marionella Mik	RDB 1
Cordyla nitidula Edwards	Notable	Docosia pallipes Edwards	Notable
Cosmetopus dentimanus (Zetterstedt)	RDB 1	Docosia setosa	Notable
Crassivenula brachyptera	RDB 3	Docosia sp. indet. of Hudson et. al. (1980)	RDB 3
Criorhina asilica (Fallen)	Notable	Dolichocephala ocellata (Costa)	RDB 3
Criorhina ranunculi (Panzer)	Notable	Dolichopus acuticornis Wiedemann	Notable
Cryptaciura rotundiventris (Fal.)	Notable	Dolichopus agilis Meigen	RDB 2
Cryptonevra consimilis (Collin)	RDB 2	Dolichopus andalusiacus Strobl	RDB 3
Cryptonevra nigritarsis	Notable	Dolichopus arbustorum Stannius	RDB 3
Ctenophora atrata (Linnaeus)	Notable	Dolichopus argyrotarsis Wahlberg	Notable
Ctenophora flaveolata (Fabricius)	RDB 2	Dolichopus caligatus Wahlberg	Notable
Ctenophora nigricornis Meigen	RDB 3	Dolichopus cilifemoratus Macquart	RDB K
Ctenophora ornata Meigen	RDB 1	Dolichopus laticola Verrall	RDB 1
Ctenophora pectinicornis (Linnaeus)	Notable	Dolichopus latipennis Fallen	RDB 3
Culiseta longiareolata (Macquart)	RDB K	Dolichopus linearis Meigen	Notable
Cylindromyia brassicaria (Fabricius)	RDB 1	Dolichopus lineatocornis Zetterstedt	RDB 1
Cyturella albosetosa (Strobl)	RDB 1	Dolichopus maculipennis Zetterstedt	RDB 2
		Dolichopus mediicornis Verrall	RDB 2
Dactylolabis sexmaculata (Macquart)	Notable	Dolichopus melanopus Meigen	Extinct
Dactylolabis transversa (Meigen)	Notable	Dolichopus migrans Zetterstedt	RDB 3
Dasiops occultus Collin	Notable	Dolichopus nigripes Fallen	RDB 1
Dasiops spatiosus (Becker)	Notable	Dolichopus notatus Staeger	Notable
Dasiops trichosternalis Morge	Notable	Dolichopus plumitarsis Fallen	RDB 1
Dasyhelea saxicola (Edwards, 1929)	RDB 2	Dolichopus signifer Haliday	RDB 2
Dasypogon diadema Fabricius	RDB 1	Dolichopus strigipes Verrall	Notable
Delia caledonica Fonseca	RDB K	Dolichopus virgultorum Haliday	Notable
Delia flavogrisea (Ringdahl)	RDB K	Doros conopseus (Fabricius)	RDB 2
Delia hirtitibia (Stein)	RDB K	Dorycera graminum (Fabricius)	RDB 3
Delia pilifemur (Ringdahl)	RDB K	Dorylomorpha beckeri Aczel	Notable
Delia tarsifimbria (Pandelle)	RDB K	Dorylomorpha clavifemora Coe	RDB 1
Delia tumidula Ringdahl	RDB K	Dorylomorpha hungarica (Aczel)	Notable
Dexiopsis lacustris Karl	Notable	Dorylomorpha infirmata (Collin)	Notable
Dexiopsis minutalis (Zetterstedt)	Notable	Drapetis arcuata Loew	Notable
Diadocidia valida Mik, 1874	RDB 2	Drapetis convergens Collin	RDB K
Dialineura anilis (Linnaeus)	RDB 3	Drapetis curvipes (Meigen)	Notable
Diaphorus hoffmannseggii Meigen	RDB 1	Drapetis infitialis Collin	Notable
Diaphorus winthemi Meigen	RDB 1	Drapetis setigera Loew	RDB 3
Diastata vagans Loew	Notable	Drapetis simulans Collin	Notable
Diazosma hirtipennis (Siebke)	Notable	Drino lota (Meigen)	Notable
Dichetophora finlandica Verbeke	RDB 3	Dryodromia testacea (Rondani)	Notable
Dicraeus napaeus Collin	RDB K	Dynatosoma cochleare Strobl	RDB 2
Dicraeus raptus (Haliday)	Notable	Dynatosoma nigromaculatum Lundstroem	RDB 3
Dicraeus scibilis Collin	Notable	Dziedzickia marginata (Dziedzicki))	Notable
Dicraeus styriacus (Strobl)	Notable		
Dicraeus tibialis (Macquart)	Notable	Earomyia schistopyga Collin	Notable
Dicraeus vallaris Collin	Notable	Eccoptemera pallescens (Meigen)	Notable
Dicranoptycha fuscescens (Schummel)	RDB 1	Eccoptomera ornata Loew	Notable
Dicranota gracilipes Wahlgren	Notable	Ectinocera borealis (Zetterstedt)	RDB 3
Dicranota guerini Zetterstedt	Notable	Ectrepesthoneura colyeri Chandler	RDB 2
Dicranota robusta Lundstroem	Notable	Ectrepesthoneura pubescens (Zetterstedt)	RDB 1
Dicranota simulans Lackschewitz	RDB 3	Eggisops pecchiolii Rondani	Notable
Dictya umbrarum (Linnaeus)	Notable	Egle subarctica Huckett, 1965	RDB K
Didea alneti (Fallen)	RDB 1	Elachiptera pubescens (Thalhammar)	Notable
Didea fasciata Macquart	Notable	Elachiptera rufifrons Duda	RDB 3
Didea intermedia Loew	Notable	Elachiptera uniseta Collin	Notable
Dioctria cothurnata Meigen	RDB 3	Elliptera omissa Schiner	RDB K
Dioctria oelandica (Linnaeus)	Notable	Eloceria delecta (Meigen)	Notable
Diogma glabrata (Meigen)	Notable	Elodia ambulatoria (Meigen)	RDB 3
Dionaea aurifrons (Meigen)	RDB 1	Empis decora Meigen	Notable

Empis laetabilis Collin	RDB 3	*Exechia exigua* Lundstroem	Notable
Empis limata Collin	RDB 1	*Exechia lucidula* (Zetterstedt)	RDB 2
Empis melaena Bezzi	RDB 1	*Exechia lundstroemi* Landrock	RDB K
Empis picipes Meigen	Notable	*Exechia pectinivalva* Stackelberg	RDB 3
Empis prodromus Loew	RDB 1	*Exechia pseudofestiva*	Notable
Empis rufiventris Meigen	Notable	*Exechia sororcula* Lachschewitz	RDB 3
Empis volucris Meigen	Notable	*Exechia sp. nov.*	RDB 1
Empis woodi Collin	RDB 3	*Exechiopsis crucigera* (Lundstroem)	Notable
Epichlorops puncticollis (Zetterstedt)	Notable	*Exechiopsis dryaspagensis* Chandler	RDB 1
Epicypta limnophila Chandler	Notable	*Exechiopsis dumitrescae* Burghele-Balace	Notable
Epistophella euchroma (Kowarz)	RDB 3	*Exechiopsis fimbriata* (Lundstroem)	Notable
Epistrophe diaphana (Zetterstedt)	Notable	*Exechiopsis furcata* (Lundstroem)	Notable
Epitriptus arthriticus (Zeller)	RDB 1	*Exechiopsis jenkinsoni* (Edwards)	Notable
Epitriptus cowini Hobby	RDB K	*Exechiopsis ligulata* (Lundstroem)	Notable
Eremomyia anderssoni Hennig	RDB K	*Exechiopsis magnicauda* (Lundstroem)	RDB 2
Eribolus gracilior (de Meijere)	Notable	*Exechiopsis membranacea* (Lundstroem)	Notable
Eribolus nana (Zetterstedt)	Notable	*Exechiopsis pollicata* (Edwards)	Notable
Eribolus slesvicensis (Becker)	Notable	*Exechiopsis pseudindecisa*	Notable
Erioptera bivittata (Loew)	RDB 2	*Exorista glossatorum* (Rondani)	RDB 2
Erioptera limbata Loew	RDB 2		
Erioptera meigeni (Zetterstedt)	RDB 3	*Fannia atripes* Stein	RDB K
Erioptera meijerei Edwards	RDB 2	*Fannia carbonaria* (Meigen)	Notable
Erioptera nielseni de Meijere	Notable	*Fannia clara* Collin	Notable
Erioptera nigripalpis Goetghebuer	RDB 3	*Fannia collini* Fonseca	RDB K
Erioptera pusilla (Schiner)	RDB 1	*Fannia coracula* Collin	Notable
Erioptera scotica Edwards	RDB 1	*Fannia gotlandica* Ringdahl	Notable
Erioptera sordida Zetterstedt	RDB 3	*Fannia hirticeps* (Stein)	RDB K
Eristalis cryptarum (Fabricius)	RDB 2	*Fannia hirundinis* Ringdahl	RDB K
Eristalis rupium Fabricius	Notable	*Fannia immutica* Collin	Notable
Ernestia puparum (Fabricius)	RDB 2	*Fannia latipalpis* (Stein)	RDB K
Ernoneura argus (Zetterstedt)	RDB 2	*Fannia lineata* Stein	RDB K
Erycia furibunda (Zetterstedt)	RDB 2	*Fannia melania* (Dufour)	Notable
Erynnia ocypterata Fallen	RDB 2	*Fannia metallipennis* (Zetterstedt)	Notable
Estheria bohemani Rondani	RDB 1	*Fannia nidica* Collin	Notable
Eudicrana nigriceps (Lundstroem)	RDB 1	*Fannia nigra* Malloch	Notable
Eudorylas arcanus Coe	Notable	*Fannia norvegica* Ringdahl	Notable
Eudorylas dissimilis Coe	RDB 1	*Fannia novalis* Pont	RDB K
Eudorylas halteratus (Meigen)	Notable	*Fannia ornata* (Meigen)	RDB K
Eudorylas horridus (Becker)	Notable	*Fannia pseudonorvegica* Fonseca	RDB K
Eudorylas inferus Collin	Notable	*Fannia ringdahlana* Collin	Notable
Eudorylas jenkinsoni Coe	Notable	*Fannia speciosa* (Villeneuve)	Notable
Eudorylas kowarzi (Becker)	Notable	*Fannia subatripes* Fonseca	RDB K
Eudorylas melanostolus (Becker)	Notable	*Fannia subpubescens* Collin	Notable
Eudorylas montium (Becker)	Notable	*Fannia tuberculata* (Zetterstedt)	Notable
Eudorylas obliquus Coe	Notable	*Fannia umbratica* Collin	RDB K
Eudorylas restrictus Coe	RDB 1	*Fannia verrallii* (Stein)	Notable
Eudorylas ruralis (Meigen)	RDB 1	*Fannia vespertilionis* Ringdahl	Notable
Eudorylas terminalis (Thomson)	RDB 2	*Ferdinandea ruficornis* (Fabricius)	Notable
Eudorylas unicolor (Zetterstedt)	Notable	*Fiebrigella palposa* (Fallen)	Notable
Eudorylas zermattensis (Becker)	Notable	*Fiebrigella parcepilosa* (Collin)	RDB K
Eumerus ornatus Meigen	Notable	*Freraea gagatea* Robineau-Desvoidy	RDB 3
Eumerus sabulonum (Fallen)	Notable	*Frontina laeta* (Meigen)	RDB 3
Eupachygaster tarsalis (Zetterstedt)	Notable		
Euphranta toxoneura (Loew)	Notable	*Gampsocera inornata* Corti	RDB K
Eurina lurida Meigen	RDB 3	*Gasterophilus haemorrhoidalis* (Linnaeus)	RDB 1
Eurithia conjugata (Zett.)	Notable	*Gasterophilus intestinalis* (Degeer)	Notable
Eurygnathomyia bicolor (Zetterstedt)	RDB 1	*Gasterophilus nasalis* (Linnaeus)	RDB 1
Eurysthaea scutellaris (Robineau-Desvoidy)	RDB 1	*Gasterophilus pecorum* (Fabricius)	RDB 1
Eustalomyia hilaris (Fal.)	RDB 3	*Gaurax brittanicus* Deeming	RDB K
Eustalomyia vittipes (Zetterstedt)	Notable	*Gaurax niger* (Czerny)	RDB K
Euthyneura albipennis	RDB 1	*Geomyza angustipennis* Zetterstedt	RDB 3
Euthyneura gyllenhali (Zetterstedt)	Notable	*Geomyza apicalis* (Meigen)	Notable
Euthyneura halidayi Collin	Notable	*Geomyza breviseta* (Czerny)	Notable
Euthyneura inermis Becker	RDB 1	*Geomyza hendeli* Czerny	RDB 3
Eutolmus rufibarbis (Meigen)	RDB 3	*Geomyza majuscula* (Loew)	Notable
Eutropha fulvifrons (Haliday)	Notable	*Geomyza venusta* (Meigen)	Notable
Evibrissa vittata (Meigen)	RDB 3	*Germaria angustata* (Zetterstedt)	RDB 2
Exechia cincta Winnertz	RDB 3	*Germaria ruficeps* (Fallen)	RDB 1
Exechia dizona Edwards	RDB 1	*Gimnomera tarsea* (Fallen)	Notable

Gnophomyia elsneri Stary	RDB 1
Gnophomyia viridipennis (Gimmerthal)	Notable
Gnoriste bilineata Zetterstedt	Notable
Gnoriste longirostris Siebke	RDB 2
Gonatherus planiceps (Fallen)	RDB 3
Gonia capitata (Degeer)	RDB 2
Gonia divisa Mg	RDB 3
Goniglossum wiedemanni (Meigen)	Notable
Goniocera versicolor (Fallen)	RDB 2
Gonomyia abbreviata Tjeder	RDB 3
Gonomyia alboscutellata (von Roser)	RDB 1
Gonomyia bifida Tonnoir	Notable
Gonomyia bradleyi Edwards	RDB 2
Gonomyia connexa Loew	RDB 1
Gonomyia conoviensis Barnes	Notable
Gonomyia edwardsii	RDB K
Gonomyia limbata	RDB 1
Gonomyia punctata Edwards	RDB 2
Gonomyia sexguttata (Dale)	RDB 1
Graphogaster brunnescens Villeneuve	RDB 3
Grzegorzekia collaris (Meigen)	RDB 3
Gymnosoma globosum (Fabricius)	RDB 1
Gymnosoma nitens (Meigen)	RDB 1
Gymnosoma rotundatum (Linnaeus)	RDB 3
Haematopota bigoti Gobert	RDB 3
Haematopota grandis Meigen	RDB 3
Hammerschmidtia ferruginea (Fallen)	RDB 1
Heleodromia irwini	RDB 1
Heleomyza captiosa Gorodkov	RDB K
Helina abdominalis (Zetterstedt)	Notable
Helina annosa (Zetterstedt)	RDB 3
Helina arctata Collin	Notable
Helina calceata (Rondani)	Notable
Helina cilipes (Schnabl and Dz	RDB 1
Helina concolor (Czerny)	RDB 3
Helina cothurnata (Rondani)	RDB 3
Helina crinita Collin	RDB 2
Helina flagripes (Rondani)	RDB 3
Helina intermedia (Villeneuve)	RDB 2
Helina parcepilosa (Stein)	RDB 2
Helina pubescens (Stein)	RDB 3
Helina pulchella (Ringdahl)	RDB 3
Helina quadrinotata (Meigen)	RDB 3
Helina vicina (Czerny)	Notable
Helius pallirostris Edwards	Notable
Helophilus groenlandicus (Fabricius)	RDB 2
Hemerodromia adulatoria Collin	Notable
Hemerodromia laudatoria Collin	Notable
Hemerodromia melangyna Collin	RDB 2
Hemimacquartia paradoxa Brauer and Berg	RDB 1
Hercostomus angustifrons (Staeger)	RDB 2
Hercostomus chalybeus (Wiedemann)	Notable
Hercostomus fulvicaudis (Haliday)	RDB 3
Hercostomus nigrilamellatus (Macquart)	Notable
Hercostomus nigrocoerulea Latreille	Notable
Hercostomus plagiatus (Loew)	Notable
Hercostomus praetextatus (Haliday)	Notable
Hercostomus sahlbergi (Zetterstedt)	RDB 1
Herina oscillans (Meigen)	RDB 3
Herina paludum (Fallen)	RDB 3
Herina palustris (Meigen)	Notable
Heteromeringia nigrimana (Loew)	RDB 1
Hilara abdominalis Zetterstedt	Notable
Hilara aeronetha Mik	RDB 1
Hilara albipennis von Roser	Notable
Hilara albitarsis von Roser	Notable
Hilara albiventris von Roser	Notable
Hilara apta Collin	Notable

Hilara barbipes Frey	RDB 3
Hilara biseta Collin	Notable
Hilara brevivittata Macquart	RDB 3
Hilara clypeata Meigen	Notable
Hilara discoidalis Lundbeck	Notable
Hilara gallica (Meigen)	RDB 1
Hilara germanica Engel	Notable
Hilara hirta Strobl	RDB 2
Hilara hirtella Collin	RDB 2
Hilara implicata Collin	Notable
Hilara lugubris (Zetterstedt)	Notable
Hilara medeterifrons Collin	RDB 2
Hilara media Collin	Notable
Hilara merula Collin	RDB 1
Hilara morata Collin	Notable
Hilara nigrohirta Collin	Notable
Hilara pilosopectinata Strobl	RDB 1
Hilara platyura Loew	Notable
Hilara primula Collin	Notable
Hilara quadriseta Collin	RDB 3
Hilara recedens Walker	RDB 3
Hilara scrobiculata Loew	Notable
Hilara setosa Collin	RDB 2
Hilara submaura Collin	RDB 1
Hilara woodi Collin	Notable
Hippobosca equina Linnaeus	RDB K
Homocephala albitarsis Zetterstedt	RDB 1
Homocephala bipunctata (Loew)	RDB K
Homoneura consobrina (Zetterstedt)	Notable
Homoneura interstincta (Fallen)	RDB 3
Homoneura limnea (Becker)	RDB 2
Homoneura tesquae (Becker)	Notable
Hormopeza obliterata Zetterstedt	RDB 1
Huebneria affinis (Fallen)	RDB 1
Hyalurgus lucidus (Meigen)	RDB 3
Hybomitra ciureai Seguy	RDB 3
Hybomitra expollicata (Pandelle)	RDB 2
Hybomitra lurida (Fallen)	RDB 3
Hybomitra micans (Meigen)	RDB 2
Hybomitra muhlfeldi (Brauer)	RDB 3
Hydrophoria spiniclunis (Pandelle)	RDB K
Hydrophorus rufibarbis Gerstaecker	Notable
Hydrophorus viridis (Meigen)	RDB 3
Hydrotaea basdeni Collin	RDB 3
Hydrotaea borussica Stein	Notable
Hydrotaea cinerea Robineau-Desvoidyi	Notable
Hydrotaea glabricula (Fallen)	RDB 3
Hydrotaea meridionalis Portschinsky	RDB 3
Hydrotaea nidicola Malloch	RDB 3
Hydrotaea pandellei Stein	RDB K
Hydrotaea parva Meade	Notable
Hydrotaea pilipes Stein	Notable
Hydrotaea pilitibia Stein	RDB 3
Hydrotaea velutina Robineau-Desvoidyi	RDB 2
Hypoderma bovis (Linnaeus)	RDB 2
Hypoderma diana Brauer	RDB 3
Hypoderma lineatum (Villers)	RDB 2
Hypophyllus discipes (Ahrens)	Notable
Icterica westermanni (Mg.)	Notable
Incertella scotica (Collin)	Notable
Keroplatus testaceus Dalman	Notable
Labigastera forcipata (Meigen)	RDB 1
Lamprochromus elegans (Meigen)	Notable
Laphria flava (Linnaeus)	RDB 3
Laphria gilva (Linnaeus)	RDB K
Laphria marginata (Linnaeus)	Notable

Lasiamba baliola Collin	Notable
Lasiamba brevibucca Duda	Notable
Lasiopogon cinctus (Fabricius)	Notable
Leia bifasciata Gimmerthal	Notable
Leia longiseta Barendrecht	RDB 2
Leia piffardi Edwards	Notable
Lejogaster splendida (Meigen)	Notable
Lejops vittata (Meigen)	RDB 2
Leopoldius brevirostris (Germar)	RDB 2
Leopoldius signatus (Wiedemann)	Notable
Leptometopa niveipennis (Strobl)	RDB K
Leptopeza borealis Zetterstedt	RDB 2
Leskia aurea (Fallen)	RDB 1
Leucopis griseola (Fallen)	Notable
Leucopis morgei Smith	RDB K
Leucopis silesiaca Eggers	Notable
Leucostoma simplex (Fallen)	RDB 3
Limnophila abdominalis Staeger	Notable
Limnophila apicata (Loew)	Notable
Limnophila fasciata (Linnaeus)	RDB 1
Limnophila glabricula (Meigen)	Notable
Limnophila heterogyna Bergroth	RDB 1
Limnophila mundata (Loew)	Notable
Limnophila pictipennis (Meigen)	RDB 2
Limnophila pulchella (Meigen)	Notable
Limnophila trimaculata (Zetterstedt)	Notable
Limnophila verralli (Bergroth)	Notable
Limnophora nigripes (Robineau-Desvoidy)	Notable
Limnophora scrupulosa (Zetterstedt)	Notable
Limnophora uniseta Stein	Notable
Limonia annulata (Linnaeus)	RDB 3
Limonia aperta (Wahlgren)	RDB 1
Limonia aquosa (Verrall)	Notable
Limonia bezzii (Alexander & Leonard)	RDB 2
Limonia caledonica (Edwards)	Notable
Limonia complicata (de Meijere)	Notable
Limonia consimilis (Zetterstedt)	RDB 3
Limonia ctenophora (Loew)	RDB 2
Limonia danica (Kuntze)	RDB 3
Limonia distendens (Lundstroem)	Notable
Limonia frontalis (Staeger)	RDB 1
Limonia goritiensis (Mik)	RDB 3
Limonia halterata Osten Sacken	RDB K
Limonia halterella (Edwards)	Notable
Limonia inusta (Meigen)	Notable
Limonia lucida (de Meijere)	Notable
Limonia magnicauda	RDB 2
Limonia masoni (Edwards)	RDB 3
Limonia occidua (Edwards)	Notable
Limonia omissinervis (de Meijere)	RDB 2
Limonia ornata (Meigen)	Notable
Limonia quadrimaculata (Linnaeus)	RDB 2
Limonia rufiventris (Strobl)	RDB 3
Limonia stigmatica (Meigen)	Notable
Limonia stylifera (Lackschewitz)	RDB 2
Limonia trivittata (Schummel)	Notable
Limonia uniseriata (Schiner)	RDB 3
Limonia ventralis (Schummel)	Notable
Linnaemya comta (Fallen)	RDB 3
Lipara rufitarsis (Loew)	Notable
Lipara similis Schiner	RDB 2
Lipsothrix ecucullata Edwards	RDB 3
Lipsothrix errans (Walker)	Notable
Lipsothrix nigristigma Edwards	RDB 1
Lispe caesia Meigen	Notable
Lispe consanguinea Loew	RDB 2
Lispe hydromyzina Fallen	Extinct
Lispe loewi Ringdahl	Notable
Lispe nana Macquart	Notable

Lispe uliginosa Fallen	Notable
Lithophasia hyalipennis (Fallen)	Extinct
Lonchaea britteni Collin	Notable
Lonchaea collini Hackman	Notable
Lonchaea corusca Czerny	Notable
Lonchaea hirticeps Zetterstedt	Notable
Lonchaea laxa Collin	Notable
Lonchaea nitens (Bigot)	Notable
Lonchaea palposa Zetterstedt	Notable
Lonchaea peregrina Becker	Notable
Lonchaea ultima Collin	Notable
Lonchoptera meijeri Collin, 1938	Notable
Lonchoptera nigrociliata Duda	Notable
Lonchoptera nitidifrons Strobl	Notable
Lonchoptera scutellata Stein, P.	Notable
Lophosia fasciata Meigen	Notable
Loxocera nigrifrons Macquart	RDB 2
Lyciella laeta (Zetterstedt)	RDB 3
Machimus rusticus (Meigen)	RDB 2
Macrocera aterrima Stackelberg	RDB 3
Macrocera crassicornis Winnertz	Notable
Macrocera estonica Landrock	Notable
Macrocera fascipennis Staeger	RDB 3
Macrocera fastuosa Loew	RDB 1
Macrocera inversa Loew, 1869	RDB 2
Macrocera longibrachiata Landrock	RDB 1
Macrocera maculata Meigen	Notable
Macrocera nana Macquart, 1826	Notable
Macrocera propleuralis Edwards	RDB 1
Macrocera tusca Loew	Notable
Macrocera zetterstedti Lundstroem	RDB 1
Macronychia griseola (Fallen)	RDB 3
Macronychia polyodon (Meigen)	RDB 3
Macronychia ungulans (Pandelle)	Notable
Madiza britanica Hennig	RDB 2
Madiza pachymera Becker	RDB 3
Mallota cimbiciformis (Fallen)	Notable
Manota unifurcata Lundstroem	RDB 2
Medetera ambigua (Zetterstedt)	Notable
Medetera borealis Thuneberg	RDB 2
Medetera cuspidata Collin	RDB 3
Medetera excellens Frey	RDB 2
Medetera infumata Loew	RDB 3
Medetera inspissata Collin	RDB 3
Medetera jugalis Collin	Notable
Medetera melancholica Lundbeck	RDB 3
Medetera nitida (Macquart)	Notable
Medetera obscura (Zetterstedt)	Notable
Medetera oscillans Allen	RDB 3
Medetera parenti Stackleberg	RDB K
Medetera petrophila Kowarz	Notable
Medetera pinicola Kowarz	Notable
Medetera striata Parent	RDB 3
Medetera unisetosa Collin	RDB 3
Megalopelma nigroclavatum (Strobl)	Notable
Megamerina dolium (Fabricius)	Notable
Megasyrphus annulipes (Zetterstedt)	Notable
Megophtalmidia crassicornis (Curtis)	Notable
Meigenia majuscula (Rondani)	RDB 2
Melangyna barbifrons (Fallen)	Notable
Melangyna ericarum (Collin)	RDB 3
Melangyna guttata (Fallen)	Notable
Melangyna triangulifera (Zetterstedt)	Notable
Melanochaeta capreolus (Haliday)	Notable
Melanostolus melancholicus (Loew)	RDB 3
Melanostoma dubium (Zetterstedt)	Notable
Melanostoma species A Stubbs	Notable
Melanum fumipenne Loew	RDB K

Melieria cana (Loew)	Notable	Mycetophila v-nigrum Lundstroem	RDB 2
Melieria picta (Mg)	Notable	Mycomya britteni Kidd	RDB 2
Meonura freta Collin	RDB K	Mycomya clavigera	RDB 2
Meonura lacteipennis (Fallen)	RDB 3	Mycomya collini Edwards	RDB 2
Meonura minutissima (Zetterstedt)	Notable	Mycomya digitifera Edwards	RDB 2
Meonura neglecta Collin	RDB 3	Mycomya flavicollis (Zetterstedt)	Notable
Meonura prima Becker	Notable	Mycomya fuscata (Winnertz)	RDB 3
Meonura triangularis Collin	Notable	Mycomya griseovittata (Zetterstedt, 1852)	RDB 3
Meromyza coronoseta Hubicka	Notable	Mycomya insignis (Winnertz, 1863)	RDB 2
Meromyza curvinervis Zetterstedt	RDB K	Mycomya lambi Edwards	RDB 3
Meromyza hispanica	RDB K	Mycomya nigricornis (Zetterstedt, 1852)	RDB 3
Meromyza laeta Meigen	RDB K	Mycomya occultans (Zetterstedt, 1852)	RDB 1
Meromyza mosquensis Fedoseeva	Notable	Mycomya ornata (Meigen)	RDB 3
Meromyza pluriseta Peterfi	Notable	Mycomya parva (Dziedzicki)	Notable
Meromyza sp. indet.	Notable	Mycomya pectinifera Edwards	RDB 3
Meroplius minutus Wiedemann	RDB 3	Mycomya permixta Vaisanen, 1984	RDB 1
Metasyrphus lapponicus (Zetterstedt)	Notable	Mycomya punctata (Meigen)	RDB 1
Metasyrphus latilunulatus (Collin)	Notable	Mycomya rosalba Hutson	RDB 1
Metasyrphus nielseni Dusek & Laska	Notable	Mycomya shermani Garrett, 1924	RDB 2
Metasyrphus nitens (Zetterstedt)	Notable	Mycomya trivittata (Zettertstedt, 1838)	Notable
Metopomyza ornata (Meigen)	Notable	Mycomya vittiventris (Zetterstedt)	RDB 2
Microdon devius (Linnaeus)	RDB 2	Mydaea deserta (Zetterstedt)	Notable
Microdon eggeri Mik	Notable	Mydaea maculiventris	RDB 3
Microdon mutabilis (L.)	Notable	Mydaea obscurella Malloch	RDB 2
Micromorphus albipes (Zetterstedt)	Notable	Myennis octopunctata (Coquebert)	RDB 2
Micropeza lateralis Meigen	Notable	Myolepta luteola (Gmelin)	Notable
Microphorus anomalus (Meigen)	Notable	Myolepta potens (Harris)	RDB 1
Microprosopa pallidicauda (Zetterstedt)	RDB 3	Myopa curtirostris Krober	RDB 3
Microsania straeleni Collart	RDB 3	Myopa extricata Collin	RDB 3
Miltogramma germari Meigen	RDB 3	Myopa fasciata Meigen	RDB 3
Minettia dissimilis Collin	RDB 3	Myopa occulta Wiedemann	RDB 1
Minettia flaviventris (Costa)	RDB 3	Myopa polystigma Rondani	RDB 3
Mintho rufiventris (Fal.)	Notable	Myopa strandi Duda	RDB 3
Molophilus bihamatus de Meijere	Notable	Myopa vicaria Walker	RDB 2
Molophilus corniger de Meijere	Notable	Myopites eximia Seguy	RDB 3
Molophilus czizeki Lackschewitz	RDB 3	Myopites inulaedyssentericae Blot	RDB 3
Molophilus lackschewitzianus Alexander	RDB 3		
Molophilus niger Goetghebuer	Notable	Nanna brevifrons (Zetterstedt)	Notable
Molophilus propinquus (Egger)	Notable	Nematoproctus distendens (Meigen)	RDB 2
Molophilus variispinus Stary	Notable	Nemopoda pectinulata Loew	Notable
Monocentrota favonii Chandler	RDB 1	Nemoraea pellucida (Meigen)	RDB 2
Morpholeria dudai (Czerny)	RDB 3	Neoascia geniculata (Meigen)	Notable
Mycetobia pallipes Meigen	Notable	Neoascia interrupta (Meigen)	Notable
Mycetophila abbreviata Landrock	RDB 3	Neoascia obliqua Coe	Notable
Mycetophila autumnalis Lundstroem	RDB 3	Neocnemodon brevidens (Egger)	Notable
Mycetophila bialorussica Dziedzicki	RDB 3	Neocnemodon latitarsis (Egger)	Notable
Mycetophila bohemica (Lastovka)	RDB 2	Neocnemodon pubescens Delucchi & Psch	Notable
Mycetophila caudata Staeger	RDB 2	Neocnemodon verrucula (Collin)	Notable
Mycetophila confusa Dziedzicki	RDB 3	Neoempheria bimaculata	RDB 2
Mycetophila czizeki (Landrock)	RDB 3	Neoempheria lineola (Meigen)	RDB 1
Mycetophila dziedzickii	RDB 3	Neoempheria striata (Meigen, 1818)	RDB 1
Mycetophila freyi Lundstroem	Notable	Neoempheria winnertzi Edwards, 1913	RDB 1
Mycetophila gratiosa Winnertz	RDB 1	Neoitamus cothurnatus (Meigen)	RDB 1
Mycetophila hetschkoi Landrock	Notable	Neoleria propinqua Collin	Notable
Mycetophila immaculata (Dziedzicki)	RDB 3	Neolimnophila carteri (Tonnoir)	Notable
Mycetophila lapponica Lundstroem	RDB 2	Neolimnophila placida (Meigen)	Notable
Mycetophila lastovkia Caspers	RDB 2	Neolimnophora maritima (Roder)	RDB 2
Mycetophila lubomirskii Dziedzicki	RDB 1	Neolimnophora virgo (Villeneuve)	RDB 3
Mycetophila magnicauda Strobl	Notable	Neopachygaster meromelaena (Austen)	Notable
Mycetophila mitis Johannsen	Notable	Neoplatyura biumbrata (Edwards, 1913)	RDB 2
Mycetophila mohilevensis Dziedzicki	RDB 2	Neossos nidicola (Frey)	RDB 3
Mycetophila morosa Winnertz	RDB 2	Nephrocerus flavicornis Zetterstedt	Notable
Mycetophila schnabli (Dziedzicki)	RDB 1	Nephrocerus scutellatus Macquart	RDB 1
Mycetophila scotica Edwards	RDB 2	Nephrotoma aculeata (Loew)	RDB 2
Mycetophila signata Meigen	Notable	Nephrotoma crocata (Linnaeus)	RDB 3
Mycetophila sp. nov.	RDB 2	Nephrotoma dorsalis (Fabricius)	Notable
Mycetophila stolida Walker	Notable	Nephrotoma lunulicornis (Schummel)	Notable
Mycetophila strigata Staeger	Notable	Nephrotoma quadristriata (Schummel)	RDB 2
Mycetophila strigatoides (Landrock)	RDB 2	Nephrotoma sullingtonensis Edwards	RDB 1

Neuratelia nigricornis Edwards	Notable	Paradelphomyia fuscula (Loew)	Notable
Neurigona abdominalis (Fallen)	RDB 1	Paradelphomyia nielseni (Kuntze)	Notable
Neurigona suturalis (Fallen)	Notable	Paragus albifrons (Fallen)	RDB 2
Norellia spinipes Robineau-Desvoidyi	Notable	Paragus tibialis (Fal.)	Notable
Nostima semialata (Collin)	RDB K	Parallelomma paridis Hering	RDB 2
		Parallelomma vittatum (Meigen)	Notable
Ochthera manicata	RDB 3	Paraprosalpia albipennis (Ringdahl)	RDB K
Ochthera schembrii Rondani	RDB 1	Parasetigena silvestris (Robineau-Desvoidy	RDB 2
Ocydromia melanopleura Loew	Notable	Parasyrphus nigritarsis (Zetterstedt)	RDB 1
Odinia hendeli Collin	RDB 2	Parhelophilus consimilis (Malm)	RDB 2
Odinia maculata (Meigen)	RDB 3	Parochthiphila coronata (Loew)	RDB 1
Odinia meijerei Collin	Notable	Parochthiphila spectabilis (Loew)	RDB 1
Odinia ornata (Zett.)	RDB 2	Paroxyna absinthii	Notable
Odinia pomona Cogan	RDB 1	Paroxyna lhommei Hering	RDB 1
Odinia xanthocera Collin	RDB 2	Paroxyna producta	Notable
Odontomyia angulata (Panzer)	RDB 1	Paroxyna solidagensis White	Notable
Odontomyia argentata (Fabricius)	RDB 2	Parydroptera discomyzina Collin	RDB 2
Odontomyia hydroleon (L., 1758)	RDB 1	Pedicia lucidipennis (Edwards)	Notable
Odontomyia ornata (Linnaeus)	RDB 2	Pedicia unicolor (Schummel)	Notable
Odontomyia tigrina (Fabricius)	Notable	Pegohylemyia apiciseta (Ringdahl)	RDB K
Oecothea praecox Loew	Notable	Pegohylemyia flavisquama (Stein)	RDB K
Oedalea apicalis Loew	Notable	Pegohylemyia norvegica Ringdahl	RDB K
Oedalea oriunda Collin	RDB 1	Pegohylemyia sanctimarci (Czerny)	RDB K
Oedalea ringdahli Chvala	RDB 1	Pegomya argyrocephala (Meigen)	RDB K
Oedalea tibialis Macquart	Notable	Pelecocera tricincta Meigen	RDB 3
Oedalea zetterstedti Collin	Notable	Peleteria rubescens Robineau-Desvoidyi	Extinct
Oestrus ovis L.	RDB 3	Pelidnoptera nigripennis (Fabricius)	Notable
Ogcodes gibbosus (Linnaeus)	Notable	Peribaea fissicornis (Strobl)	Notable
Ogcodes pallipes Latreille	Notable	Periscelis annulata (Fallen)	Notable
Oldenbergiella brumalis Czerny	RDB 1	Periscelis annulipes Loew	RDB K
Opesia cana (Meigen)	RDB 3	Periscelis nigra (Zetterstedt)	RDB 1
Opomyza lineatopunctata von Roser	Notable	Periscelis winnertzi Egger	RDB 1
Opomyza punctata Haliday	Notable	Periscepsia prunaria (Rondani)	RDB K
Opomyza punctella Fallen	RDB 3	Phalacrocera replicata (Linnaeus)	Notable
Orchisia costata (Meigen)	RDB 2	Phania thoracica (Meigen)	RDB 3
Orellia falcata (Scopoli)	Notable	Phaonia amabilis (Mg)	RDB 2
Orimarga juvenilis (Zetterstedt)	Notable	Phaonia apicalis Stein	RDB 2
Orimarga virgo (Zetterstedt)	RDB 3	Phaonia atriceps	Notable
Ormosia aciculata Edwards	RDB 2	Phaonia bitincta (Rondani)	RDB 3
Ormosia bicornis (de Meijere)	RDB 2	Phaonia canescens Stein	RDB 3
Ormosia staegeriana Alexander	Notable	Phaonia colbrani Collin	RDB K
Orthoceratium lacustre (Scopoli)	Notable	Phaonia consobrina (Zetterstedt)	Notable
Orthonevra brevicornis Loew	Notable	Phaonia exoleta (Meigen)	RDB 3
Orthonevra geniculata Meigen	Notable	Phaonia falleni Michelsen	Notable
Orthopodomyia pulcripalpis (Rondani)	RDB 3	Phaonia fusca (Meade)	RDB 3
Oscinella angularis Collin	Notable	Phaonia gracilis Stein	RDB 1
Oscinella angustipennis Duda	Notable	Phaonia jaroschewskii (Schnabl)	RDB 2
Oscinomorpha arcuata (Duda)	Notable	Phaonia laeta (Fal.)	RDB 3
Oscinomorpha sordissima (Strobl)	Notable	Phaonia latipalpis Schnabl	RDB 2
Oscinosoma gilvipes	Notable	Phaonia lugubris (Meigen)	Notable
Oxycera analis Meigen	RDB 2	Phaonia mediterranea Hennig	Notable
Oxycera dives Loew	RDB 3	Phaonia nymphaearum R-D	RDB 2
Oxycera leonina (Panzer, 1798)	RDB 1	Phaonia pratensis (Robineau-Desvoidy	Notable
Oxycera morrisii Curtis	Notable	Phaonia pullata (Czerny)	RDB K
Oxycera pardalina Meigen	Notable	Phaonia scutellata (Zetterstedt)	Extinct
Oxycera pygmaea (Fallen)	Notable	Phaonia siebecki Schnabl & Dzeidzicki	Notable
Oxycera terminata Meigen	RDB 2	Phaonia subfuscinervis (Zetterstedt)	Notable
Oxycera varipes Loew,1870	RDB 1	Phaonia zugmayeriae Schnabl	Notable
Oxyna flavipennis (Loew)	Notable	Pharyngomyia picta (Meigen)	Extinct
Oxyna nebulosa (Wiedemann)	RDB 3	Phebellia nigripalpis Robineau-Desvoidyi	RDB 2
		Phebellia stulta (Zetterstedt)	Extinct
Palaedocosia flava (Edwards)	RDB 1	Pherbellia annulipes (Zetterstedt)	Notable
Palaeodocosia alpicola (Strobl)	RDB K	Pherbellia argyra Verbeke	RDB 2
Palloptera ambusta (Meigen)	RDB 3	Pherbellia brunnipes Meigen	Notable
Palloptera laetabilis Loew	RDB 2	Pherbellia dorsata (Zetterstedt)	Notable
Palloptera usta (Meigen)	RDB 3	Pherbellia griseola (Fallen)	Notable
Pamponerus germanicus (Linnaeus)	RDB 3	Pherbellia grisescens (Meigen)	Notable
Paraclusia tigrina (Fallen)	RDB 2	Pherbellia knutsoni Verbeke	RDB 3
Paradelphomyia ecalcarata (Edwards)	RDB 2	Pherbellia nana (Fallen)	Notable

Phora obscura (Zetterstedt)	RDB K	*Platypalpus ochrocera* (Collin)	RDB 1
Phora praepandens Schmitz	RDB K	*Platypalpus pallidicoxa* Frey	RDB 2
Phorbia atrogrisea Tiensuu	Notable	*Platypalpus pallidiseta*	RDB 1
Phorbia longipilis (Pandelle)	RDB K	*Platypalpus politus* (Collin)	Notable
Phorbia nuditibia Fonseca	RDB K	*Platypalpus praecinctus* (Collin)	Notable
Phronia caliginosa Dziedzecki	RDB 1	*Platypalpus pseudociliaris* Strobl	Notable
Phronia disgrega Dziedzicki	Notable	*Platypalpus pulicarius* (Meigen)	Notable
Phronia egregia Dziedzecki	RDB 3	*Platypalpus pygialis* Chvala	RDB 1
Phronia egregia	Notable	*Platypalpus rapidus* (Meigen)	RDB 3
Phronia electa Dziedzecki	RDB 2	*Platypalpus ruficornis* (von Roser)	Notable
Phronia interstincta Dziedzicki	RDB 3	*Platypalpus stabilis* (Collin)	Notable
Phronia longelamellata Strobl	RDB 3	*Platypalpus stigma* (Collin)	Notable
Phronia mutabilis Dziedzicki	RDB 1	*Platypalpus stigmatellus* (Zetterstedt)	Notable
Phronia persimilis Hackman	RDB 2	*Platypalpus subtilis* (Collin)	RDB 3
Phronia silvatica Dziedzicki	RDB 1	*Platypalpus sylvicola* (Collin)	RDB 3
Phronia sp. nov.	RDB 1	*Platypalpus tonsus* (Collin)	Notable
Phronia sudetica Dziedzicki	RDB 2	*Platypalpus tuomikoskii* Chvala	RDB 3
Phthiria pulicaria	Notable	*Platypalpus unicus* Collin	RDB 2
Physocephala nigra (Degeer)	RDB 3	*Platyparea discoidea* (Fabricius)	RDB 2
Phytomyza orobanchia Kaltenbach	Notable	*Platypeza hirticeps* Verrall	Notable
Piezura boletorum (Rondani)	RDB K	*Plectanocnema nudipes* (Becker)	RDB K
Pilaria fuscipennis (Meigen)	Notable	*Pocota personata* (Harris)	RDB 2
Pilaria meridiana (Staeger)	Notable	*Poecilobothrus ducalis* (Loew)	RDB 2
Pilaria scutellata (Staeger)	Notable	*Poecilobothrus majesticus* Fonseca	RDB 1
Piophila signata (Fallen)	RDB 2	*Poecilobothrus principalis* (Loew)	Notable
Pipiza lugubris (Fabricius)	Notable	*Policheta unicolor* (Fallen)	RDB 2
Pipizella maculipennis (Meigen)	RDB 3	*Polietes steinii* (Ringdahl)	RDB 1
Pipizella virens (Fabricius)	Notable	*Polyodaspis sulcicollis* (Meigen)	RDB 1
Pipunculus fonsecai Coe	Notable	*Potamia setifemur* (Stein)	RDB 1
Pipunculus phaeton Coe	Notable	*Prionocera pubescens* Loew	RDB 2
Pipunculus zugmayeriae Kowarz	Notable	*Prionocera subserricornis* (Zetterstedt)	RDB 2
Platycephala umbraculata (Fabricius)	RDB 2	*Psacadina verbekei* Rozkonsky	Notable
Platycheirus discimanus Loew	Notable	*Psacadina vittigera* (Schiner)	RDB 2
Platycheirus immarginatus (Zetterstedt)	Notable	*Psacadina zernyi* Mayer	RDB 2
Platycheirus melanopsis Loew	RDB 3	*Pseudexechia aurivernica* Chandler	RDB 3
Platycheirus perpallidus Verrall	Notable	*Pseudexechia parallela* (Edwards)	Extinct
Platycheirus podagratus (Zetterstedt)	Notable	*Pseudomyopina moriens* (Zetterstedt)	RDB K
Platycheirus sticticus (Meigen)	Notable	*Pseudonesia puberula* (Zetterstedt)	Notable
Platypalpus aeneus (Macquart)	RDB 3	*Pseudopachychaeta approximatonervis* (Zett.)	Notable
Platypalpus albicornis (Zetterstedt)	Notable	*Pseudopachychaeta heleocharis*	Notable
Platypalpus albiseta (Panzer)	Notable	*Pseudopachychaeta ruficeps*	Notable
Platypalpus albocapillatus (Fallen)	Notable	*Pseudopomyza atrimana* Meigen	RDB 1
Platypalpus alter (Collin)	RDB 3	*Pseudorymosia fovea* (Dziedzicki)	RDB 3
Platypalpus analis (Meigen)	RDB 1	*Psila clunalis* Collin	Notable
Platypalpus aristatus (Collin)	Notable	*Psila luteola* Collin	RDB 3
Platypalpus articulatoides	Notable	*Psilocephala melaleuca* (Loew)	RDB 1
Platypalpus articulatus Macquart	Notable	*Psilocephala rustica* (Panzer)	RDB 3
Platypalpus aurantiacus (Collin)	RDB 3	*Psilopa marginella* Fallen	Notable
Platypalpus carteri (Collin)	RDB 2	*Psilota anthracina* Meigen	RDB 2
Platypalpus confinis (Zetterstedt)	RDB 3	*Pterella grisea* (Meigen)	Notable
Platypalpus cothurnatus Macquart	Notable	*Pteromicra glabricula* (Fallen)	Notable
Platypalpus cryptospina Frey	Notable	*Pteromicra leucopeza* (Meigen)	RDB 2
Platypalpus difficilis Frey	Notable	*Pteromicra pectorosa* (Hendel)	RDB 2
Platypalpus divisus Walker	Notable	*Ptiolina atra* Staeger	Notable
Platypalpus ecalceatus (Zetterstedt)	Notable	*Ptiolina obscura* (Fallen)	Notable
Platypalpus excisus (Becker)	RDB 3	*Ptychoptera longicauda* (Tonnoir)	Notable
Platypalpus incertus (Collin)	Notable	*Pyratula perpusilla* (Edwards, 1913)	RDB 3
Platypalpus inexpectatus Smith & Chvala	RDB 1	*Pyrellia rapax* (Harris)	RDB 2
Platypalpus infectus (Collin)	RDB 2		
Platypalpus ingenuus (Collin)	RDB 2	*Ragas unica* Walker	Notable
Platypalpus interpolus (Collin)	RDB 3	*Rainieria calceata* (Fallen)	RDB 1
Platypalpus leucothrix (Strobl)	Notable	*Redtenbacheria insignis* Egger	RDB 2
Platypalpus longimanus (Corti)	RDB 1	*Renocera striata* (Meigen)	Notable
Platypalpus luteolus (Collin)	RDB 3	*Rhabdomastix hilaris* Edwards	RDB 3
Platypalpus macula (Zetterstedt)	Notable	*Rhabdomastix inclinata* Edwards	RDB 2
Platypalpus melancholicus (Collin)	RDB 3	*Rhadiurgus variabilis* (Zetterstedt)	RDB 3
Platypalpus mikii (Becker)	RDB 3	*Rhagio annulatus* Degeer	RDB 3
Platypalpus niger (Meigen)	Notable	*Rhagio strigosus* (Meigen)	RDB 3
Platypalpus niveiseta Zetterstedt	RDB 3	*Rhagoletis meigenii* (Loew)	Extinct

Rhamphomyia aethiops Zetterstedt	RDB 3	*Sarcophila latifrons* (Fallen)	Notable
Rhamphomyia albidiventris Strobl	RDB 1	*Scatella callosicosta* Bezzi	RDB 2
Rhamphomyia albitarsis Collin	Notable	*Scatella crassicosta* Becker	RDB 2
Rhamphomyia albosegmentata Zett.	Notable	*Scatella fusca* Macquart	Extinct
Rhamphomyia breviventris Frey	RDB 1	*Scathophaga decipiens* Haliday	Notable
Rhamphomyia caliginosa Collin	Notable	*Scathophaga pictipennis* Oldenburg	RDB 3
Rhamphomyia culicina (Fallen)	Notable	*Scathophaga scybalaria* (Linnaeus)	Notable
Rhamphomyia curvula Frey	Notable	*Scathophaga tinctinervis* (Becker)	RDB 2
Rhamphomyia hirtula Zetterstedt	RDB 3	*Scenopinus niger* (Degeer)	Notable
Rhamphomyia ignobilis Zetterstedt	RDB 1	*Sceptonia concolor* Winnertz	RDB 3
Rhamphomyia lamellata Collin	Notable	*Sceptonia costata* (Wulp)	Notable
Rhamphomyia marginata (Fabricius)	RDB K	*Sceptonia flavipuncta* Edwards	RDB 3
Rhamphomyia micropyga Collin	Notable	*Sceptonia fuscipalpis* Edwards	Notable
Rhamphomyia morio Zetterstedt	Notable	*Sceptonia humerella* Edwards	RDB 2
Rhamphomyia murina Collin	RDB 2	*Sceptonia tenuis* Edwards	RDB 1
Rhamphomyia nitidula Zetterstedt	Notable	*Schoenophilus versutus* (Haliday)	Notable
Rhamphomyia obscura Zetterstedt	Notable	*Schroederella iners* (Meigen)	RDB K
Rhamphomyia physoprocta Frey	RDB 1	*Sciapus contristans* (Wiedemann)	Notable
Rhamphomyia plumipes (Meigen)	RDB 3	*Sciapus heteropygus* Parent	RDB 1
Rhamphomyia sulcatina Collin	Notable	*Sciapus laetus* (Meigen)	Notable
Rhamphomyia tibialis Meigen	Notable	*Sciapus loewi* (Becker)	Notable
Rhamphomyia trigemina Oldenburg	RDB 1	*Sciomyza dryomyzina* Zetterstedt	RDB 2
Rhamphomyia vesiculosa (Fallen)	RDB 1	*Sciomyza simplex* Fallen	Notable
Rhaphiochaeta breviseta (Zetterstedt)	RDB 1	*Sciophila adamsi* Edwards	RDB 1
Rhaphium antennatum Carlier	Notable	*Sciophila antiqua* Chandler	RDB 1
Rhaphium auctum (Loew)	Notable	*Sciophila buxtoni* Freeman	RDB 2
Rhaphium fascipes (Meigen)	Notable	*Sciophila cliftoni* Edwards	Extinct
Rhaphium fractum Loew	Notable	*Sciophila fenestella* Curtis	Notable
Rhaphium gravipes Haliday	Notable	*Sciophila fridolini* Stackelberg	RDB 1
Rhaphium lanceolatum Loew	Notable	*Sciophila geniculata* Zetterstedt	Notable
Rhaphium micans (Meigen)	Notable	*Sciophila interrupta* (Winnertz)	RDB 1
Rhaphium nasutum (Fallen)	Notable	*Sciophila limbatella* Zetterstedt	RDB 1
Rhaphium patulum (Raddatz)	Notable	*Sciophila nigronitida* Landrock	Notable
Rhaphium pectinatum (Loew)	Extinct	*Sciophila nonnisilva* Hutson	Notable
Rhaphium penicillatum Loew	RDB 2	*Sciophila ochracea* Walker	RDB 1
Rhaphium rivale (Loew)	Notable	*Sciophila plurisetosa* Edwards	RDB 2
Rhingia rostrata (Linnaeus)	RDB 3	*Sciophila quadriterga* Hutson	RDB 1
Rhinotachina modesta (Meigen)	RDB 2	*Sciophila rufa* Meigen	Notable
Rhopalopterum atricilla (Zetterstedt)	Notable	*Sciophila sp. nov.*	RDB 1
Rhopalopterum brunneipennis Besch. & Lansb.	RDB K	*Sciophila varia* (Winnertz)	RDB 1
Rhopalopterum crucicarinatus Besch. & Lansb.	RDB K	*Scleroprocta pentagonalis* (Loew)	RDB 3
Rhopalopterum femorale (Collin)	Notable	*Scleroprocta sororcula* (Zetterstedt)	Notable
Rocetelion humerale (Zetterstedt, 1850)	RDB 1	*Scoliocentra scutellaris* (Zett.)	RDB 3
Rondania fasciata (Macquart)	Notable	*Sepsis biflexuosa* Strobl	Notable
Rutylapa ruficornis (Zetterstedt, 1851)	RDB 1	*Sepsis nigripes* Meigen	RDB 3
Rymosia acta Dziedzicki	RDB 2	*Seri obscuripennis* (Oldenburg)	RDB 2
Rymosia affinis Winnertz	RDB 2	*Sicus abdominalis* Krober	RDB 1
Rymosia armata Lackschewitz	RDB 3	*Siphonella oscinina* (Fallen)	Notable
Rymosia britteni Edwards	RDB 2	*Siphunculina aenea* (Macquart)	RDB 3
Rymosia connexa Winnertz	RDB 2	*Solva maculata* (Meigen)	RDB 2
Rymosia placida Winnertz	Notable	*Solva marginata* (Meigen)	Notable
Rymosia setiger Dziedzicki	Notable	*Solva varia* (Meigen)	Extinct
Rymosia sp. nov.	RDB 1	*Spania nigra* Meigen	Notable
Rymosia spinipes Winnertz	Notable	*Speccafrons halophila* Duda	Notable
Rymosia winnertzi Barendrecht	Notable	*Sphaerophoria loewi* Zetterstedt	RDB 2
		Sphaerophoria virgata Goeldlin de Tie	Notable
Salticella fasciata (Meigen)	RDB 2	*Sphegina verecunda* Collin	Notable
Sapromyza albiceps Fallen	Notable	*Spilogona alpica* (Zetterstedt)	RDB K
Sapromyza basalis Zetterstedt	Notable	*Spilogona baltica* (Ringdahl)	Notable
Sapromyza bipunctata Meigen	Notable	*Spilogona biseriata* (Stein)	Notable
Sapromyza obsoleta Fallen	Notable	*Spilogona depressiuscula* (Zetterstedt)	RDB 3
Sapromyza opaca Becker	Notable	*Spilogona griseola* (Collin)	RDB 3
Sapromyza zetterstedti Hendel	Notable	*Spilogona litorea* (Fallen)	RDB 3
Sarcophaga arcipes Pandelle	Notable	*Spilogona scutulata* (Schnabl and Dz	RDB 3
Sarcophaga ebrachiata Pandelle	RDB 3	*Spilogona septemnotata* (Zetterstedt)	RDB 3
Sarcophaga exuberans Pandelle	RDB 1	*Spilogona setigera* (Stein)	Notable
Sarcophaga laciniata Pandelle	Notable	*Spilogona triangulifera* (Zetterstedt)	Notable
Sarcophaga similis Meade	Notable	*Spilogona trianguligera* (Zetterstedt)	RDB 3
Sarcophaga villeneuvei Bottcher	RDB 3	*Staurochaeta albocingulata* (Fallen)	RDB K

Stegana coleoptrata (Scopoli)	Notable	*Tetanocera freyi* Stackelberg	RDB 3
Stegana hypoleuca Meigen	RDB K	*Tetanocera phyllophora* Melander	Notable
Stegana longifibula Takada	RDB 3	*Tetanocera punctifrons* Rondani	Notable
Stegana nigrithorax Strobl	Notable	*Tetanops myopinus* Fallen	Notable
Stenomicra cogani Irwin	RDB 3	*Tethina incisuralis* (Macquart)	RDB K
Stenomicra delicata (Collin)	RDB 2	*Tethina simplex* (Collin)	RDB K
Stilpon lunata (Haliday)	Notable	*Thaumalea truncata* Edwards	Notable
Stilpon sublunata Collin	Notable	*Thaumastoptera calceata* Mik	Notable
Stomatomyia acuminata (Rondani)	RDB 2	*Thaumatomyia rufa* (Macquart)	Notable
Stratiomys chamaeleon	RDB 1	*Thecocarcelia acutangula* (Macqart)	RDB 2
Stratiomys longicornis	RDB 2	*Thecophora fulvipes* Robineau-Desvoidyi	Notable
Stratiomys potamida	Notable	*Thelymorpha marmorata* (F)	Notable
Stratiomys singularior (Harris)	Notable	*Themira biloba* Andersson	RDB K
Strongylophthalmyia ustulata (Zetterstedt)	RDB 1	*Themira germanica* Duda	Notable
Subclytia rotundiventris (Fallen)	RDB 3	*Themira gracilis* (Zetterstedt)	Notable
Suillia dawnae Withers	RDB K	*Themira nigricornis* (Meigen)	RDB 3
Suillia dumicola (Collin)	Notable	*Thereva fulva* (Meigen)	RDB 3
Suillia oxyphora (Mik)	RDB 2	*Thereva handlirschi* Krober	RDB 3
Suillia vaginata (Loew)	Notable	*Thereva inornata* Verrall	RDB 3
Symballophthalmus dissimilis (Fallen)	Notable	*Thereva lunulata* Zetterstedt	RDB 3
Symballophthalmus pictipes (Becker)	RDB 3	*Thereva plebeia* (Linnaeus)	Notable
Symballophthalmus scapularis	Notable	*Thereva strigata* Fabricius	RDB 3
Symphoromyia immaculata (Meizen)	Notable	*Thereva valida* Loew	RDB 3
Sympycnus spiculatus Gerstaecker	Notable	*Thinophilus ruficornis* (Haliday)	Notable
Symtormon macula Parent	RDB 3	*Thricops aculeipes* (Zetterstedt)	Notable
Syndyas nigripes (Zetterstedt)	RDB 2	*Thricops albibasalis* (Zetterstedt)	Notable
Syneches muscarius (Fabricius)	RDB 1	*Thricops foveolatus* (Zett.)	Notable
Syntemma nitidula Edwards	RDB 3	*Thricops hirtulus* (Zett.)	Notable
Syntemna stylata Hutson	RDB 1	*Thricops innocuus* (Zett.)	Notable
Syntormon filiger Verrall	Notable	*Thricops separ* (Zetterstedt)	RDB 2
Syntormon mikii Strobl	RDB 2	*Thrypticus cuneatus* (Becker)	RDB 1
Syntormon spicatus (Loew)	Notable	*Thrypticus divisus* (Strobl)	RDB 3
Syntormon zelleri (Loew)	Notable	*Thrypticus laetus* Verrall	Notable
Systenus bipartitus (Loew)	RDB 3	*Thrypticus nigricauda* Wood	Notable
Systenus leucurus Loew	Notable	*Thrypticus pollinosus* Verrall	Notable
Systenus pallipes (von Roser)	Notable	*Thrypticus tarsalis* Parent	RDB 3
Systenus scholtzii (Loew)	Notable	*Thyridanthrax fenestratus* (Fallen)	RDB 3
Systenus tener Loew	RDB 3	*Tipula alpina* Loew	RDB 3
		Tipula bistilata Lundstroem	RDB 2
Tabanus bovinus Linnaeus	RDB K	*Tipula cheethami* Edwards	Notable
Tabanus cordiger Meigen	Notable	*Tipula coerulescens* Lackschewitz	RDB 3
Tabanus glaucopis Meigen	RDB 3	*Tipula dilatata* Shummel	RDB 2
Tabanus miki Brauer	RDB K	*Tipula gimmerthali* Lackschewitz	RDB 3
Tachina magnicornis (Zetterstedt)	RDB K	*Tipula grisescens*	RDB 3
Tachydromia acklandi Chvala	RDB 2	*Tipula helvola* Loew	Notable
Tachydromia connexa Meigen	RDB 3	*Tipula holoptera* Edwards	Notable
Tachydromia costalis (von Roser)	RDB 3	*Tipula hortorum* Linnaeus	RDB 3
Tachydromia halidayi (Collin)	RDB 3	*Tipula limbata* Zetterstedt	RDB 3
Tachydromia halterata (Collin)	RDB 2	*Tipula livida* Wulp	Notable
Tachydromia lundstroemi Frey	RDB 1	*Tipula luridirostris* Schummel	RDB 3
Tachydromia terricola	RDB 1	*Tipula marginata* Meigen	RDB 3
Tachydromia woodi (Collin)	RDB 2	*Tipula mutila* Wahlgren	RDB 1
Tachypeza fuscipennis (Fallen)	Notable	*Tipula nodicornis* Meigen	RDB 3
Tachypeza heeri Zetterstedt	RDB 2	*Tipula nubeculosa* Meigen	Notable
Tachypeza truncorum (Fallen)	RDB 3	*Tipula peliostigma* Schummel	Notable
Tachytrechus consobrinus (Haliday)	Notable	*Tipula pseudovariipennis* Czizek	Notable
Tachytrechus ripicola Loew	RDB 3	*Tipula sarajevensis* Strobl	RDB 1
Tanypeza longimana Fallen	RDB 2	*Tipula selene*	RDB 3
Tarnania dziedzickii (Edwards)	RDB 2	*Tipula serrulifera* Alexander	RDB 1
Tarnania tarnanii (Dziedzicki)	RDB 3	*Tipula siebkei* Zetterstedt	RDB 1
Tasiocera collini Freeman	RDB 1	*Tipula truncorum* Meigen	Notable
Tasiocera fuscescens (Lackschewitz)	RDB 1	*Tipula yerburyi* Edwards	Notable
Tasiocera jenkinsoni Freeman	RDB 1	*Tlephusa diligens* (Zetterstedt)	RDB 3
Tasiocera laminata Freeman	Notable	*Tomosvaryella cilitarsis* (Strobl)	Notable
Telmaturgus tumidulus (Raddatz)	RDB 3	*Tomosvaryella minima* (Becker)	RDB 3
Tephritis praecox (Loew)	RDB 1	*Tomosvaryella palliditarsis* (Collin)	Notable
Tephritis sp. nov.	RDB K	*Trachysiphonella carinfacies* Narchuk	RDB K
Terellia vectensis (Collin)	RDB 3	*Trachysiphonella pygmaea* (Meigen)	Notable
Terellia winthemi (Mg.)	RDB 3	*Trachysiphonella ruficeps* (Macquart)	Notable

Trachysiphonella scutellata (von Roser)	Notable
Trichina opaca Loew	Notable
Trichina pallipes (Zetterstedt)	Notable
Trichocera maculipennis Meigen	Notable
Trichonta bicolor Landrock	RDB 1
Trichonta clavigera Lundstrom	Notable
Trichonta flavicauda Lundstroem	RDB 1
Trichonta fragilis	RDB 3
Trichonta fragilis Gagne	RDB 3
Trichonta fusca Landrock	RDB 1
Trichonta icenica Edwards	RDB 3
Trichonta nigritula Edwards	RDB 1
Trichonta pulchra Gagne	RDB 1
Trichonta sp. nov.	RDB 1
Trichonta vulcani (Dziedzicki)	Notable
Trichopareia seria (Meigen)	RDB 2
Triglyphus primus Loew	Notable
Triogma trisulcata (Schummel)	RDB 3
Triphleba excisa (Lundbeck)	RDB K
Triphleba flexipalpis Schmitz	RDB K
Triphleba smithi Disney	RDB K
Trixoscelis marginella (Fallen)	Notable
Trupanea amoena Frauenfeld	RDB 2
Ulidia erythrophthalma Meigen	RDB 3
Urophora cuspidata (Mg.)	Notable
Urophora solstitialis	RDB 3
Urophora spoliata (Haliday)	RDB 3
Urytalpa atriceps (Edwards, 1913)	RDB 3
Urytalpa macrocera (Edwards, 1913)	RDB 1
Vanoyia tenuicornis (Macquart)	Notable
Vidalia cornuta (Scopoli)	RDB 3
Vidalia spinifrons Schroeder	RDB 3
Villa cingulata (Meigen)	RDB 1
Villa circumdata (Meigen)	RDB 2
Volucella inanis (Linnaeus)	Notable
Volucella inflata (Fabricius)	Notable
Volucella zonaria (Poda)	Notable

Wagneria costata (Fallen)	RDB 2
Wagneria gagatea Robineau-Desvoidyi	RDB 3
Weidemannia impudica Mik	RDB 1
Weidemannia lamellata (Loew)	RDB 1
Wiedemannia lota Walker	Notable
Wiedemannia phantasma Mik	RDB 3
Woodiphora retroversa (Wood)	RDB K
Xanthandrus comtus (Harris)	Notable
Xylophagus cinctus Degeer	RDB 3
Xylophagus junki Szilady	RDB 1
Xylota abiens Meigen	Notable
Xylota coeruleiventris Zetterstedt	Notable
Xylota florum (Fabricius)	Notable
Xylota tarda Meigen	Notable
Xylota xanthocnema Collin	Notable
Xylotachina diluta (Meigen)	RDB 1
Zabrachia minutissima (Zetterstedt)	Notable
Zodion cinereum (Fabricius)	Notable
Zodion notatum Meigen	RDB 3
Zophomyia temula (Scopoli)	Notable

Appendix 3 Nationally rare and nationally scarce species listed by status category.

EXTINCT (No records since 1900)

Mycetophilidae	*Pseudexechia parallela* (Edwards)
	Sciophila cliftoni Edwards
Stratiomyidae	*Clitellaria ephippium* (Fabricius)
Xylomyiidae	*Solva varia* (Meigen)
Dolichopodidae	*Dolichopus melanopus* Meigen
	Rhaphium pectinatum (Loew)
Tephritidae	*Rhagoletis meigenii* (Loew)
Ephydridae	*Scatella fusca* Macquart
Oestridae	*Pharyngomyia picta* (Meigen)
Tachinidae	*Lithophasia hyalipennis* (Fallen)
	Peleteria rubescens Robineau-Desvoidyi
	Phebellia stulta (Zetterstedt)
Muscidae	*Lispe hydromyzina* Fallen
	Phaonia scutellata (Zetterstedt)

Category 1 ENDANGERED

Tipulidae	*Ctenophora ornata* Meigen
	Dicranoptycha fuscescens (Schummel)
	Erioptera pusilla (Schiner)
	Erioptera scotica Edwards
	Gnophomyia elsneri Stary
	Gonomyia alboscutellata (von Roser)
	Gonomyia connexa Loew
	Gonomyia limbata
	Gonomyia sexguttata (Dale)
	Limnophila fasciata (Linnaeus)
	Limnophila heterogyna Bergroth
	Limonia aperta (Wahlgren)
	Limonia frontalis (Staeger)
	Lipsothrix nigristigma Edwards
	Nephrotoma sullingtonensis Edwards
	Tasiocera collini Freeman
	Tasiocera fuscescens (Lackschewitz)
	Tasiocera jenkinsoni Freeman
	Tipula mutila Wahlgren
	Tipula sarajevensis Strobl
	Tipula serrulifera Alexander
	Tipula siebkei Zetterstedt
Mycetophilidae	*Anatella pseudogibba* Plassmann
	Boletina pectinunguis Edwards
	Boletina silvatica Dziedzicki
	Bolitophila fumida Edwards
	Brevicornu griseolum (Zetterstedt)
	Docosia marionella Mik
	Ectrepesthoneura pubescens (Zetterstedt)
	Eudicrana nigriceps (Lundstroem)
	Exechia dizona Edwards
	Exechia sp. nov.
	Exechiopsis dryaspagensis Chandler
	Macrocera fastuosa Loew
	Macrocera longibrachiata Landrock
	Macrocera propleuralis Edwards
	Macrocera zetterstedti Lundstroem
	Monocentrota favonii Chandler
	Mycetophila gratiosa Winnertz
	Mycetophila lubomirskii Dziedzicki
	Mycetophila schnabli (Dziedzicki)
	Mycomya occultans (Zetterstedt, 1852)
	Mycomya permixta Vaisanen, 1984
	Mycomya punctata (Meigen)
	Mycomya rosalba Hutson
	Neoempheria lineola (Meigen)
	Neoempheria striata (Meigen, 1818)

	Neoempheria winnertzi Edwards, 1913
	Palaedocosia flava (Edwards)
	Phronia caliginosa Dziedzecki
	Phronia mutabilis Dziedzicki
	Phronia silvatica Dziedzicki
	Phronia sp. nov.
	Rocetelion humerale (Zetterstedt, 1850)
	Rutylapa ruficornis (Zetterstedt, 1851)
	Rymosia sp. nov.
	Sceptonia tenuis Edwards
	Sciophila adamsi Edwards
	Sciophila antiqua Chandler
	Sciophila fridolini Stackelberg
	Sciophila interrupta (Winnertz)
	Sciophila limbatella Zetterstedt
	Sciophila ochracea Walker
	Sciophila quadriterga Hutson
	Sciophila sp. nov.
	Sciophila varia (Winnertz)
	Syntemna stylata Hutson
	Trichonta bicolor Landrock
	Trichonta flavicauda Lundstroem
	Trichonta fusca Landrock
	Trichonta nigritula Edwards
	Trichonta pulchra Gagne
	Trichonta sp. nov.
	Urytalpa macrocera (Edwards, 1913)
Stratiomyidae	*Odontomyia angulata* (Panzer)
	Odontomyia hydroleon (L., 1758)
	Oxycera leonina (Panzer, 1798)
	Oxycera varipes Loew,1870
	Stratiomys chamaeleon
Xylophagidae	*Xylophagus junki* Szilady
Rhagionidae	*Chrysopilus laetus* (Zetterstedt)
Tabanidae	*Atylotus plebeius* (Fallen)
	Atylotus rusticus (Linnaeus)
	Chrysops sepulchralis (Fabricius)
Asilidae	*Dasypogon diadema* Fabricius
	Epitriptus arthriticus (Zeller)
	Neoitamus cothurnatus (Meigen)
Therevidae	*Psilocephala melaleuca* (Loew)
Bombyliidae	*Villa cingulata* (Meigen)
Empididae	*Athalia sp. indet.*
	Chelifera astigma Collin
	Empis limata Collin
	Empis melaena Bezzi
	Empis prodromus Loew
	Euthyneura albipennis
	Euthyneura inermis Becker
	Heleodromia irwini Wagner
	Hilara aeronetha Mik
	Hilara gallica (Meigen)
	Hilara merula Collin
	Hilara pilosopectinata Stroble
	Hilara submaura Collin
	Hormopeza obliterata Zetterstedt
	Oedalea oriunda Collin
	Oedalea ringdahli Chvala
	Platypalpus analis (Meigen)
	Platypalpus inexpectatus Smith & Chvala
	Platypalpus longimanus (Corti)
	Platypalpus ochrocera (Collin)
	Platypalpus pallidiseta
	Platypalpus pygialis Chvala
	Rhamphomyia albidiventris Strobl
	Rhamphomyia breviventris Frey

	Rhamphomyia ignobilis Zetterstedt
	Rhamphomyia physoprocta Frey
	Rhamphomyia trigemina Oldenburg
	Rhamphomyia vesiculosa (Fallen)
	Syneches muscarius (Fabricius)
	Tachydromia lundstroemi Frey
	Tachydromia terricola
	Weidemannia impudica Mik
	Weidemannia lamellata (Loew)
Dolichopodidae	*Acropsilus niger* (Loew)
	Cyturella albosetosa (Strobl)
	Diaphorus hoffmannseggii Meigen
	Diaphorus winthemi Meigen
	Dolichopus laticola Verrall
	Dolichopus lineatocornis Zetterstedt
	Dolichopus nigripes Fallen
	Dolichopus plumitarsis Fallen
	Hercostomus sahlbergi (Zetterstedt)
	Neurigona abdominalis (Fallen)
	Poecilobothrus majesticus Fonseca
	Sciapus heteropygus Parent
	Thrypticus cuneatus (Becker)
Pipunculidae	*Cephalops curtifrons* Coe
	Dorylomorpha clavifemora Coe
	Eudorylas dissimilis Coe
	Eudorylas restrictus Coe
	Eudorylas ruralis (Meigen)
	Nephrocerus scutellatus Macquart
Syrphidae	*Blera fallax* (Linnaeus)
	Caliprobola speciosa (Rossi)
	Callicera spinolae Rondani
	Chamaesyrphus caledonicus Collin
	Cheilosia species B Stubbs
	Chrysotoxum vernale Loew
	Didea alneti (Fallen)
	Hammerschmidtia ferruginea (Fallen)
	Myolepta potens (Harris)
	Parasyrphus nigritarsis (Zetterstedt)
Conopidae	*Myopa occulta* Wiedemann
	Sicus abdominalis Krober
Tephritidae	*Acinia corniculata* (Zetterstedt)
	Paroxyna lhommei Hering
	Tephritis praecox (Loew)
Otitidae	*Homocephala albitarsis* Zetterstedt
Micropezidae	*Rainieria calceata* (Fallen)
Pseudopomyzidae	*Pseudopomyza atrimana* Meigen
Tanypezidae	*Strongylophthalmyia ustulata* (Zetterstedt)
Chamaemyiidae	*Parochthiphila coronata* (Loew)
	Parochthiphila spectabilis (Loew)
Heleomyzidae	*Borboropsis puberula* (Zetterstedt)
	Oldenbergiella brumalis Czerny
Chyromyidae	*Aphaniosoma propinquans* Collin
	Aphaniosoma socium Collin
Pallopteridae	*Eurygnathomyia bicolor* (Zetterstedt)
Piophilidae	*Centrophlebomyia furcata* (Fabricius)
Clusiidae	*Heteromeringia nigrimana* (Loew)
Odiniidae	*Odinia pomona* Cogan
Periscelididae	*Periscelis nigra* (Zetterstedt)
	Periscelis winnertzi Egger
Ephydridae	*Athyroglossa ordinata* Becker
	Ochthera schembrii Rondani
Drosophilidae	*Amiota variegata* (Fallen)
Chloropidae	*Polyodaspis sulcicollis* (Meigen)
Gasterophilidae	*Gasterophilus haemorrhoidalis* (Linnaeus)
	Gasterophilus nasalis (Linnaeus)
	Gasterophilus pecorum (Fabricius)
Tachinidae	*Actia exoleta* (Meigen)
	Belida angelicae (Meigen)
	Carcelia intermedia (Herting)

	Ceromya silacea (Meigen)
	Chrysosomopsis auratus (Fallen)
	Clemelis pullata (Meigen)
	Cylindromyia brassicaria (Fabricius)
	Dionaea aurifrons (Meigen)
	Estheria bohemani Rondani
	Eurysthaea scutellaris (Robineau-Desvoidy
	Germaria ruficeps (Fallen)
	Gymnosoma globosum (Fabricius)
	Gymnosoma nitens (Meigen)
	Hemimacquartia paradoxa Brauer & Berg
	Huebneria affinis (Fallen)
	Labigastera forcipata (Meigen)
	Leskia aurea (Fallen)
	Rhaphiochaeta breviseta (Zetterstedt)
	Xylotachina diluta (Meigen)
Rhinophoridae	*Angioneura acerba* (Meigen)
Sarcophagidae	*Agria affinis* (Fallen)
	Angiometopa ruralis (Fallen)
	Sarcophaga exuberans Pandelle
Scathophagidae	*Cordilura hyalinipennis* Ringdahl
	Cosmetopus dentimanus (Zetterstedt)
Muscidae	*Helina cilipes* (Schnabl and Dz
	Phaonia gracilis Stein
	Polietes steinii (Ringdahl)
	Potamia setifemur (Stein)

Category 2 VULNERABLE

Tipulidae	*Arctoconopa melampodia* (Loew)
	Ctenophora flaveolata (Fabricius)
	Erioptera bivittata (Loew)
	Erioptera limbata Loew
	Erioptera meijerei Edwards
	Gonomyia bradleyi Edwards
	Gonomyia punctata Edwards
	Limnophila pictipennis (Meigen)
	Limonia bezzii (Alexander & Leonard)
	Limonia ctenophora (Loew)
	Limonia magnicauda
	Limonia omissinervis (de Meijere)
	Limonia quadrimaculata (Linnaeus)
	Limonia stylifera (Lackschewitz)
	Nephrotoma aculeata (Loew)
	Nephrotoma quadristriata (Schummel)
	Ormosia aciculata Edwards
	Ormosia bicornis (de Meijere)
	Paradelphomyia ecalcarata (Edwards)
	Prionocera pubescens Loew
	Prionocera subserricornis (Zetterstedt)
	Rhabdomastix inclinata Edwards
	Tipula bistilata Lundstroem
	Tipula dilatata Shummel
Culicidae	*Aedes flavescens* (Muller)
Ceratopogonidae	*Dasyhelea saxicola* (Edwards, 1929)
Mycetophilidae	*Acnemia amoena* Winnertz
	Allodia angulata Lundstroem
	Allodia czernyi (Landrock)
	Allodia retracta Plassman
	Allodiopsis rufilatera (Edwards)
	Asindulum nigrum Latreille
	Boletina digitata Lundstroem
	Boletina nigrofusca Dziedzicki
	Bolitophila bimaculata Zetterstedt
	Brachypeza armata Winnertz
	Brevicornu fennicum Landrock
	Cordyla insons Lastovaska & Matile
	Diadocidia valida Mik, 1874
	Dynatosoma cochleare Strobl

Ectrepesthoneura colyeri Chandler
Exechia lucidula (Zetterstedt)
Exechiopsis magnicauda (Lundstroem)
Gnoriste longirostris Siebke
Leia longiseta Barendrecht
Macrocera inversa Loew, 1869
Manota unifurcata Lundstroem
Mycetophila bohemica (Lastovka)
Mycetophila caudata Staeger
Mycetophila lapponica Lundstroem
Mycetophila lastovkia Caspers
Mycetophila mohilevensis Dziedzicki
Mycetophila morosa Winnertz
Mycetophila scotica Edwards
Mycetophila sp. nov.
Mycetophila strigatoides (Landrock)
Mycetophila v-nigrum Lundstroem
Mycomya britteni Kidd
Mycomya clavigera
Mycomya collini Edwards
Mycomya digitifera Edwards
Mycomya insignis (Winnertz, 1863)
Mycomya shermani Garrett, 1924
Mycomya vittiventris (Zetterstedt)
Neoempheria bimaculata
Neoplatyura biumbrata (Edwards, 1913)
Phronia electa Dziedzecki
Phronia persimilis Hackman
Phronia sudetica Dziedzicki
Rymosia acta Dziedzicki
Rymosia affinis Winnertz
Rymosia britteni Edwards
Rymosia connexa Winnertz
Sceptonia humerella Edwards
Sciophila buxtoni Freeman
Sciophila plurisetosa Edwards
Tarnania dziedzickii (Edwards)

Stratiomyidae *Odontomyia argentata* (Fabricius)
Odontomyia ornata (Linnaeus)
Oxycera analis Meigen
Oxycera terminata Meigen
Stratiomys longicornis

Xylomyiidae *Solva maculata* (Meigen)
Rhagionidae *Chrysopilus erythrophthalmus* Loew
Tabanidae *Hybomitra expollicata* (Pandelle)
Hybomitra micans (Meigen)
Asilidae *Machimus rusticus* (Meigen)
Bombyliidae *Bombylius minor* Linnaeus
Villa circumdata (Meigen)
Empididae *Hemerodromia melangyna* Collin
Hilara hirta Strobl
Hilara hirtella Collin
Hilara medeterifrons Collin
Hilara setosa Collin
Leptopeza borealis Zetterstedt
Platypalpus carteri (Collin)
Platypalpus infectus (Collin)
Platypalpus ingenuus (Collin)
Platypalpus pallidicoxa Frey
Platypalpus unicus Collin
Rhamphomyia murina Collin
Syndyas nigripes (Zetterstedt)
Tachydromia acklandi Chvala
Tachydromia halterata (Collin)
Tachydromia woodi (Collin)
Tachypeza heeri Zetterstedt
Dolichopodidae *Argyra auricollis* (Meigen)
Argyra grata Loew
Dolichopus agilis Meigen

Dolichopus maculipennis Zetterstedt
Dolichopus mediicornis Verrall
Dolichopus signifer Haliday
Hercostomus angustifrons (Staeger)
Medetera borealis Thuneberg
Medetera excellens Frey
Nematoproctus distendens (Meigen)
Poecilobothrus ducalis (Loew)
Rhaphium penicillatum Loew
Syntormon mikii Strobl

Platypezidae *Agathomyia collini* Verrall
Callomyia elegans Meigen
Seri obscuripennis (Oldenburg)
Pipunculidae *Cephalops perspicuus* (de Meijere)
Eudorylas terminalis (Thomson)
Syrphidae *Chalcosyrphus eunotus* (Loew)
Cheilosia sahlbergi Becker
Chrysotoxum octomaculatum Curtis
Doros conopseus (Fabricius)
Eristalis cryptarum (Fabricius)
Helophilus groenlandicus (Fabricius)
Lejops vittata (Meigen)
Microdon devius (Linnaeus)
Paragus albifrons (Fallen)
Parhelophilus consimilis (Malm)
Pocota personata (Harris)
Psilota anthracina Meigen
Sphaerophoria loewi Zetterstedt
Conopidae *Leopoldius brevirostris* (Germar)
Myopa vicaria Walker
Tephritidae *Campiglossa grandinata* (Rondani)
Chaetorellia ioricata (Rondani)
Chetostoma curvinerve Rondani
Platyparea discoidea (Fabricius)
Trupanea amoena Frauenfeld
Otitidae *Myennis octopunctata* (Coquebert)
Tanypezidae *Tanypeza longimana* Fallen
Psilidae *Loxocera nigrifrons* Macquart
Chamaemyiidae *Acrometopia wahlbergi* (Zetterstedt)
Chamaemyia paludosa Collin
Lauxaniidae *Homoneura limnea* (Becker)
Heleomyzidae *Suillia oxyphora* (Mik)
Sciomyzidae *Antichaeta brevipennis* (Zetterstedt)
Antichaeta obliviosa Enderlein
Colobaea pectoralis (Zetterstedt)
Pherbellia argyra Verbeke
Psacadina vittigera (Schiner)
Psacadina zernyi Mayer
Pteromicra leucopeza (Meigen)
Pteromicra pectorosa (Hendel)
Salticella fasciata (Meigen)
Sciomyza dryomyzina Zetterstedt
Pallopteridae *Palloptera laetabilis* Loew
Piophilidae *Piophila signata* (Fallen)
Clusiidae *Paraclusia tigrina* (Fallen)
Odiniidae *Odinia hendeli* Collin
Odinia ornata (Zett.)
Odinia xanthocera Collin
Aulacigastridae *Stenomicra delicata* (Collin)
Anthomyzidae *Anagnota collini* Czerny
Asteiidae *Asteia elegantula* Zetterstedt
Astiosoma rufifrons Duda
Ephydridae *Parydroptera discomyzina* Collin
Scatella callosicosta Bezzi
Scatella crassicosta Becker
Drosophilidae *Amiota albilabris* Zett.
Amiota basdeni Fonseca
Milichiidae *Madiza britanica* Hennig
Chloropidae *Aphanotrigonum meijerei* (Duda)

	Cryptonevra consimilis (Collin)		*Tipula coerulescens* Lackschewitz
	Lipara similis Schiner		*Tipula gimmerthali* Lackschewitz
	Platycephala umbraculata (Fabricius)		*Tipula grisescens*
Oestridae	*Hypoderma bovis* (Linnaeus)		*Tipula hortorum* Linnaeus
	Hypoderma lineatum (Villers)		*Tipula limbata* Zetterstedt
Tachinidae	*Asiphona verralli* (Wainwright)		*Tipula luridirostris* Schummel
	Carcelia excisa (Fallen)		*Tipula marginata* Meigen
	Ceromya monstrosicornis (Stein)		*Tipula nodicornis* Meigen
	Ernestia puparum (Fabricius)		*Tipula selene*
	Erycia furibunda (Zetterstedt)		*Triogma trisulcata* (Schummel)
	Erynnia ocypterata Fallen	Culicidae	*Aedes dorsalis* (Meigen)
	Exorista glossatorum (Rondani)		*Orthopodomyia pulcripalpis* (Rondani)
	Germaria angustata (Zetterstedt)	Mycetophilidae	*Allodia embla* Hackman
	Gonia capitata (Degeer)		*Allodia triangularis* Strobl
	Goniocera versicolor (Fallen)		*Anatella alpina* Plassman
	Meigenia majuscula (Rondani)		*Anatella ankeli* Plassman
	Nemoraea pellucida (Meigen)		*Anatella dampfi* Landrock
	Parasetigena silvestris (R-D)		*Boletina groenlandica* Staeger
	Phebellia nigripalpis Robineau-Desvoidy		*Boletina nasuta* (Haliday)
	Policheta unicolor (Fallen)		*Boletina villosa* Landrock
	Redtenbacheria insignis Egger		*Brevicornu foliatum* (Edwards)
	Rhinotachina modesta (Meigen)		*Brevicornu kingi* (Edwards)
	Stomatomyia acuminata (Rondani)		*Brevicornu serenum* Winnertz
	Thecocarcelia acutangula (Macqart)		*Docosia sp. indet.* of Hudson et. al. (1980)
	Trichopareia seria (Meigen)		*Dynatosoma nigromaculatum* Lundstroem
	Wagneria costata (Fallen)		*Exechia cincta* Winnertz
Rhinophoridae	*Angioneura cyrtoneurina* (Zetterstedt)		*Exechia pectinivalva* Stackelberg
Scathophagidae	*Ernoneura argus* (Zetterstedt)		*Exechia sororcula* Lachschewitz
	Parallelomma paridis Hering		*Grzegorzekia collaris* (Meigen)
	Scathophaga tinctinervis (Becker)		*Macrocera aterrima* Stackelberg
Muscidae	*Helina crinita* Collin		*Macrocera fascipennis* Staeger
	Helina intermedia (Villeneuve)		*Mycetophila abbreviata* Landrock
	Helina parcepilosa (Stein)		*Mycetophila autumnalis* Lundstroem
	Hydrotaea velutina Robineau-Desvoidyi		*Mycetophila bialorussica* Dziedzicki
	Lispe consanguinea Loew		*Mycetophila confusa* Dziedzicki
	Mydaea obscurella Malloch		*Mycetophila czizeki* (Landrock)
	Neolimnophora maritima (Roder)		*Mycetophila dziedzickii*
	Orchisia costata (Meigen)		*Mycetophila immaculata* (Dziedzicki)
	Phaonia amabilis (Mg)		*Mycomya fuscata* (Winnertz)
	Phaonia apicalis Stein		*Mycomya griseovittata* (Zetterstedt, 1852)
	Phaonia jaroschewskii (Schnabl)		*Mycomya lambi* Edwards
	Phaonia latipalpis Schnabl		*Mycomya nigricornis* (Zetterstedt, 1852)
	Phaonia nymphaearum R-D		*Mycomya ornata* (Meigen)
	Pyrellia rapax (Harris)		*Mycomya pectinifera* Edwards
	Thricops separ (Zetterstedt)		*Phronia egregia* Dziedzecki
			Phronia interstincta Dziedzicki
Category 3 RARE			*Phronia longelamellata* Strobl
			Pseudexechia aurivernica Chandler
Tipulidae	*Ctenophora nigricornis* Meigen		*Pseudorymosia fovea* (Dziedzicki)
	Dicranota simulans Lackschewitz		*Pyratula perpusilla* (Edwards, 1913)
	Erioptera meigeni (Zetterstedt)		*Rymosia armata* Lackschewitz
	Erioptera nigripalpis Goetghebuer		*Sceptonia concolor* Winnertz
	Erioptera sordida Zetterstedt		*Sceptonia flavipuncta* Edwards
	Gonomyia abbreviata Tjeder		*Syntemma nitidula* Edwards
	Limonia annulata (Linnaeus)		*Tarnania tarnanii* (Dziedzicki)
	Limonia consimilis (Zetterstedt)		*Trichonta fragilis*
	Limonia danica (Kuntze)		*Trichonta fragilis* Gagne
	Limonia goritiensis (Mik)		*Trichonta icenica* Edwards
	Limonia masoni (Edwards)		*Urytalpa atriceps* (Edwards, 1913)
	Limonia rufiventris (Strobl)	Stratiomyidae	*Oxycera dives* Loew
	Limonia uniseriata (Schiner)	Xylophagidae	*Xylophagus cinctus* Degeer
	Lipsothrix ecucullata Edwards	Rhagionidae	*Atrichops crassipes* (Meigen)
	Molophilus czizeki Lackschewitz		*Rhagio annulatus* Degeer
	Molophilus lackschewitzianus Alexander		*Rhagio strigosus* (Meigen)
	Nephrotoma crocata (Linnaeus)	Tabanidae	*Atylotus latistriatus* (Brauer)
	Orimarga virgo (Zetterstedt)		*Haematopota bigoti* Gobert
	Rhabdomastix hilaris Edwards		*Haematopota grandis* Meigen
	Scleroprocta pentagonalis (Loew)		*Hybomitra ciureai* Seguy
	Tipula alpina Loew		*Hybomitra lurida* (Fallen)

Asilidae	*Hybomitra muhlfeldi* (Brauer)		*Systenus tener* Loew
	Tabanus glaucopis Meigen		*Tachytrechus ripicola* Loew
	Dioctria cothurnata Meigen		*Telmaturgus tumidulus* (Raddatz)
	Eutolmus rufibarbis (Meigen)		*Thrypticus divisus* (Strobl)
	Laphria flava (Linnaeus)		*Thrypticus tarsalis* Parent
	Pamponerus germanicus (Linnaeus)	Platypezidae	*Agathomyia falleni* (Zetterstedt)
	Rhadiurgus variabilis (Zetterstedt)		*Microsania straeleni* Collart
Therevidae	*Dialineura anilis* (Linnaeus)	Pipunculidae	*Tomosvaryella minima* (Becker)
	Psilocephala rustica (Panzer)	Syrphidae	*Anasimyia interpuncta* (Harris)
	Thereva fulva (Meigen)		*Brachyopa bicolor* (Fallen)
	Thereva handlirschi Krober		*Callicera aenea* (Fabricius)
	Thereva inornata Verrall		*Callicera rufa* Schummel
	Thereva lunulata Zetterstedt		*Chamaesyrphus scaevoides* (Fallen)
	Thereva strigata Fabricius		*Cheilosia chrysocoma* (Meigen)
	Thereva valida Loew		*Cheilosia nebulosa* Verrall
Bombyliidae	*Thyridanthrax fenestratus* (Fallen)		*Cheilosia nigripes* (Meigen)
Empididae	*Clinocera nivalis* (Zetterstedt)		*Cheilosia semifasciata* Becker
	Clinocera tenella (Wahlberg)		*Chrysotoxum elegans* Loew
	Dolichocephala ocellata (Costa)		*Epistophella euchroma* (Kowarz)
	Drapetis setigera Loew		*Melangyna ericarum* (Collin)
	Empis laetabilis Collin		*Pelecocera tricincta* Meigen
	Empis woodi Collin		*Pipizella maculipennis* (Meigen)
	Hilara barbipes Frey		*Platycheirus melanopsis* Loew
	Hilara brevivittata Macquart		*Rhingia rostrata* (Linnaeus)
	Hilara quadriseta Collin	Conopidae	*Myopa curtirostris* Krober
	Hilara recedens Walker		*Myopa extricata* Collin
	Platypalpus aeneus (Macquart)		*Myopa fasciata* Meigen
	Platypalpus alter (Collin)		*Myopa polystigma* Rondani
	Platypalpus aurantiacus (Collin)		*Myopa strandi* Duda
	Platypalpus confinis (Zetterstedt)		*Physocephala nigra* (Degeer)
	Platypalpus excisus (Becker)		*Zodion notatum* Meigen
	Platypalpus interpolus (Collin)	Tephritidae	*Campiglossa argyrocephala* (Loew)
	Platypalpus luteolus (Collin)		*Myopites eximia* Seguy
	Platypalpus melancholicus (Collin)		*Myopites inulaedyssentericae* Blot
	Platypalpus mikii (Becker)		*Oxyna nebulosa* (Wiedemann)
	Platypalpus niveiseta Zetterstedt		*Terellia vectensis* (Collin)
	Platypalpus rapidus (Meigen)		*Terellia winthemi* (Mg.)
	Platypalpus subtilis (Collin)		*Urophora solstitialis*
	Platypalpus sylvicola (Collin)		*Urophora spoliata* (Haliday)
	Platypalpus tuomikoskii Chvala		*Vidalia cornuta* (Scopoli)
	Rhamphomyia aethiops Zetterstedt		*Vidalia spinifrons* Schroeder
	Rhamphomyia hirtula Zetterstedt	Otitidae	*Dorycera graminum* (Fabricius)
	Rhamphomyia plumipes (Meigen)		*Herina oscillans* (Meigen)
	Symballophthalmus pictipes (Becker)		*Herina paludum* (Fallen)
	Tachydromia connexa Meigen		*Ulidia erythrophthalma* Meigen
	Tachydromia costalis (von Roser)	Micropezidae	*Calobata stylifera* Loew
	Tachydromia halidayi (Collin)	Psilidae	*Chyliza extenuatum* (Rossi)
	Tachypeza truncorum (Fallen)		*Psila luteola* Collin
	Wiedemannia phantasma Mik	Lauxaniidae	*Cnemacantha muscaria* (Fallen)
Dolichopodidae	*Aphrosylus mitis* Verrall		*Homoneura interstincta* (Fallen)
	Argyra elongata (Zetterstedt)		*Lyciella laeta* (Zetterstedt)
	Campsicnemus magius (Loew)		*Minettia dissimilis* Collin
	Chrysotus verralli Parent		*Minettia flaviventris* (Costa)
	Dolichopus andalusiacus Strobl	Heleomyzidae	*Morpholeria dudai* (Czerny)
	Dolichopus arbustorum Stannius		*Neossos nidicola* (Frey)
	Dolichopus latipennis Fallen		*Scoliocentra scutellaris* (Zett.)
	Dolichopus migrans Zetterstedt	Sepsidae	*Meroplius minutus* Wiedemann
	Hercostomus fulvicaudis (Haliday)		*Sepsis nigripes* Meigen
	Hydrophorus viridis (Meigen)		*Themira nigricornis* (Meigen)
	Medetera cuspidata Collin	Sciomyzidae	*Antichaeta analis* (Meigen)
	Medetera infumata Loew		*Dichetophora finlandica* Verbeke
	Medetera inspissata Collin		*Ectinocera borealis* (Zetterstedt)
	Medetera melancholica Lundbeck		*Pherbellia knutsoni* Verbeke
	Medetera oscillans Allen		*Tetanocera freyi* Stackelberg
	Medetera striata Parent	Pallopteridae	*Palloptera ambusta* (Meigen)
	Medetera unisetosa Collin		*Palloptera usta* (Meigen)
	Melanostolus melancholicus (Loew)	Neottiophilidae	*Actenoptera hilarella* (Zetterstedt)
	Symtormon macula Parent	Opomyzidae	*Geomyza angustipennis* Zetterstedt
	Systenus bipartitus (Loew)		*Geomyza hendeli* Czerny

Clusiidae	*Opomyza punctella* Fallen	
Odiniidae	*Clusiodes geomyzina* (Fallen)	
Carniidae	*Odinia maculata* (Meigen)	
	Meonura lacteipennis (Fallen)	
	Meonura neglecta Collin	
Acartophthalmidae	*Acartophthalmus bicolor* Oldenberg	
Aulacigastridae	*Stenomicra cogani* Irwin	
Ephydridae	*Ochthera manicata*	
Drosophilidae	*Acletoxenus formosus* (Loew)	
	Stegana longifibula Takada	
Milichiidae	*Madiza pachymera* Becker	
Chloropidae	*Crassivenula brachyptera*	
	Elachiptera rufifrons Duda	
	Eurina lurida Meigen	
	Siphunculina aenea (Macquart)	
Oestridae	*Hypoderma diana* Brauer	
	Oestrus ovis L.	
Tachinidae	*Anthomyiopsis nigrisquama* (Zetterstedt)	
	Bactromyia aurulenta (Meigen)	
	Diplostichus janithrix (Hartig)	
	Elodia ambulatoria (Meigen)	
	Evibrissa vittata (Meigen)	
	Freraea gagatea Robineau-Desvoidy	
	Frontina laeta (Meigen)	
	Gonia divisa Mg	
	Graphogaster brunnescens Villeneuve	
	Gymnosoma rotundatum (Linnaeus)	
	Hyalurgus lucidus (Meigen)	
	Leucostoma simplex (Fallen)	
	Linnaemya comta (Fallen)	
	Opesia cana (Meigen)	
	Phania thoracica (Meigen)	
	Subclytia rotundiventris (Fallen)	
	Tlephusa diligens (Zetterstedt)	
	Wagneria gagatea Robineau-Desvoidyi	
Sarcophagidae	*Agria mamillata* (Pandelle)	
	Blaesoxipha erythrura (Meigen)	
	Blaesoxipha rossica Villeneuve	
	Macronychia griseola (Fallen)	
	Macronychia polyodon (Meigen)	
	Miltogramma germari Meigen	
	Sarcophaga ebrachiata Pandelle	
	Sarcophaga villeneuvei Bottcher	
Calliphoridae	*Calliphora alpina* (Zetterstedt)	
	Calliphora uralensis Villeneuve	
Scathophagidae	*Acanthocnema nigrimana* (Zetterstedt)	
	Cordilura aemula Collin	
	Cordilura picipes Mg.	
	Cordilura similis Siebke	
	Gonatherus planiceps (Fallen)	
	Microprosopa pallidicauda (Zetterstedt)	
	Scathophaga pictipennis Oldenburg	
Anthomyiidae	*Eustalomyia hilaris* (Fal.)	
Muscidae	*Caricea brachialis* (Rondani)	
	Caricea rubricornis (Zetterstedt)	
	Coenosia flavimana (Zett.)	
	Coenosia paludis Tiensuu	
	Coenosia stigmatica Wood	
	Coenosia vibrissata Collin	
	Helina annosa (Zetterstedt)	
	Helina concolor (Czerny)	
	Helina cothurnata (Rondani)	
	Helina flagripes (Rondani)	
	Helina pubescens (Stein)	
	Helina pulchella (Ringdahl)	
	Helina quadrinotata (Meigen)	
	Hydrotaea basdeni Collin	
	Hydrotaea glabricula (Fallen)	
	Hydrotaea meridionalis Portschinsky	

Hydrotaea nidicola Malloch
Hydrotaea pilitibia Stein
Mydaea maculiventris
Neolimnophora virgo (Villeneuve)
Phaonia bitincta (Rondani)
Phaonia canescens Stein
Phaonia exoleta (Meigen)
Phaonia fusca (Meade)
Phaonia laeta (Fal.)
Spilogona depressiuscula (Zetterstedt)
Spilogona griseola (Collin)
Spilogona litorea (Fallen)
Spilogona scutulata (Schnabl and Dz)
Spilogona septemnotata (Zetterstedt)
Spilogona trianguligera (Zetterstedt)

Category K INSUFFICIENTLY KNOWN

Tipulidae	*Elliptera omissa* Schiner	
	Gonomyia edwardsii	
	Limonia halterata Osten Sacken	
Culicidae	*Aedes communis* (Degeer)	
	Aedes leucomelas (Meigen)	
	Aedes sticticus (Meigen)	
	Anopheles algeriensis Theobald	
	Culiseta longiareolata (Macquart)	
Mycetophilidae	*Exechia lundstroemi* Landrock	
	Palaeodocosia alpicola (Strobl)	
Tabanidae	*Tabanus bovinus* Linnaeus	
	Tabanus miki Brauer	
Asilidae	*Epitriptus cowini* Hobby	
	Laphria gilva (Linnaeus)	
Empididae	*Drapetis convergens* Collin	
	Rhamphomyia marginata (Fabricius)	
Dolichopodidae	*Dolichopus cilifemoratus* Macquart	
	Medetera parenti Stackleberg	
Phoridae	*Aenigmatias brevifrons* Schmitz	
	Aenigmatias franzi Schmitz	
	Aenigmatias lubbocki (Verrall)	
	Phora obscura (Zetterstedt)	
	Phora praepandens Schmitz	
	Plectanocnema nudipes (Becker)	
	Triphleba excisa (Lundbeck)	
	Triphleba flexipalpis Schmitz	
	Triphleba smithi Disney	
	Woodiphora retroversa (Wood)	
Tephritidae	*Tephritis* sp. nov.	
Otitidae	*Homocephala bipunctata* (Loew)	
Chamaemyiidae	*Leucopis morgei* Smith	
Heleomyzidae	*Heleomyza captiosa* Gorodkov	
	Schroederella iners (Meigen)	
	Suillia dawnae Withers	
Sepsidae	*Themira biloba* Andersson	
Carniidae	*Meonura freta* Collin	
Periscelididae	*Periscelis annulipes* Loew	
Ephydridae	*Nostima semialata* (Collin)	
Drosophilidae	*Chymomyza distincta* (Egger)	
	Stegana hypoleuca Meigen	
Milichiidae	*Leptometopa niveipennis* (Strobl)	
Tethinidae	*Tethina incisuralis* (Macquart)	
	Tethina simplex (Collin)	
Chloropidae	*Calamoncosis aspistylina* Duda	
	Cetema transversa Collin	
	Chlorops citrinella (Zetterstedt)	
	Conioscinella zetterstedti	
	Dicraeus napaeus Collin	
	Fiebrigella parcepilosa (Collin)	
	Gampsocera inornata Corti	

186

Gaurax brittanicus Deeming
Gaurax niger (Czerny)
Melanum fumipenne Loew
Meromyza curvinervis Zetterstedt
Meromyza hispanica
Meromyza laeta Meigen
Rhopalopterum brunneipennis B. & L.
Rhopalopterum crucicarinatus B. & L.
Trachysiphonella carinfacies Narchuk

Tachinidae
Actia nudibasis Stein
Periscepsia prunaria (Rondani)
Staurochaeta albocingulata (Fallen)
Tachina magnicornis (Zetterstedt)

Anthomyiidae
Chirosia aberrans Collin
Chirosia montana Pokorny
Delia caledonica Fonseca
Delia flavogrisea (Ringdahl)
Delia hirtitibia (Stein)
Delia pilifemur (Ringdahl)
Delia tarsifimbria (Pandelle)
Delia tumidula Ringdahl
Egle subarctica Huckett, 1965
Eremomyia anderssoni Hennig
Hydrophoria spiniclunis (Pandelle)
Paraprosalpia albipennis (Ringdahl)
Pegohylemyia apiciseta (Ringdahl)
Pegohylemyia flavisquama (Stein)
Pegohylemyia norvegica Ringdahl
Pegohylemyia sanctimarci (Czerny)
Pegomya argyrocephala (Meigen)
Phorbia longipilis (Pandelle)
Phorbia nuditibia Fonseca
Pseudomyopina moriens (Zetterstedt)

Fanniidae
Fannia atripes Stein
Fannia collini Fonseca
Fannia hirticeps (Stein)
Fannia hirundinis Ringdahl
Fannia latipalpis (Stein)
Fannia lineata Stein
Fannia novalis Pont
Fannia ornata (Meigen)
Fannia pseudonorvegica Fonseca
Fannia subatripes Fonseca
Fannia umbratica Collin
Piezura boletorum (Rondani)

Muscidae
Coenosia brevisquama Fonseca
Coenosia dubiosa Hennig
Hydrotaea pandellei Stein
Phaonia colbrani Collin
Phaonia pullata (Czerny)
Spilogona alpica (Zetterstedt)

Hippoboscidae
Hippobosca equina Linnaeus

NATIONALLY NOTABLE (NATIONALLY SCARCE)

Trichoceridae
Diazosma hirtipennis (Siebke)
Trichocera maculipennis Meigen

Tipulidae
Cheilotrichia imbuta (Meigen)
Ctenophora atrata (Linnaeus)
Ctenophora pectinicornis (Linnaeus)
Dactylolabis sexmaculata (Macquart)
Dactylolabis transversa (Meigen)
Dicranota gracilipes Wahlgren
Dicranota guerini Zetterstedt
Dicranota robusta Lundstroem
Diogma glabrata (Meigen)
Erioptera nielseni de Meijere
Gnophomyia viridipennis (Gimmerthal)

Gonomyia bifida Tonnoir
Gonomyia conoviensis Barnes
Helius pallirostris Edwards
Limnophila abdominalis Staeger
Limnophila apicata (Loew)
Limnophila glabricula (Meigen)
Limnophila mundata (Loew)
Limnophila pulchella (Meigen)
Limnophila trimaculata (Zetterstedt)
Limnophila verralli (Bergroth)
Limonia aquosa (Verrall)
Limonia caledonica (Edwards)
Limonia complicata (de Meijere)
Limonia distendens (Lundstroem)
Limonia halterella (Edwards)
Limonia inusta (Meigen)
Limonia lucida (de Meijere)
Limonia occidua (Edwards)
Limonia ornata (Meigen)
Limonia stigmatica (Meigen)
Limonia trivittata (Schummel)
Limonia ventralis (Schummel)
Lipsothrix errans (Walker)
Molophilus bihamatus de Meijere
Molophilus corniger de Meijere
Molophilus niger Goetghebuer
Molophilus propinquus (Egger)
Molophilus variispinus Stary
Neolimnophila carteri (Tonnoir)
Neolimnophila placida (Meigen)
Nephrotoma dorsalis (Fabricius)
Nephrotoma lunulicornis (Schummel)
Orimarga juvenilis (Zetterstedt)
Ormosia staegeriana Alexander
Paradelphomyia fuscula (Loew)
Paradelphomyia nielseni (Kuntze)
Pedicia lucidipennis (Edwards)
Pedicia unicolor (Schummel)
Phalacrocera replicata (Linnaeus)
Pilaria fuscipennis (Meigen)
Pilaria meridiana (Staeger)
Pilaria scutellata (Staeger)
Scleroprocta sororcula (Zetterstedt)
Tasiocera laminata Freeman
Thaumastoptera calceata Mik
Tipula cheethami Edwards
Tipula helvola Loew
Tipula holoptera Edwards
Tipula livida Wulp
Tipula nubeculosa Meigen
Tipula peliostigma Schummel
Tipula pseudovariipennis Czizek
Tipula truncorum Meigen
Tipula yerburyi Edwards

Ptychopteridae
Ptychoptera longicauda (Tonnoir)

Dixidae
Dixa maculata Meigen
Dixella attica Pandazis
Dixella filicornis Edwards
Dixella obscura
Dixella serotina Meigen

Thaumaleidae
Thaumalea truncata Edwards

Anisopodidae
Mycetobia pallipes Meigen

Mycetophilidae
Acnemia longipes Winnertz
Allodia barbata (Lundstroem)
Allodia neglecta Edwards
Allodia pistillata (Lundstroem)
Allodia silvatica Landrock
Allodiopsis ingeniosa Kidd
Allodiopsis maculosa (Meigen)

Anaclileia dispar (Winnertz)
Anatella lenis Dziedzicki
Azana anomala (Staeger)
Boletina dispecta Dziedzicki
Boletina moravica Landrock
Boletina nitida Grzegorzek
Boletina pallidula Edwards
Boletina rejecta Edwards
Bolitophila basicornis (Mayer)
Bolitophila glabrata Loew
Bolitophila rossica Landrock
Brachypeza bisignata Winnertz
Brevicornu boreale (Lundstroem)
Brevicornu nigrofuscum (Lundstroem)
Brevicornu proximum (Staeger)
Coelosia silvatica Landrock
Cordyla nitidula Edwards
Ditomyia fasciata (Meigen)
Docosia carbonaria Edwards
Docosia fuscipes (Roser)
Docosia pallipes Edwards
Docosia setosa
Dziedzickia marginata (Dziedzicki))
Epicypta limnophila Chandler
Exechia exigua Lundstroem
Exechia pseudofestiva
Exechiopsis crucigera (Lundstroem)
Exechiopsis dumitrescae Burghele-Balace
Exechiopsis fimbriata (Lundstroem)
Exechiopsis furcata (Lundstroem)
Exechiopsis jenkinsoni (Edwards)
Exechiopsis ligulata (Lundstroem)
Exechiopsis membranacea (Lundstroem)
Exechiopsis pollicata (Edwards)
Exechiopsis pseudindecisa
Gnoriste bilineata Zetterstedt
Keroplatus testaceus Dalman
Leia bifasciata Gimmerthal
Leia piffardi Edwards
Macrocera crassicornis Winnertz
Macrocera estonica Landrock
Macrocera maculata Meigen
Macrocera nana Macquart, 1826
Macrocera tusca Loew
Megalopelma nigroclavatum (Strobl)
Megophtalmidia crassicornis (Curtis)
Mycetophila freyi Lundstroem
Mycetophila hetschkoi Landrock
Mycetophila magnicauda Strobl
Mycetophila mitis Johannsen
Mycetophila signata Meigen
Mycetophila stolida Walker
Mycetophila strigata Staeger
Mycomya flavicollis (Zetterstedt)
Mycomya parva (Dziedzicki)
Mycomya trivittata (Zettertstedt, 1838)
Neuratelia nigricornis Edwards
Phronia disgrega Dziedzicki
Phronia egregia
Rymosia placida Winnertz
Rymosia setiger Dziedzicki
Rymosia spinipes Winnertz
Rymosia winnertzi Barendrecht
Sceptonia costata (Wulp)
Sceptonia fuscipalpis Edwards
Sciophila fenestella Curtis
Sciophila geniculata Zetterstedt
Sciophila nigronitida Landrock
Sciophila nonnisilva Hutson

Sciophila rufa Meigen
Trichonta clavigera Lundstrom
Trichonta vulcani (Dziedzicki)

Stratiomyidae

Beris clavipes (Linnaeus)
Beris fuscipes Meigen
Chorisops nagatomii Rozkosny
Eupachygaster tarsalis (Zetterstedt)
Neopachygaster meromelaena (Austen)
Odontomyia tigrina (Fabricius)
Oxycera morrisii Curtis
Oxycera pardalina Meigen
Oxycera pygmaea (Fallen)
Stratiomys potamida
Stratiomys singularior (Harris)
Vanoyia tenuicornis (Macquart)
Zabrachia minutissima (Zetterstedt)

Xylomyiidae

Solva marginata (Meigen)

Rhagionidae

Ptiolina atra Staeger
Ptiolina obscura (Fallen)
Spania nigra Meigen
Symphoromyia immaculata (Meizen)

Tabanidae

Atylotus fulvus (Meigen)
Tabanus cordiger Meigen

Asilidae

Asilus crabroniformis Linnaeus
Dioctria oelandica (Linnaeus)
Laphria marginata (Linnaeus)
Lasiopogon cinctus (Fabricius)

Therevidae

Thereva plebeia (Linnaeus)

Scenopinidae

Scenopinus niger (Degeer)

Acroceridae

Ogcodes gibbosus (Linnaeus)
Ogcodes pallipes Latreille

Bombyliidae

Bombylius canescens Mikan
Bombylius discolor Mikan
Phthiria pulicaria

Empididae

Bicellaria halterata Collin
Bicellaria mera Collin
Chelifera angusta Collin
Chelifera aperticauda Collin
Chelifera concinnicauda Collin
Chelifera monostigma (Meigen)
Chelifera subangusta Collin
Chersodromia cursitans (Zetterstedt)
Chersodromia speculifera Haliday
Clinocera wesmaelii (Macquart)
Drapetis arcuata Loew
Drapetis curvipes (Meigen)
Drapetis infitialis Collin
Drapetis simulans Collin
Dryodromia testacea (Rondani)
Empis decora Meigen
Empis picipes Meigen
Empis rufiventris Meigen
Empis volucris Meigen
Euthyneura gyllenhali (Zetterstedt)
Euthyneura halidayi Collin
Hemerodromia adulatoria Collin
Hemerodromia laudatoria Collin
Hilara abdominalis Zetterstedt
Hilara albipennis von Roser
Hilara albitarsis von Roser
Hilara albiventris von Roser
Hilara apta Collin
Hilara biseta Collin
Hilara clypeata Meigen
Hilara discoidalis Lundbeck
Hilara germanica Engel
Hilara implicata Collin
Hilara lugubris (Zetterstedt)
Hilara media Collin

Hilara morata Collin
Hilara nigrohirta Collin
Hilara platyura Loew
Hilara primula Collin
Hilara scrobiculata Loew
Hilara woodi Collin
Microphorus anomalus (Meigen)
Ocydromia melanopleura Loew
Oedalea apicalis Loew
Oedalea tibialis Macquart
Oedalea zetterstedti Collin
Platypalpus albicornis (Zetterstedt)
Platypalpus albiseta (Panzer)
Platypalpus albocapillatus (Fallen)
Platypalpus aristatus (Collin)
Platypalpus articulatoides
Platypalpus articulatus Macquart
Platypalpus cothurnatus Macquart
Platypalpus cryptospina Frey
Platypalpus difficilis Frey
Platypalpus divisus Walker
Platypalpus ecalceatus (Zetterstedt)
Platypalpus incertus (Collin)
Platypalpus leucothrix (Strobl)
Platypalpus macula (Zetterstedt)
Platypalpus niger (Meigen)
Platypalpus politus (Collin)
Platypalpus praecinctus (Collin)
Platypalpus pseudociliaris Strobl
Platypalpus pulicarius (Meigen)
Platypalpus ruficornis (von Roser)
Platypalpus stabilis (Collin)
Platypalpus stigma (Collin)
Platypalpus stigmatellus (Zetterstedt)
Platypalpus tonsus (Collin)
Ragas unica Walker
Rhamphomyia albitarsis Collin
Rhamphomyia albosegmentata Zett.
Rhamphomyia caliginosa Collin
Rhamphomyia culicina (Fallen)
Rhamphomyia curvula Frey
Rhamphomyia lamellata Collin
Rhamphomyia micropyga Collin
Rhamphomyia morio Zetterstedt
Rhamphomyia nitidula Zetterstedt
Rhamphomyia obscura Zetterstedt
Rhamphomyia sulcatina Collin
Rhamphomyia tibialis Meigen
Stilpon lunata (Haliday)
Stilpon sublunata Collin
Symballophthalmus dissimilis (Fallen)
Symballophthalmus scapularis
Tachypeza fuscipennis (Fallen)
Trichina opaca Loew
Trichina pallipes (Zetterstedt)
Wiedemannia lota Walker

Dolichopodidae Achalcus melanotrichus Mik
Aphrosylus raptor Haliday
Argyra atriceps Loew
Campsicnemus compeditus Loew
Campsicnemus marginatus Loew
Campsicnemus pectinulatus Loew
Campsicnemus pusillus (Meigen)
Chrysotimus concinnus (Zetterstedt)
Chrysotus angulicornis Kowarz
Chrysotus collini Parent
Chrysotus kowarzi Lundbeck
Chrysotus melampodius Loew
Chrysotus monochaetus Kowarz

Chrysotus palustris Verrall
Chrysotus suavis Loew
Dolichopus acuticornis Wiedemann
Dolichopus argyrotarsis Wahlberg
Dolichopus caligatus Wahlberg
Dolichopus linearis Meigen
Dolichopus notatus Staeger
Dolichopus strigipes Verrall
Dolichopus virgultorum Haliday
Hercostomus chalybeus (Wiedemann)
Hercostomus nigrilamellatus (Macquart)
Hercostomus nigrocoerulea Latreille
Hercostomus plagiatus (Loew)
Hercostomus praetextatus (Haliday)
Hydrophorus rufibarbis Gerstaecker
Hypophyllus discipes (Ahrens)
Lamprochromus elegans (Meigen)
Medetera ambigua (Zetterstedt)
Medetera jugalis Collin
Medetera nitida (Macquart)
Medetera obscura (Zetterstedt)
Medetera petrophila Kowarz
Medetera pinicola Kowarz
Micromorphus albipes (Zetterstedt)
Neurigona suturalis (Fallen)
Orthoceratium lacustre (Scopoli)
Poecilobothrus principalis (Loew)
Rhaphium antennatum Carlier
Rhaphium auctum (Loew)
Rhaphium fascipes (Meigen)
Rhaphium fractum Loew
Rhaphium gravipes Haliday
Rhaphium lanceolatum Loew
Rhaphium micans (Meigen)
Rhaphium nasutum (Fallen)
Rhaphium patulum (Raddatz)
Rhaphium rivale (Loew)
Schoenophilus versutus (Haliday)
Sciapus contristans (Wiedemann)
Sciapus laetus (Meigen)
Sciapus loewi (Becker)
Sympycnus spiculatus Gerstaecker
Syntormon filiger Verrall
Syntormon spicatus (Loew)
Syntormon zelleri (Loew)
Systenus leucurus Loew
Systenus pallipes (von Roser)
Systenus scholtzii (Loew)
Tachytrechus consobrinus (Haliday)
Thinophilus ruficornis (Haliday)
Thrypticus laetus Verrall
Thrypticus nigricauda Wood
Thrypticus pollinosus Verrall

Lonchopteridae Lonchoptera meijeri Collin, 1938
Lonchoptera nigrociliata Duda
Lonchoptera nitidifrons Strobl
Lonchoptera scutellata Stein, P.

Platypezidae Agathomyia elegantula (Fallen)
Agathomyia species 1
Agathomyia species 2
Atelestus dissonans Collin
Callomyia dives Zetterstedt
Platypeza hirticeps Verrall

Pipunculidae Cephalops carinatus (Verrall)
Cephalops oberon Coe
Chalarus argenteus Coe
Chalarus basalis Loew
Chalarus griseus Coe
Chalarus parmenteri Coe

	Dorylomorpha beckeri Aczel		*Platycheirus immarginatus* (Zetterstedt)
	Dorylomorpha hungarica (Aczel)		*Platycheirus perpallidus* Verrall
	Dorylomorpha infirmata (Collin)		*Platycheirus podagratus* (Zetterstedt)
	Eudorylas arcanus Coe		*Platycheirus sticticus* (Meigen)
	Eudorylas halteratus (Meigen)		*Sphaerophoria virgata* Goeldlin de Tie
	Eudorylas horridus (Becker)		*Sphegina verecunda* Collin
	Eudorylas inferus Collin		*Triglyphus primus* Loew
	Eudorylas jenkinsoni Coe		*Volucella inanis* (Linnaeus)
	Eudorylas kowarzi (Becker)		*Volucella inflata* (Fabricius)
	Eudorylas melanostolus (Becker)		*Volucella zonaria* (Poda)
	Eudorylas montium (Becker)		*Xanthandrus comtus* (Harris)
	Eudorylas obliquus Coe		*Xylota abiens* Meigen
	Eudorylas unicolor (Zetterstedt)		*Xylota coeruleiventris* Zetterstedt
	Eudorylas zermattensis (Becker)		*Xylota florum* (Fabricius)
	Nephrocerus flavicornis Zetterstedt		*Xylota tarda* Meigen
	Pipunculus fonsecai Coe		*Xylota xanthocnema* Collin
	Pipunculus phaeton Coe	Conopidae	*Conops strigata* Wiedemann
	Pipunculus zugmayeriae Kowarz		*Conops vesicularis* Linnaeus
	Tomosvaryella cilitarsis (Strobl)		*Leopoldius signatus* (Wiedemann)
	Tomosvaryella palliditarsis (Collin)		*Thecophora fulvipes* Robineau-Desvoidyi
Syrphidae	*Anasimyia lunulata* (Meigen)		*Zodion cinereum* (Fabricius)
	Brachyopa insensilis Collin	Tephritidae	*Acanthiophilus helianthi* (Rossi)
	Brachyopa pilosa Collin		*Cryptaciura rotundiventris* (Fal.)
	Brachypalpus laphriformis (Fallen)		*Dioxyna bidentis* (Robineau-Desvoidy)
	Cheilosia barbata Loew		*Euphranta toxoneura* (Loew)
	Cheilosia carbonaria Egger		*Goniglossum wiedemanni* (Meigen)
	Cheilosia cynocephala Loew		*Icterica westermanni* (Mg.)
	Cheilosia mutabilis (Fallen)		*Orellia falcata* (Scopoli)
	Cheilosia pubera (Zetterstedt)		*Oxyna flavipennis* (Loew)
	Cheilosia soror (Zett.)		*Paroxyna absinthii*
	Cheilosia velutina Loew		*Paroxyna producta*
	Chrysogaster macquarti Loew		*Paroxyna solidagensis* White
	Criorhina asilica (Fallen)		*Urophora cuspidata* (Mg.)
	Criorhina ranunculi (Panzer)	Otitidae	*Herina palustris* (Meigen)
	Didea fasciata Macquart		*Melieria cana* (Loew)
	Didea intermedia Loew		*Melieria picta* (Mg)
	Epistrophe diaphana (Zetterstedt)		*Tetanops myopinus* Fallen
	Eristalis rupium Fabricius	Micropezidae	*Micropeza lateralis* Meigen
	Eumerus ornatus Meigen	Megamerinidae	*Megamerina dolium* (Fabricius)
	Eumerus sabulonum (Fallen)	Psilidae	*Chyliza fuscipennis* (Robineau-Desvoidy
	Ferdinandea ruficornis (Fabricius)		*Chyliza nova* Collin
	Lejogaster splendida (Meigen)		*Chyliza vittata* Meigen
	Mallota cimbiciformis (Fallen)		*Psila clunalis* Collin
	Megasyrphus annulipes (Zetterstedt)	Chamaemyiidae	*Chamaemyia elegans* Panzer
	Melangyna barbifrons (Fallen)		*Chamaemyia fasciata* Loew
	Melangyna guttata (Fallen)		*Leucopis griseola* (Fallen)
	Melangyna triangulifera (Zetterstedt)		*Leucopis silesiaca* Eggers
	Melanostoma dubium (Zetterstedt)	Lauxaniidae	*Aulogastromyia anisodactyla* (Loew)
	Melanostoma species A Stubbs		*Homoneura consobrina* (Zetterstedt)
	Metasyrphus lapponicus (Zetterstedt)		*Homoneura tesquae* (Becker)
	Metasyrphus latilunulatus (Collin)		*Sapromyza albiceps* Fallen
	Metasyrphus nielseni Dusek & Laska		*Sapromyza basalis* Zetterstedt
	Metasyrphus nitens (Zetterstedt)		*Sapromyza bipunctata* Meigen
	Microdon eggeri Mik		*Sapromyza obsoleta* Fallen
	Microdon mutabilis (L.)		*Sapromyza opaca* Becker
	Myolepta luteola (Gmelin)		*Sapromyza zetterstedti* Hendel
	Neoascia geniculata (Meigen)	Heleomyzidae	*Chaetomus confusus* (Wahlgren)
	Neoascia interrupta (Meigen)		*Chaetomus flavotestaceus* (Zett.)
	Neoascia obliqua Coe		*Eccoptemera pallescens* (Meigen)
	Neocnemodon brevidens (Egger)		*Eccoptemera ornata* Loew
	Neocnemodon latitarsis (Egger)		*Neoleria propinqua* Collin
	Neocnemodon pubescens Delucchi & Psch		*Oecothea praecox* Loew
	Neocnemodon verrucula (Collin)		*Suillia dumicola* (Collin)
	Orthonevra brevicornis Loew		*Suillia vaginata* (Loew)
	Orthonevra geniculata Meigen		*Trixoscelis marginella* (Fallen)
	Paragus tibialis (Fal.)	Sepsidae	*Nemopoda pectinulata* Loew
	Pipiza lugubris (Fabricius)		*Sepsis biflexuosa* Strobl
	Pipizella virens (Fabricius)		*Themira germanica* Duda
	Platycheirus discimanus Loew		*Themira gracilis* (Zetterstedt)

Sciomyzidae — *Colobaea bifasciella* (Fallen)
Colobaea distincta (Meigen)
Colobaea punctata (Lundbeck)
Dictya umbrarum (Linnaeus)
Pelidnoptera nigripennis (Fabricius)
Pherbellia annulipes (Zetterstedt)
Pherbellia brunnipes Meigen
Pherbellia dorsata (Zetterstedt)
Pherbellia griseola (Fallen)
Pherbellia grisescens (Meigen)
Pherbellia nana (Fallen)
Psacadina verbekei Rozkonsky
Pteromicra glabricula (Fallen)
Renocera striata (Meigen)
Sciomyza simplex Fallen
Tetanocera phyllophora Melander
Tetanocera punctifrons Rondani

Lonchaeidae — *Dasiops occultus* Collin
Dasiops spatiosus (Becker)
Dasiops trichosternalis Morge
Earomyia schistopyga Collin
Lonchaea britteni Collin
Lonchaea collini Hackman
Lonchaea corusca Czerny
Lonchaea hirticeps Zetterstedt
Lonchaea laxa Collin
Lonchaea nitens (Bigot)
Lonchaea palposa Zetterstedt
Lonchaea peregrina Becker
Lonchaea ultima Collin

Opomyzidae — *Geomyza apicalis* (Meigen)
Geomyza breviseta (Czerny)
Geomyza majuscula (Loew)
Geomyza venusta (Meigen)
Opomyza lineatopunctata von Roser
Opomyza punctata Haliday

Clusiidae — *Clusiodes apicalis* (Zetterstedt)
Clusiodes caledonica (Collin)

Odiniidae — *Odinia meijerei* Collin

Carniidae — *Meonura minutissima* (Zetterstedt)
Meonura prima Becker
Meonura triangularis Collin

Periscelididae — *Periscelis annulata* (Fallen)

Aulacigastridae — *Aulacigaster leucopeza* (Meigen)

Anthomyzidae — *Anagnota bicolor* (Meigen)
Anthomyza bifasciata Wood

Ephydridae — *Psilopa marginella* Fallen

Diastatidae — *Diastata vagans* Loew

Drosophilidae — *Amiota alboguttata* (Wahlberg)
Chymomyza costata (Zetterstedt)
Stegana coleoptrata (Scopoli)
Stegana nigrithorax Strobl

Agromyzidae — *Metopomyza ornata* (Meigen)
Phytomyza orobanchia Kaltenbach

Chloropidae — *Cetema myopina* (Loew)
Chlorops adjuncta Meigen
Chlorops gracilis Meigen
Chlorops laeta Meigen
Chlorops planifrons Loew
Chlorops rufina (Zetterstedt)
Chlorops triangularis Becker
Chlorops troglodytes (Zetterstedt)
Chlorops varsoviensis Becker
Cryptonevra nigritarsis
Dicraeus raptus (Haliday)
Dicraeus scibilis Collin
Dicraeus styriacus (Strobl)
Dicraeus tibialis (Macquart)
Dicraeus vallaris Collin

Elachiptera pubescens (Thalhammar)
Elachiptera uniseta Collin
Epichlorops puncticollis (Zetterstedt)
Eribolus gracilior (de Meijere)
Eribolus nana (Zetterstedt)
Eribolus slesvicensis (Becker)
Eutropha fulvifrons (Haliday)
Fiebrigella palposa (Fallen)
Incertella scotica (Collin)
Lasiamba baliola Collin
Lasiamba brevibucca Duda
Lipara rufitarsis (Loew)
Melanochaeta capreolus (Haliday)
Meromyza coronoseta Hubicka
Meromyza mosquensis Fedoseeva
Meromyza pluriseta Peterfi
Meromyza sp. indet.
Oscinella angularis Collin
Oscinella angustipennis Duda
Oscinomorpha arcuata (Duda)
Oscinomorpha sordissima (Strobl)
Oscinosoma gilvipes
Pseudopachychaeta approximatonervis (Z.)
Pseudopachychaeta heleocharis
Pseudopachychaeta ruficeps
Rhopalopterum atricilla (Zetterstedt)
Rhopalopterum femorale (Collin)
Siphonella oscinina (Fallen)
Speccafrons halophila Duda
Thaumatomyia rufa (Macquart)
Trachysiphonella pygmaea (Meigen)
Trachysiphonella ruficeps (Macquart)
Trachysiphonella scutellata (von Roser)

Oestridae — *Cephenemyia auribarbis* (Mg.)

Gasterophilidae — *Gasterophilus intestinalis* (Degeer)

Tachinidae — *Brachicheta strigata* (Meigen)
Drino lota (Meigen)
Eloceria delecta (Meigen)
Eurithia conjugata (Zett.)
Lophosia fasciata Meigen
Mintho rufiventris (Fal.)
Peribaea fissicornis (Strobl)
Rondania fasciata (Macquart)
Thelymorpha marmorata (F)
Zophomyia temula (Scopoli)

Sarcophagidae — *Blaesoxipha gladiatrix* (Pandelle)
Macronychia ungulans (Pandelle)
Pterella grisea (Meigen)
Sarcophaga arcipes Pandelle
Sarcophaga laciniata Pandelle
Sarcophaga similis Meade
Sarcophila latifrons (Fallen)

Calliphoridae — *Calliphora loewi* Enderlein
Eggisops pecchiolii Rondani
Pseudonesia puberula (Zetterstedt)

Scathophagidae — *Acanthocnema glaucescens* (Loew)
Cordilura atrata Zetterstedt
Cordilura rufimana Meigen
Gimnomera tarsea (Fallen)
Nanna brevifrons (Zetterstedt)
Norellia spinipes Robineau-Desvoidyi
Parallelomma vittatum (Meigen)
Scathophaga decipiens Haliday
Scathophaga scybalaria (Linnaeus)

Anthomyiidae — *Eustalomyia vittipes* (Zetterstedt)
Phorbia atrogrisea Tiensuu

Fanniidae — *Fannia carbonaria* (Meigen)
Fannia clara Collin
Fannia coracula Collin

Muscidae

Fannia gotlandica Ringdahl
Fannia immutica Collin
Fannia melania (Dufour)
Fannia metallipennis (Zetterstedt)
Fannia nidica Collin
Fannia nigra Malloch
Fannia norvegica Ringdahl
Fannia ringdahlana Collin
Fannia speciosa (Villeneuve)
Fannia subpubescens Collin
Fannia tuberculata (Zetterstedt)
Fannia verrallii (Stein)
Fannia vespertilionis Ringdahl
Caricea falculata Collin
Caricea pallipalpis (Zetterstedt)
Caricea spuria (Zetterstedt)
Coenosia atra Meigen
Coenosia campestris (R-D)
Coenosia pudorosa Collin
Coenosia pulicaria (Zetterstedt)
Coenosia pygmaea (Zetterstedt)
Coenosia trilineella (Zetterstedt)
Coenosia verralli Collin
Dexiopsis lacustris Karl
Dexiopsis minutalis (Zetterstedt)
Helina abdominalis (Zetterstedt)
Helina arctata Collin
Helina calceata (Rondani)
Helina vicina (Czerny)
Hydrotaea borussica Stein

Hydrotaea cinerea Robineau-Desvoidyi
Hydrotaea parva Meade
Hydrotaea pilipes Stein
Limnophora nigripes (Robineau-Desvoidy
Limnophora scrupulosa (Zetterstedt)
Limnophora uniseta Stein
Lispe caesia Meigen
Lispe loewi Ringdahl
Lispe nana Macquart
Lispe uliginosa Fallen
Mydaea deserta (Zetterstedt)
Phaonia atriceps
Phaonia consobrina (Zetterstedt)
Phaonia falleni Michelsen
Phaonia lugubris (Meigen)
Phaonia mediterranea Hennig
Phaonia pratensis (Robineau-Desvoidy
Phaonia siebecki Schnabl & Dzeidzicki
Phaonia subfuscinervis (Zetterstedt)
Phaonia zugmayeriae Schnabl
Spilogona baltica (Ringdahl)
Spilogona biseriata (Stein)
Spilogona setigera (Stein)
Spilogona triangulifera (Zetterstedt)
Thricops aculeipes (Zetterstedt)
Thricops albibasalis (Zetterstedt)
Thricops foveolatus (Zett.)
Thricops hirtulus (Zett.)
Thricops innocuus (Zett.)

"Research & survey in nature conservation" series

No. 1   The use of permanent quadrats to record changes in the structure
          and composition of Wytham Woods, Oxfordshire. A S Horsfall and
          K J Kirby. 1985.

No. 2   Monitoring the abundance of butterflies 1976-1985.   E Pollard,
          M L Hall and T J Bibby. 1986.

No. 3   Saltmarsh survey of Great Britain: Bibliography.   Compiled by
          Kevin Charman, Wanda Fojt and Shirley Penny. 1986.

No. 4   A survey of the numbers and breeding distribution of the North
          Atlantic gannet Sula bassana and an assessment of the changes
          which have occurred since Operation Seafarer 1969/70.
          Sarah Wanless. 1987.

No. 5   Agricultural structures policy and nature conservation in Upland
          Grampian: a pilot study. J R Crabtree, Sue Evans, Brian J Revell
          and Philip M K Leat. 1987.

No. 6   Changes in the Cumbrian countryside. First report of the National
          Countryside Monitoring Scheme. 1987.

No. 7   The Wash and its environment. Report of a conference held on
          8-10 April 1987 at Horncastle, Lincolnshire. Edited by Pat Doody
          and Brian Barnett. 1987.

No. 8   The moths of Ceredigion. A P Fowles. 1988.

No. 9   Long-term monitoring in unmanaged woodland nature reserves.
          G F Peterken and Christa Backmeroff. 1988.

No. 10   The woods of Argyll and Bute. Jane MacKintosh. 1988.

No. 11   A woodland survey handbook. K J Kirby. 1988.

No. 12   The reintroduction of the white-tailed sea eagle to Scotland:
          1975-1987. Prepared by John A Love. 1988.

No. 13   Saltmarsh vegetation of the Wash. An assessment of change from
          1971 to 1985. Margaret I Hill. 1988.

No. 14   The peatland management handbook. T A Rowell. 1988.

No. 15   Woodland conservation and research in the clay vale of Oxfordshire
          and Buckinghamshire. Proceedings of a symposium . . . on
          14 March 1987. Edited by K J Kirby and F J Wright. 1988.

No. 16   NCC research in the uplands. Proceedings of a seminar, 1986.
          Edited by D B A Thompson, S Whyte and P H Oswald. 1988.

No. 17   The saltmarsh survey of Great Britain. An inventory of British
          saltmarshes. Fiona Burd. 1989.

No. 18   A sea-cliff bibliography. Compiled by Jonathan Mitchley. 1989.

No. 19   A botanical classification of standing waters in Great Britain and
          a method for the use of macrophyte flora in assessing changes in
          water quality. Margaret Palmer. 1989.

No. 20   Vegetated shingle structures survey of Great Britain:
          Bibliography. Pippa Sneddon and R E Randall. 1989.

No. 21 Dungeness bibliography. Compiled by Helen Riley (assisted by Brian Ferry). 1989.

No. 22 Inventories of ancient, long-established and semi-natural woodland for Scotland. G J Walker and K J Kirby. 1989.

No. 23 The Nature Conservancy Council's research programme (1989/90 edition). Compiled and edited by Philip Oswald and Stefa Kaznowska. 1989. Reprinted with minor corrections 1991.

No. 24 Cut-over lowland raised mires. Proceedings of a conference held on 4 and 5 October 1988 at Doncaster. Edited by Wanda Fojt and Roger Meade. 1989.

No. 25 Moorland management: a literature review. M A Mowforth and C Sydes. 1989.

No. 26 Dungeness: a vegetation survey of a shingle beach. Brian Ferry, Ned Lodge and Stephen Waters. 1990.

No. 27 Methods for monitoring heather cover. Angus MacDonald and Helen Armstrong. 1989.

No. 28 Heather damage: a guide to types of damage and their causes. Angus MacDonald. 1990.

No. 29 A review of the scarcer Ephemeroptera and Plecoptera of Great Britain. John H Bratton. 1990.

No. 30 Wildlife habitat in Cumbria. P G Kelly and K A Perry. 1990.

No. 31 Grazing research and nature conservation in the uplands: proceedings of a seminar, 1988. Edited by D B A Thompson and K J Kirby. 1990.

No. 32 A review of the Trichoptera of Great Britain. I D Wallace. 1991.

No. 33 Goose damage and management workshop. Proceedings of a meeting organised by The Wildfowl & Wetlands Trust at Martin Mere, Lancashire, on 27 April 1990. Edited by Myrfyn Owen and M W Pienkowski. 1991.

No. 34 A review of the scarcer Neuroptera of Great Britain. P Kirby. 1991.

No. 35 A review of the scarce and threatened bees, wasps and ants of Great Britain. Steven Falk. 1991.

No. 36 The Nature Conservancy Council's research programme (1990/91 supplement). Compiled and edited by Philip Oswald and Stefa Kaznowska. 1991.

No. 37 An atlas of wildlife habitat in Cumbria. P G Kelly and S E Hunt. 1991.

No. 38 An atlas of wildlife habitat in Bedfordshire. S E Hunt and P G Kelly. 1991.

No. 39 A review of the scarce and threatened flies of Great Britain (Part 1). Steven Falk. 1991.